142

Mechanical engineering scien

Consulting Editor

C. T. Butler

*Head of Department of Mechanical and Production Engineering,
Nottingham Regional College of Technology*

Mechanical engineering science

D. Titherington
BEng (Liverpool), CEng, MIMechE and
J. G. Rimmer
BSc (Eng) (London), CEng MIMechE
Wigan and District Mining and Technical College

London · New York · St. Louis · San Francisco
Düsseldorf · Johannesburg · Kuala Lumpur · Mexico
Montreal · New Delhi · Panama · Paris · São Paulo
Singapore · Sydney · Toronto

Published by

McGRAW-HILL Publishing Company Limited

MAIDENHEAD · BERKSHIRE · ENGLAND

07 094252 8

PRINTED AND BOUND IN GREAT BRITAIN

Preface

In May 1965, the British Government announced its intention to adopt the Système International d'Unités (SI units), a coherent system of units based on the metre, kilogramme, and second, together with three other fundamental units: the kelvin for temperature; the ampere for electric current; and the candela for luminous intensity. Since that time, the move towards the adoption of SI units, both in the United Kingdom and in Europe, has proceeded with gathering momentum. In Britain, both students and practising engineers are therefore faced with a change, not only from Imperial to metric units, but also from a gravitational to an absolute system of units.

This book has been designed to cover the syllabus for the subject of Mechanical Engineering Science (0.1) as set out in the current rules governing the award of Ordinary National Certificates and Diplomas in Engineering, and SI units have been used exclusively throughout. Although primarily intended for ONC and OND students, it is also hoped that practising engineers in industry may find the book useful during the inevitable period of re-training which they will find necessary with the advent of 'metrication'.

It is the authors' belief that the practice of conversion of units is a bad one, and familiarity with the new units should be gained by associating them directly with the corresponding physical quantities. For this reason, no conversion factors have been included, and no reference whatever has been made to the Imperial system. Particular attention has been paid to the application of basic principles to engineering problems; for example, a careful distinction has been drawn between 'mass' and 'gravitational force'. Bearing in mind that some students may elect not to extend their mechanical engineering knowledge further than this first year of the ONC course, the treatment of each topic dealt with has been as complete as possible.

The authors would like to thank Mrs M. Robinson for her assistance in the typing of the manuscript, and Miss G. Tyldesley for the tracing of the diagrams. They would also like to express their appreciation of the friendly co-operation and helpful advice given to them by the publishers.

v

Finally, a word of thanks to their wives, Sheila and Norah, not only for their assistance with the onerous task of proof checking, but also for their patience during the preparation of the book.

D. TITHERINGTON
J. G. RIMMER

SI Units

Quantity	Name of unit	Unit symbol
Mass	kilogramme	kg
Length	metre	m
Time	second	s
Temperature	kelvin	K
Electric current	ampere	A
Luminous intensity	candela	cd

Names of multiples and submultiples

Factor by which the unit is to be multiplied	Prefix	Symbol
$1\,000\,000\,000\,000 = 10^{12}$	tera	T
$1\,000\,000\,000 = 10^9$	giga	G
$1\,000\,000 = 10^6$	mega	M
$1000 = 10^3$	kilo	k
$100 = 10^2$	hecto*	h
$10 = 10^1$	deca*	da
$0{\cdot}1 = 10^{-1}$	deci*	d
$0{\cdot}01 = 10^{-2}$	centi*	c
$0{\cdot}001 = 10^{-3}$	milli	m
$0.000\,001 = 10^{-6}$	micro	μ
$0{\cdot}000\,000\,001 = 10^{-9}$	nano	n
$0{\cdot}000\,000\,000\,001 = 10^{-12}$	pico	p
$0{\cdot}000\,000\,000\,000\,001 = 10^{-15}$	femto	f
$0{\cdot}000\,000\,000\,000\,000\,001 = 10^{-18}$	atto	a

* Not recommended.

Contents

1. Vectors

1.1 Vector quantities

In the fields of science and engineering, many different physical quantities are encountered. These quantities may be divided into two groups.

The first of these groups contains those physical quantities with which the concept of direction can never be associated. Such quantities are known as 'scalar' quantities. Examples of scalar quantities are mass, volume, energy, and time.

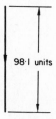

98·1 units

Figure 1.1

All the physical quantities in the second group possess *direction* as well as magnitude. These are called *vector quantities*. Examples of vector quantities are displacement, velocity, acceleration, force, and momentum. In order to define a vector quantity, it is necessary always to specify both the magnitude and the direction of the quantity. Furthermore, in addition to describing the direction of the quantity, an indication should be made of its *sense*. For example, the force due to gravity acting on a mass of 10 kg is defined thus:

magnitude: 98·1 newtons (see section 6.4)
  direction: vertical
    sense: downwards

A fourth consideration may be important in certain types of problem: this is its position in space, or line of action, relative to some body.

Vector quantities can most conveniently be represented by means of

1

vectors. A vector is a straight line drawn parallel to the direction of the quantity, and of a length proportional to the magnitude of the quantity. The sense may be indicated by an appropriate arrow on the vector. It is, however, important to understand that a vector does not represent the position of the quantity in space.

Figure 1.1 shows a vector representing the force due to gravity on the 10 kg mass referred to above.

1.2 Addition and subtraction of vectors

When two or more physical quantities of the same type are allowed to exert their influence on a particular situation, it is important to know the total, or resultant, effect on the situation. This is, in fact, the purpose of addition (or subtraction if negative quantities are involved). In the case of scalar quantities, numerical addition is all that is needed to achieve the total effect. With vector quantities, however, mere numerical addition is valid only if the quantities all happen to possess the same direction. In general, of course, the vector quantities will tend to have different

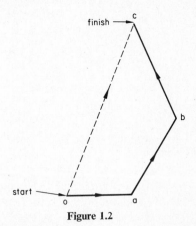

Figure 1.2

directions and, in the addition process, the effect of these different directions must be taken into account.

Perhaps the simplest example of vector addition occurs when a body undergoes a series of displacements. With reference to Fig. 1.2, suppose a body is initially at **o**; is subsequently moved from **o** to **a**; then from **a** to **b**; and finally from **b** to **c**. The net result is that the body has been displaced *from* **o** *to* **c**. This is expressed mathematically as follows:

$$\text{vector sum} = \mathbf{oa} + \mathbf{ab} + \mathbf{bc} = \mathbf{oc} \tag{1.1}$$

The same rules of addition apply to all vector quantities, so that eq. 1.1 and Fig. 1.2 represent the vector addition of any three vector quantities, whether they be displacements, velocities, accelerations, forces, etc.

Note that:

the sense of the vector sum is *from* the starting point *to* the finishing point;

the magnitude of **oc** is markedly different from the numerical sum of the magnitudes of **oa**, **ab**, and **bc**;

small letters are always used to designate vectors;

the order in which the letters are quoted is indicative of the sense of the vector—thus, the resultant is **oc** and not **co**, which would have the opposite sense.

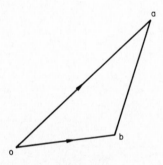

Figure 1.3

Suppose now the difference between two vector quantities is required. In general, they will not have the same direction, so that the two quantities could be represented by the vectors **oa** and **ob**, as shown in Fig. 1.3. Notice that in this case the vectors are drawn radiating from the same point o, whereas in the previous case the vectors were drawn end-to-end (Fig. 1.2).

$$\text{Vector difference } (\mathbf{oa} - \mathbf{ob}) = \mathbf{oa} + (-\mathbf{ob}) = \mathbf{oa} + \mathbf{bo}$$
$$= \mathbf{bo} + \mathbf{oa} = \mathbf{ba} \qquad (1.2)$$

By appreciating that a negative vector is one of opposite sense, the vector difference has been converted into a vector sum in which **b** is the starting point and **a** is the finishing point.

In the same way, the vector difference (**ob** − **oa**) is given by

$$(\mathbf{ob} - \mathbf{oa}) = \mathbf{ob} + \mathbf{ao} = \mathbf{ao} + \mathbf{ob} = \mathbf{ab} \qquad (1.3)$$

which has, of course, the opposite sense.

2

1.3 Resolution of vectors

Figure 1.2 shows how a number of vector quantities may be combined to give their resultant effect. It is conversely true that a single vector quantity, as represented by **oc** (Fig. 1.2), may be replaced by the three vector quantities **oa**, **ab**, and **bc**, since their combined effect is the same. When this is done, the vector quantity is said to have been *resolved* into component parts. A single vector quantity can always be resolved, in this way, into *any* number of components in an infinite variety of different ways.

The resolution of a vector quantity into component parts can sometimes simplify the solution of an engineering problem. Usually, however, the most convenient resolution is one in which the vector quantity is resolved into two components at right-angles.

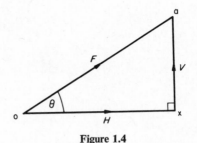

Figure 1.4

For example, the vector **oa** in Fig. 1.4 could be resolved into the horizontal and vertical components **ox** and **xa**, respectively. By simple trigonometry,

$$\cos \theta = H/F; \qquad \sin \theta = V/F$$

$$\text{Thus the horizontal component, } H = F\cos \theta \qquad (1.4)$$

$$\text{and the vertical component, } V = F\sin \theta \qquad (1.5)$$

It should be noticed that the component *adjacent* to the angle θ is associated with the *cosine* of the angle; whereas the component *opposite* to the angle θ is associated with the *sine* of the angle.

Components at right-angles need not, of course, be horizontal and vertical. Figure 1.5 shows another case in which a vector **oa** has been resolved into components at right-angles. With reference to Fig.1.5, and by comparison with eq. 1.4 and 1.5,

$$X = F\cos \theta \qquad (1.6)$$

$$Y = F\sin \theta \qquad (1.7)$$

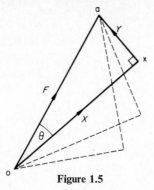

Figure 1.5

since X is the component adjacent to the angle θ, and Y is the component opposite to the angle θ.

There is, in fact, an infinite number of different ways in which a single vector may be resolved into two components at right-angles.

An alternative method of illustrating the resolution of a vector quantity into two components at right-angles is given in Fig. 1.6. The right-angled triangle employed previously is here replaced by a rectangle,

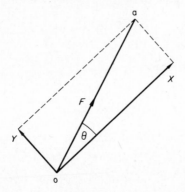

Figure 1.6

but comparison of Fig. 1.6 with Fig. 1.5 shows that the same result has been achieved. Both components, X and Y, are drawn radiating from the same point **o**. This method is convenient when the vector diagram is drawn superimposed on a space diagram, and **o** has some special significance in space. For example, **o** might be a simple pin-joint connecting two elements of a mechanism or framework; or it might be the starting point of some body destined to undergo a displacement or be given some velocity.

Worked examples

1. Draw vectors to represent the following physical quantities:

   (a) a force of 7·5 kN acting in an upward direction 30° to the horizontal.
   (b) a horizontal velocity of 20 m/s.

   (a) The vector representing the force of 7·5 kN is shown in Fig. 1.7a. The scale is 10 mm = 1 kN.
   (b) The vector representing the velocity of 20 m/s is shown in Fig. 1.7b. The scale is 10 mm = 4 m/s.

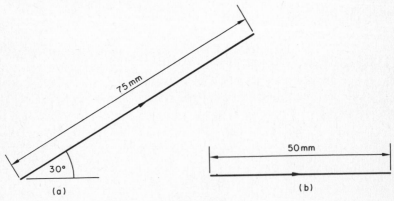

Figure 1.7

2. A fork-lift truck is capable of raising a load at the rate of 0·5 m/s. The guides of the lifting mechanism are inclined backwards at 5° to the vertical to prevent the load slipping off the forks. Determine the resultant velocity of the load if, while lifting the load at this rate, the truck moves forward at 1·5 m/s.

   The resultant velocity will be the vector sum of the two given velocities. With reference to Fig. 1.8, the resultant velocity = **oa** + **ab** = **ob** = 1·54 m/s at 18° 53′ to the horizontal.

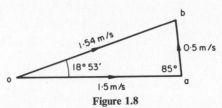

Figure 1.8

3. Determine the vector difference between two velocities of 15 m/s and 8 m/s, the angle between their directions being 30°.

The sense of the vector difference is not specified, so that, with reference to Fig. 1.9,

$$\begin{aligned}
\text{vector difference} &= (\textbf{oa} - \textbf{ob}) \quad \text{or} \quad (\textbf{ob} - \textbf{oa}) \\
&= (\textbf{bo} + \textbf{oa}) \quad \text{or} \quad (\textbf{ao} + \textbf{ob}) \\
&= \textbf{ba} \text{ or } \textbf{ab}
\end{aligned}$$

= 9·0 m/s, in a direction making an angle of 26° 23′ with the velocity of 15 m/s

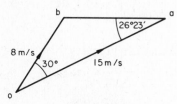

Figure 1.9

4. A force of 150 kN is applied to one end of a straight member and at 20° to its axis. The other end of the member is fixed. Calculate the axial and transverse components of the force.

The space and vector diagrams are shown in Fig. 1.10.

The axial component = $150 \cos 20° = 141·0 \, \text{kN}$
The transverse component = $150 \sin 20° = 51·3 \, \text{kN}$

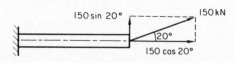

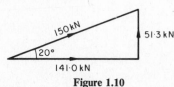

Figure 1.10

5. A projectile is given an initial velocity of 500 m/s in a direction 50° to the horizontal. The projectile is directed up a plane inclined at 7° to the

horizontal. Calculate the components of the velocity parallel to and perpendicular to the incline.

The angle between the velocity and the inclined plane $= 50° - 7° = 43°$.

Component of velocity parallel to the plane $= 500 \cos 43°$
$$= 365 \cdot 7 \text{ m/s}$$
Component of velocity perpendicular to the plane $= 500 \sin 43°$
$$= 341 \cdot 0 \text{ m/s}$$

Problems

1. Explain the difference between scalar and vector quantities, and quote five examples of each.

2. Choose suitable scales and draw vectors to represent the following physical quantities:

   (a) an acceleration of 5 m/s^2 in a direction 25° to the horizontal and with an upward sense;
   (b) a horizontal momentum of 85 kg m/s;
   (c) a velocity of 65 km/h in a direction 20° west of north.

3. Four forces, F_1, F_2, F_3, F_4, act outwards from the same point. Their magnitudes are, respectively, 2·5 kN, 4·0 kN, 1·2 kN, and 6·0 kN. The forces, F_2, F_3, and F_4, are in directions making angles of 70°, 200°, and 280°, respectively, with F_1, all these angles being measured in the same sense.
   Determine the vector sum of the forces.
   (*Answer.* 4·57 kN at 325° 54' to F_1.)

4. The velocity of a body changes from 5 m/s vertically upwards to 4 m/s in a horizontal direction. Determine the magnitude, direction, and sense of the change by subtracting the initial velocity from the final velocity.
   (*Answer.* 6·4 m/s, 38° 39' to the vertical, downwards.)

5. The force on a piston is known to be 4·4 kN when the connecting rod makes an angle of 15° to the line of stroke.
   Determine the axial and transverse components of this force relative to the connecting rod.
   (*Answer.* 4·25 kN, 1·14 kN.)

6. In order to drill a hole in the correct position, it is necessary to move the drilling head a distance of 50 mm in a direction 35° to one edge of a rectangular plate.

Calculate the components of this displacement parallel and perpendicular to this edge.

(*Answer*. 40·96 mm, 28·68 mm.)

2. Forces and moments

2.1 Representation of forces by vectors

A force is a vector quantity, and as such possesses magnitude, direction, and sense. In specifying a force, therefore, all three must be given. The most convenient method is to represent the force by means of a vector, as in Fig. 2.1b. If the point of application of a force is important, it may be shown on a space diagram, as in Fig. 2.1a.

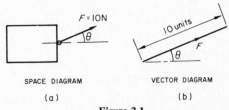

SPACE DIAGRAM   VECTOR DIAGRAM

(a)   (b)

Figure 2.1

The total effect, or *resultant*, of a number of forces acting on a body may be determined by vector addition, as explained in chapter 1. Conversely, a single force may be resolved into components (section 1.3), such that these components have the same total effect as the original force. It is often convenient to replace a force by its two components at right-angles, and, in this respect, note should be taken of eq. 1.6 and 1.7.

2.2 Coplanar forces

Forces whose lines of action all lie in the same plane are called 'coplanar forces'. The following laws relating to coplanar forces are of importance and should be noted carefully. However, it must also be remembered that these laws are applicable only to two dimensional problems.

1. *The line of action of the resultant of any two coplanar forces must pass through the point of intersection of the lines of action of the two forces.*

2. *If any number of coplanar forces act on a body and are not in equilibrium, then they can always be reduced to a single resultant force and a couple* (see Section 2.4).

3. *If three forces acting on a body are in equilibrium, then their lines of action must be concurrent,—that is, they must all pass through the same point.*

2.3 The moment of a force

When a force is applied to a body, the effect may be either to cause the body to move in a straight line, or to cause it to rotate, or both. The turning effect of a force is called the *moment* of the force about the axis of rotation. The turning effect or moment of a force about a point is dependent on two quantities: the magnitude of the force, and the perpendicular distance of the point from the line of action of the force.

Figure 2.2

If either of these quantities is increased, the moment is increased. Therefore, with reference to Fig. 2.2,

$$\text{moment of a force, } F, \text{ about a point O} = F \times x$$

The distance x is often referred to as the 'moment arm'.

A common example of the turning effect of a force is when a door is rotated about its hinge. The door handle is always placed as far from the hinge as possible in order to reduce the force required for a given turning effect.

Where more than one force acts on a body, the total turning effect is the algebraic sum of the moments of the forces. For example, suppose it is required to calculate the resultant moment about the pivot O of the forces shown acting on the bell-crank lever in Fig. 2.3, where AO = 100 mm and OC = BC = 20 mm. The force of 10 N tends to rotate the lever clockwise, whereas the other two tend to rotate the lever anticlockwise. Clearly, the 10 N force is in opposition to the other two and must therefore be regarded as negative.

Total moment about O
$$= 3(\text{AO}\cos 30°) + 5(\text{OC}) - 10(\text{OB}\sin 60°)$$
$$= 3(0{\cdot}100\cos 30°) + 5(0{\cdot}020) - 10(0{\cdot}040\sin 60°)\,\text{N m}$$
$$= 0{\cdot}2598 + 0{\cdot}100 - 0{\cdot}3464 \text{ N m}$$
$$= 0{\cdot}0134\,\text{N m, in an anticlockwise sense.}$$

Note that the sense as well as the magnitude of the total moment is given, and that the unit of a moment is the product of the force unit, the newton (N), and the unit of length, the metre (m).

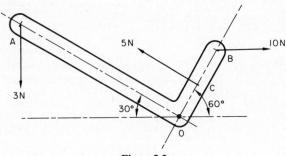

Figure 2.3

2.4 The couple

When two equal and opposite forces, not in the same straight line, act on a body, their moment about *any* point in the plane is always the same. Two such forces, as in Fig. 2.4, are said to form a *couple*. The moment of a couple is frequently referred to as a 'torque'.

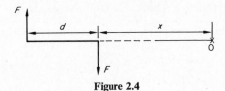

Figure 2.4

With reference to Fig. 2.4,

$$\text{total moment of the forces about O} = F(d + x) - Fx$$
$$= Fd \text{ (clockwise)}$$

The total moment of the couple about O is thus independent of the distance x, and it follows that O may be anywhere in the plane without affecting the magnitude of the couple.

2.5 Conditions of equilibrium for coplanar forces

A body is said to be in equilibrium when the total effect of all the forces acting on the body is zero. A body which is in the state of equilibrium will therefore have no tendency either to move in a straight line or to rotate.

Two conditions are therefore essential for equilibrium:

1. *The vector sum of all the forces acting on the body must be zero;*
2. *The algebraic sum of the moments about any point of all the forces acting on the body must be zero.*

If it is required to establish the equilibrium of a body, *both* conditions must be satisfied.

Conversely, if a body is known to be in equilibrium, then these conditions must apply, and their application is useful in the determination of unknown forces.

Following directly from these conditions of equilibrium are two principles widely used in problems involving static equilibrium. These are the principle of the polygon of forces, and the principle of moments.

2.6 The polygon of forces

If any number of coplanar forces acting on a body are in equilibrium, they may be represented in magnitude and direction by the sides of a closed polygon, taken in order.

This, of course, is merely a re-statement of the first condition of equilibrium, since if the vector sum is zero, the the force vector diagram must indeed form a closed polygon.

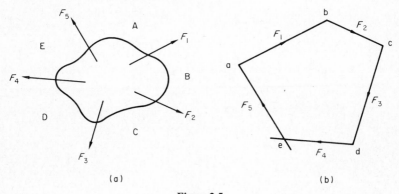

(a)   (b)

Figure 2.5

The principle is demonstrated in Fig. 2.5 which shows a space diagram depicting five forces acting on a body (Fig. 2.5a), and the corresponding force vector diagram (Fig. 2.5b). Note that, to draw the vector diagram, only three of the forces need be known in magnitude, for when vectors **ab**, **bc**, and **cd**, have been drawn to represent F_1, F_2, and F_3, respectively, the directions alone of F_4 and F_5 are sufficient to locate the point **e**.

Hence, if F_4 and F_5 are unknown in magnitude, they can be determined from the force polygon. In general, the force polygon may be drawn provided there are no more than two forces unknown in magnitude.

Bow's notation

Figure 2.5 also demonstrates the application of Bow's notation. On the space diagram, the spaces between the forces are lettered using *capital* letters. The force F_1 may then be referred to as the force AB, F_2 as the force BC, etc. Corresponding *small* letters are then used to designate the vectors in the force polygon; the force AB is therefore represented by the vector **ab**. The use of this notation will be found to be most effective in the construction and interpretation of force polygons.

2.7 The principle of moments

If any number of coplanar forces acting on a body are in equilibrium, the algebraic sum of the moments of these forces about any point in the plane must be zero.

This is, of course, the second condition of equilibrium and may also be stated in the form:

total clockwise moment   =   total anticlockwise moment
about some point   about the same point

2.8 The centre of gravity of a body

'Gravity' is the name given to the force of attraction which exists between any two bodies. The magnitude of this force is given by Newton's law of gravitation, which may be represented by the equation:

$$F = G(m_1 m_2/d^2) \qquad (2.1)$$

where m_1 and m_2 are the respective masses of the bodies, d is their distance apart, and G is some constant.

Frequently, this force is of negligible proportions and is ignored, but, if one of the bodies is the Earth whose mass is very large, the force of attraction becomes appreciable, and its effect on the smaller mass is very evident.

Most engineering problems are concerned with bodies on, or very near to, the surface of the Earth, so that for such bodies the distance d may be assumed to be constant. If this assumption is made, then it follows from eq. 2.1 that the gravitational force on a body due to the Earth will be directly proportional to the mass of the body:

$$\text{gravitational force on a body} = m \times \text{a constant} \qquad (2.2)$$
$$\text{(due to the Earth)}$$

where m is the mass of the body.

In fact, the distance d does vary slightly, since the Earth is not a perfect sphere and the height of the body above its surface may change. As a result, the 'constant' of eq. 2.2 may vary slightly, and with it the force due to gravity on the body. However, these variations are small and are usually neglected. The constant of eq. 2.2 is shown in chapter 6 to be an acceleration. This is known as the acceleration due to gravity, and is normally denoted by g. The accepted average value of g is 9·81 m/s².

The mass of a body must, of necessity, occupy some volume; that is, it must be distributed in space in a manner dependent on the shape of

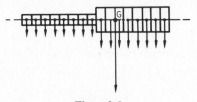

Figure 2.6

the body. The force due to gravity acting on the body will therefore be correspondingly distributed. This concept may be simplified by imagining the body to consist of a number of discrete elements of mass, as shown in Fig. 2.6, each element having its own gravitational force. It is, however, convenient to think of the force due to gravity on the whole body as a single force. This must be the resultant of the distributed gravitational forces acting on the elements. It is important to know not only the magnitude and direction of this resultant force but also its point of application G (Fig. 2.6).

The point of application of the resultant force due to gravity is called the *centre of gravity* of the body. Alternatively, the centre of gravity may be defined as the point at which all the mass of the body may be assumed to be concentrated.

The centre of gravity of a body may be determined by applying a single force at its centre of gravity to maintain the body in static equilibrium, as shown in Fig. 2.7. This may be done experimentally, by trial and error, or analytically, by assuming a position for the point of support, G, and applying the conditions for static equilibrium. In this respect, it is the second condition which is important, namely that the algebraic sum of the moments about G of all the gravitational forces acting on the body must be zero.

In practical terms, this means that, when supported on a knife-edge at its centre of gravity (as in Fig. 2.7), the body will not rotate about the

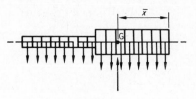

Figure 2.7

support but will remain motionless in a state of static equilibrium or balance. Application of the principle of moments will in general produce an equation in terms of $\bar{x}$, where $\bar{x}$ is the distance of the centre of gravity from some convenient datum.

Clearly, if the mass of a body is distributed uniformly along its length, then, in accordance with eq. 2.2, the gravitational forces will also be

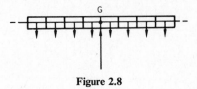

Figure 2.8

uniformly distributed along its length and the centre of gravity will be at the mid-point, as shown in Fig. 2.8. This fact can be useful when a body of non-uniform mass distribution is split up into a series of inter-connected uniformly distributed elements of mass, as in the following example.

Example. A mild steel bar ABC is 200 mm long, and B is its mid-point. The portion AB is 20 mm diameter, but BC has been turned down to 10 mm diameter. Determine the position of the centre of gravity of the bar.

Let the centre of gravity, G, be $\bar{x}$ mm from A, as shown in Fig. 2.9. The bar need only be split into two elements of mass AB and BC, since

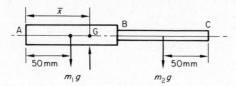

Figure 2.9

each of these is of uniform mass distribution and their respective centres of gravity are known.

Let the masses of AB and BC be m_1 and m_2, respectively.

$$\text{Gravitational force on AB} = m_1 g$$
$$\text{Gravitational force on BC} = m_2 g$$

Suppose that the bar is supported on a knife-edge at G. Then, taking moments about G,

$$m_1 g(\bar{x} - 50) = m_2 g(150 - \bar{x})$$

from which

$$\bar{x} = \frac{(50m_1 + 150m_2)}{(m_1 + m_2)}$$

If ρ = the mass density of mild steel (in appropriate units), then:

$$m_1 = \rho \,(\text{volume of AB}) = \rho(\pi \times 20^2 \times 100/4) = 10\,000\pi\rho$$
$$m_2 = \rho \,(\text{volume of BC}) = \rho(\pi \times 10^2 \times 100/4) = 2500\pi\rho$$
$$\bar{x} = (500\,000\pi\rho + 375\,000\pi\rho)/(12\,500\pi\rho)$$
$$= 8750/125$$
$$= 70{\cdot}0 \text{ mm}$$

2.9 The centre of area of a lamina

A lamina is in theory a plane area of zero thickness. Since it has no thickness, it can have no mass, and therefore the term 'gravity' has no meaning in relation to a lamina. It is nevertheless useful to apply the concept of centre of gravity to a lamina, replacing the elements of mass referred to in the previous section by elements of area. The corresponding point is referred to as the *centre of area*, or *centroid*, of the lamina.

Determination of the centre of area of a lamina is similar to the determination of the centre of gravity of a body. The principle of moments is again used, but the gravitational force on each element is replaced by its area. The concept of a 'moment of area' about an axis must therefore be realized. These concepts have important applications in the fields of mechanics of materials and mechanics of fluids in relation to areas withstanding distributed forces, that is, stress and hydraulic pressure.

Again, it is clear that a very narrow rectangular lamina will have a centroid at its mid-point, as shown in Fig. 2.10. The positions of the centroids of other areas may easily be deduced by imagining the area to consist of a series of such rectangular strips, so that the centroid must lie on a line joining the mid-points of all the strips. Thus, the centroid of a rectangle must lie at the intersection of lines joining the mid-points of opposite sides (also the point of intersection of its diagonals); and the

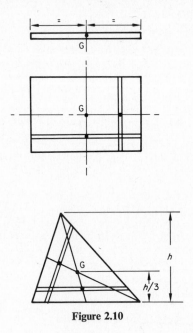

Figure 2.10

centroid of a triangle must lie at the intersection of its medians (a median being the line joining an apex to the mid-point of its opposite side). These areas are shown in Fig. 2.10.

Example. Determine the position of the centroid of the T-section shown in Fig. 2.11.

The area may be divided into two rectangular elements of area as shown. Suffixes 1 and 2 will be used to refer to these respective elements. In Fig. 2.11,

let x_1 = the distance of the centroid of area A_1 from X–X;
let x_2 = the distance of the centroid of area A_2 from X–X;
let $\bar{x}$ = the distance of the centroid, G, of the total area from X–X.

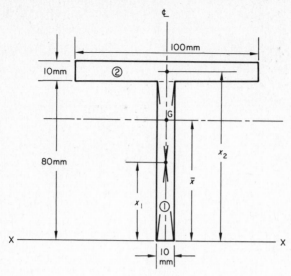

Figure 2.11

Taking moments of area about an axis through G,

$$A_1(\bar{x} - x_1) = A_2(x_2 - \bar{x})$$
$$800(\bar{x} - 40) = 1000(85 - \bar{x})$$

from which:

$$\bar{x} = 65 \text{ mm}$$

Alternatively, taking moments of area about the axis X–X,

moment of area of whole section = the sum of the moments of area
of the elements

$$(A_1 + A_2)\,\bar{x} = A_1 x_1 + A_2 x_2$$
$$1800\,\bar{x} = 800(40) + 1000(85) \text{ mm}^3$$

which gives

$$\bar{x} = 65 \text{ mm}$$

The latter method is often the more convenient.

Worked examples

1. Figure 2.12a shows a link AB which is acted upon by a horizontal and a vertical force at A, and a single force at B acting in the direction shown.

3

Determine the line of action, the magnitude, the direction, and the sense of the resultant of these forces.

The forces applied at A are first combined into a single resultant, as shown in Fig. 2.12b. This resultant and the force at B intersect at the point O. Since there are now only two forces acting, their resultant must

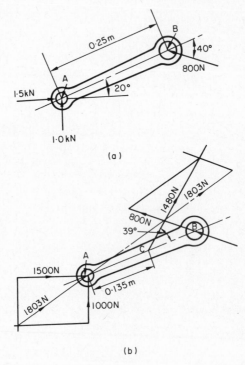

(a)

(b)

Figure 2.12

pass through O, and combining these into a single, final resultant gives:

magnitude of the resultant = 1480 N = 1·48 kN
direction and sense = 39° to AB, upwards
the line of action passes through C, where AC = 0·135 m.

2. Find the magnitude and direction of the force at B necessary to maintain the equilibrium of the link AGB (Fig. 2.13). Find also the force due to gravity acting on the link.

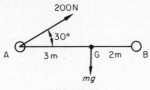

Figure 2.13

Since the link is in equilibrium under the action of three forces, the force at B must be concurrent with the forces at A and G; that is, the force at B must pass through O (Fig. 2.14).

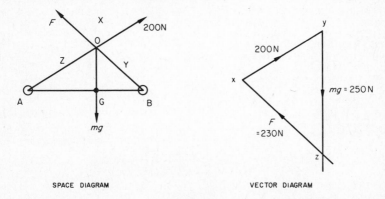

SPACE DIAGRAM   VECTOR DIAGRAM

Figure 2.14

As the directions of all three forces are known, Bow's notation may be applied and the polygon of forces drawn.

From the vector diagram of Fig. 2.14,

force at B = **zx** = 230 N at 41·5° to the horizontal,
Force of gravity on the link = **yz** = 250 N

3. A mass of 100 kg is supported by means of a bell-crank lever, as shown in Fig. 2.15. Determine the magnitude of the force F required to maintain equilibrium. Find also the magnitude and direction of the reaction at the pivot B.

Assuming $g = 10$ m/s², gravitational force on load $= mg = 1000$ N.
Taking moments about B,

$$\text{clockwise moment} = \text{anticlockwise moment}$$
$$F(1\cdot0) = 1000(0\cdot5) \text{ N m}$$
$$F = 500 \text{ N}$$

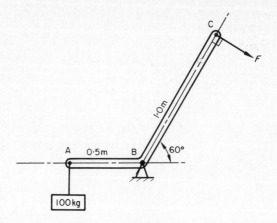

Figure 2.15

Since there are only three forces acting on the lever, the reaction R must pass through the intersection of the forces at A and C, as shown in Fig. 2.16.

From the vector diagram, $R = 1323$ N at 19° 6′ to the vertical.

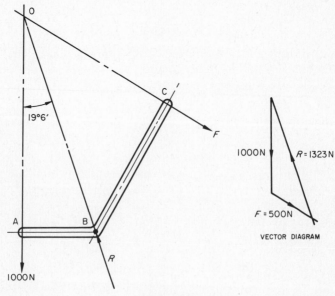

Figure 2.16

4. Determine the magnitudes of the reactions at the supports for the loaded beam shown in Fig. 2.17.

Take moments about A, so that the moment of the force R_A is zero.

total clockwise moment = total anticlockwise moment
$$100(6) + 10(12) = R_C(10) \text{ kN m}$$
$$600 + 120 = 10 \, R_C \text{ kN m}$$
$$R_C = 72 \text{ kN}$$

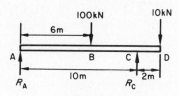

Figure 2.17

Take moments about C, so that the moment of the force R_C is zero.

total clockwise moment = total anticlockwise moment
$$R_A(10) + 10(2) = 100(4) \text{ kN m}$$
$$10 \, R_A = 400 - 20 \text{ kN m}$$
$$R_A = 38 \text{ kN}$$

Check: total upward force $= R_A + R_C = 72 + 38 = 110$ kN
total downward force $= 100 + 10 = 110$ kN.

5. Figure 2.18 shows a 40 mm diameter shaft AB carrying a 300 mm diameter eccentric at the end B. Both shaft and eccentric are made of mild steel. Determine the position of the centre of gravity of the component.

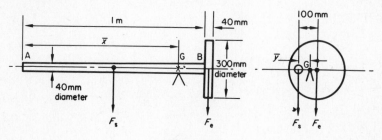

Figure 2.18

Let the centre of gravity, G, be located by the co-ordinates $\bar{x}$ and $\bar{y}$. The component may be split into two elements of mass, namely the shaft and the eccentric.

Let F_s = gravitational force on the shaft;
F_e = gravitational force on the eccentric.

Volume of shaft $= \pi(0\cdot04)^2(1\cdot0)/4 = 4\pi(10^{-4})$ m^3

If m_s is mass of shaft, $F_s = m_s g = 4\pi(10^{-4})\rho g$ N

Volume of eccentric $= \pi(0\cdot3)^2(0\cdot04)/4 = 9\pi(10^{-4})$ m^3

If m_e is mass of eccentric, $F_e = m_e g = 9\pi(10^{-4})\rho g$ N

where ρ is the density of mild steel.

With reference to the side elevation of Fig. 2.18, take moments about the centre of gravity G.

$$F_s(\bar{x} - 0\cdot5) = F_e(1\cdot020 - \bar{x}) \text{ N m}$$
$$4\pi(10^{-4})\,\rho g(\bar{x} - 0\cdot5) = 9\pi(10^{-4})\,\rho g(1\cdot020 - \bar{x}) \text{ N m}$$
$$4\bar{x} - 2\cdot0 = 9\cdot18 - 9\bar{x}$$
$$\bar{x} = 11\cdot18/13 = 0\cdot860 \text{ m} = 860 \text{ mm}$$

With reference to the end elevation of Fig. 2.18, take moments about the centre of gravity G.

$$F_s\bar{y} = F_e(0\cdot1 - \bar{y}) \text{ N m}$$
$$4\pi(10^{-4})\,\rho g\bar{y} = 9\pi(10^{-4})\,\rho g(0\cdot1 - \bar{y}) \text{ N m}$$
$$4\bar{y} = 0\cdot9 - 9\bar{y}$$
$$\bar{y} = 0\cdot9/13 = 0\cdot06923 \text{ m} = 69\cdot23 \text{ mm}$$

6. Find the centroid of the channel section shown in Fig. 2.19

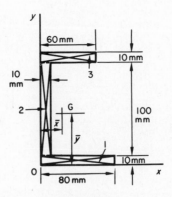

Figure 2.19

For convenience, reference axes Ox and Oy are defined as indicated in Fig. 2.19. Let G be the centre of area of the section, distance $\bar{x}$ from Oy, and $\bar{y}$ from Ox.

The area may be divided into three elemental rectangles whose centroids are known. These elemental areas are designated by the figures 1, 2, and 3, as shown, and appropriate suffixes will be used in the following calculations.

Take moments of area about the axis Oy.

$$(A_1 + A_2 + A_3)\,\bar{x} = A_1 x_1 + A_2 x_2 + A_3 x_3$$
$$(800 + 1000 + 600)\,\bar{x} = 800(40) + 1000(5) + 600(30) \text{ mm}^3$$
$$2400\,\bar{x} = 32\,000 + 5000 + 18\,000 \text{ mm}^3$$
$$\bar{x} = 55\,000/2400 = 22 \cdot 92 \text{ mm}$$

Take moments of area about the axis Ox.

$$(A_1 + A_2 + A_3)\,\bar{y} = A_1 y_1 + A_2 y_2 + A_3 y_3$$
$$(800 + 1000 + 600)\,\bar{y} = 800(5) + 1000(60) + 600(115) \text{ mm}^3$$
$$2400\,\bar{y} = 4000 + 60\,000 + 69\,000 \text{ mm}^3$$
$$\bar{y} = 133\,000/2400 = 55 \cdot 42 \text{ mm}$$

Problems

1. A uniform rod is 2 m long and the force due to gravity acting on it is 300 N. One end of the rod is hinged to the floor so that it may rotate in a vertical plane. The other end of the rod is tied to a point on the ceiling vertically above the hinge by means of a rope 2·5 m long. The vertical height of the ceiling above the floor is 3 m.

Determine the magnitude and direction of the reaction at the hinge and the magnitude of the tension in the rope. Neglect the gravitational force on the rope.

(*Answer.* 222 N at 21° 50′ to the vertical, 125 N.)

2. A garden roller has a diameter of 0·60 m, and the force due to gravity acting upon it is 750 N. The roller is drawn along a level path until it meets a step 100 mm high. Assuming the handle of the roller to be inclined at 30° to the horizontal, what is the least force which must be applied directly to the handle to cause the roller to mount the step?

(*Answer.* 588·6 N.)

3. A mass of 50 kg lies on a smooth plane inclined at 25° to the horizontal, and is maintained in a state of equilibrium by a force F.

Determine the magnitude of F and the normal reaction between the plane and the mass (a) if F is horizontal (b) if F is parallel to the plane. Assume $g = 10$ m/s^2.

(*Answer.* (a) $F = 233$ N, $R_N = 552$ N (b) $F = 211$ N, $R_N = 453$ N.)

4. ABCD is a rectangle in which AB = 1 m and BC = 2 m. A force of 20 N acts along the side AB, in the sense from A to B; a force of 30 N acts along the diagonal AC, in the sense from A to C; a force of 10 N acts along the side AD, in the sense from A to D; and a force of 20 N acts along the side DC, in the sense from D to C.

Determine the magnitude and direction of the resultant of these forces, and the distance from A that its line of action cuts the side AD.

(*Answer.* 65 N at $55\frac{1}{2}°$ to AD, 0·75 m.)

5. A beam ABCDEF is simply supported at B and E. AB = 2 m; BC = 5 m; CD = 3 m; DE = EF = 2 m. Transverse loads of 5 kN, 10 kN, 8 kN, and 3 kN, respectively, are applied at A, C, D, and F.

Calculate the reactions at the supports.

(*Answer.* $R_B = 12$ kN, $R_E = 14$ kN.)

6. A mild steel bar, ABCD, is 1 m long, and originally 30 mm uniform diameter. The portion AB, which is 0·3 m long, is turned down to 10 mm diameter; and the portion CD, which is 0·2 m long, is turned down to 20 mm diameter.

Determine the position of the centre of gravity of the stepped bar.

(*Answer.* 0·579 m from A.)

7. The stepped bar of problem 6 is suspended from a point E by two lengths of cord, EA and ED. EA is 1 m long and ED is 0·6 m long.

Assuming the mass density of mild steel to be 7840 kg/m^3, determine the tension in EA and ED, and also the angle of inclination to the vertical of the axis of the bar. Take $g = 10$ m/s^2.

(*Answer.* 23·4 N, 19·7 N, $67\frac{1}{2}°$.)

8. A rectangular plate, 0·2 m by 0·4 m, has a hole of 0·1 m diameter cut in it, as shown in Fig. 2.20.

Determine the position of the centroid of the resulting lamina.

(*Answer.* 0·189 m from the edge AB.)

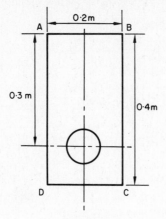

Figure 2.20

9. Determine the position of the centre of area of the section shown in Fig. 2.21.

(*Answer*. 95 mm from the upper edge of the section.)

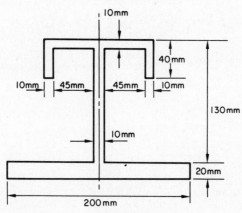

Figure 2.21

3. Simple frameworks

3.1 The simple or articulated framework

If two rigid members are connected by means of a frictionless pin-joint, then, although inseparable, each member is free to rotate relative to the other. Such joints are described as articulated joints and are incapable of resisting a torque or moment. Because of this, the only way in which force may be transmitted from one member to the other, while the members are in static equilibrium, is by means of a force whose line of action passes through the pin. Any other line of action would produce a

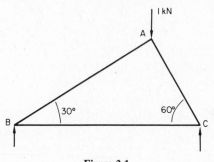

Figure 3.1

turning moment about the pin, which the joint would be unable to react, and rotation would occur. Thus, forces of interaction between members connected by pin-joints must pass through the pin.

By using only pin-joints, it is possible to build up a framework whose geometry will remain appreciably unchanged when subjected to loads. The basic example of this is shown in Fig. 3.1, in which three members are connected by pin-joints to form a triangular frame. If the members are rigid, the sides of the triangle are fixed in length and the frame cannot distort. Nevertheless, it still remains true that the pin-joints at A, B, and C, cannot resist any moment. Frames of this type, employing only pin-joints, are referred to as 'simple frameworks'.

28

3.2 Forces acting on a member

Consider the equilibrium of a single member of a simple framework. If the force due to gravity is neglected, only two forces will act on the member: these are the forces which act at the pin-joints at each end of the member. If two forces maintain a body in static equilibrium, they must be equal and opposite and must lie in the same straight line. Since these forces must also pass through the pin at each end, it follows that the common line of action of the forces is the straight line connecting these pins. Figure 3.2 illustrates this principle for a curved member as well as for a straight member.

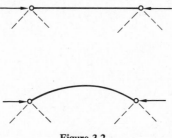

Figure 3.2

For straight members, the common line of action coincides with the axis of the member (Fig. 3.2). Such members, therefore, are subjected only to forces which tend to stretch or to compress the member and which have no transverse components (i.e., components perpendicular to the axis). Forces of this type are called *direct* loads. Those tending to stretch the member are described as *tensile* while those tending to compress are called *compressive*. The normal convention is to regard tensile loads as positive and compressive loads as negative. A member which is subjected to a direct tensile load is called a *tie*, since its function is to hold together two points in a structure. A member subjected to a direct compressive load is called a *strut*, its function being to keep two points apart.

3.3 Forces acting on a pin-joint

Figure 3.3 shows four members of a simple frame meeting at a pin-joint. Each member will exert a force on the pin, and these forces will be equal and opposite to the forces applied to the respective members. Thus, those members which are ties will exert forces on the pin radiating outwards from the pin, while those members which are struts will exert forces converging inwards on the pin (Fig. 3.3).

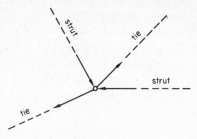

Figure 3.3

Since the members of a simple framework carry only direct loads, i.e., acting along the axis of the member, the forces acting on the pin, which are equal and opposite, are known in direction. Provided no more than two are unknown in magnitude, the polygon of forces may be drawn to represent the equilibrium of these forces (see section 2.6). From this diagram, the two unknown forces may be determined. By considering, in this way, the equilibrium of the forces acting *on the pin*, the magnitudes and senses of the forces in the members may be found.

3.4 The reciprocal diagram for a simple framework

As a simple example, consider the triangular framework of Fig. 3.1. There are three pin-joints, and at one of them, joint A, three forces act on the pin, only two of which are unknown in magnitude. All three forces are known in direction, the applied load of 1 kN being vertical and the forces applied to the pin by the members AB and AC being directed along the axes of these members. The force polygon representing their equilibrium is shown in Fig. 3.4a, Bow's notation having been used (see section 2.6).

It is apparent from Fig. 3.4a that the force exerted on the pin at A by member AC has the magnitude, direction, and sense of vector **yz**; while the force exerted on the pin at A by member AB has the magnitude, direction, and sense of vector **zx**. Both AB and AC are pushing upwards on the pin and are therefore struts.

If the member AB is pushing upwards on A with the force **zx**, it must be pushing downwards on B with the equal and opposite force **xz**. Thus, at B, there now exists a system of three forces, only two of which are unknown in magnitude, and the force polygon representing the equilibrium of the forces acting on B may be drawn. This is shown in Fig. 3.4b. Bow's notation has again been used, and it should be noticed that, since the force exerted on B by the member AB is **xz**, the appropriate letters have been used in the space diagram of Fig. 3.4b. These letters appear in the same relative positions as they did in Fig. 3.4a, provided they are read with the same sense of rotation (in this case clockwise) about the pin; i.e., X–Z–W in Fig. 3.4b and X–Y–Z in Fig. 3.4a. From the force diagram of Fig. 3.4b, the vertical support reaction at B is given by vector **wx**, while vector **zw** reveals the magnitude and sense of the force in member BC. BC is seen to be a tie.

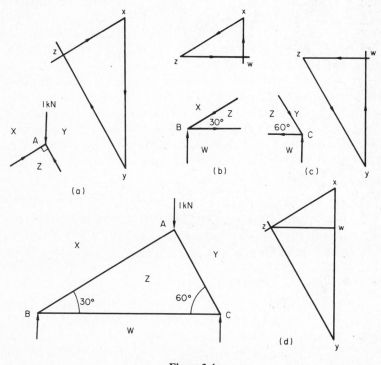

Figure 3.4

Figure 3.4c shows the space and force diagrams for the forces acting on the pin at C. This force polygon is not essential because the forces in members AB and AC are obtainable from Fig. 3.4a, and the force in member BC from Fig. 3.4b, but it is given in order to complete the picture.

Careful examination of the force vector diagrams of Fig. 3.4a, b, and c reveals that the vectors representing the forces in the members have each been drawn twice. This duplication of effort can be avoided by combining all three force polygons into a single force diagram, as shown in Fig. 3.4d. This combined diagram is called the *reciprocal* diagram for the frame.

In combining the force diagrams in this way, it becomes necessary to omit the arrows indicating the sense of the vectors, since the sense of each vector may be taken either way, depending on which joint is being considered. It is therefore imperative to adopt a *consistent* method for 'reading' the forces in the space diagram. At each pin-joint, the letters allocated to spaces in accordance with Bow's notation should be read with the same sense of rotation. For convenience, a clockwise sense has been adhered to in this book, so that, in Fig. 3.4d for example, the forces at A are: the load XY (vector **xy**); YZ (vector **yz**); and ZX (vector **zx**). Similarly, at joint B the forces are XZ (vector **xz**), ZW (vector **zw**), and WX (vector **wx**); and at joint C, the forces are ZY (vector **zy**), YW (vector **yw**), and WZ (vector **wz**).

The reciprocal diagram of Fig. 3.4d is the result of combining three polygons of forces. It should be noticed that a fourth closed polygon is present in the diagram. This is the polygon representing the equilibrium of the external forces applied to the frame. In this case, the applied load, as represented by vector **xy**, is balanced by the two support reactions, as represented by **yw** and **wx**. From the diagram,

$$\mathbf{xy} + \mathbf{yw} + \mathbf{wx} = 0$$

When the construction of a reciprocal diagram is completed, the external force polygon should always be checked for correct closure. This takes very little time, and will usually reveal the existence of any error in the diagram.

The following general rules should be followed when drawing the reciprocal diagram for a simple framework.

(a) Draw the space diagram for the frame, ensuring that all external forces, including reactions at supports, have been shown.

(b) Allocate a *capital* letter to each space separating the adjacent forces. Perhaps the best method is first to letter the spaces between external loads around the periphery of the frame, and then to letter the spaces between the various members. Letters should be chosen which do not conflict with those already used to designate pin-joints.

(c) Look for a pin-joint at which there are no more than two forces unknown in magnitude. If no such joint exists, it may be necessary to calculate an unknown support reaction by considering the equilibrium of the frame as a whole and using the principle of moments.

(d) Draw the force polygon for this joint, using Bow's notation and reading the lettered spaces in a clockwise manner around the joint. Arrows should be omitted from the force vectors, and corresponding *small* letters should be used to designate them. This determines the magnitude and sense of the two unknown forces.

(e) Indicate on the space diagram, by means of appropriate arrows, the forces exerted by the members on the pin-joint, and indicate similarly the presence of an equal and opposite force at the other end of each member.

(f) Repeat (c), (d), and (e) until the reciprocal diagram is complete.

If the forces in all the members are required, then these are best presented in a tabulated form. The Table should classify each member as a 'tie' or a 'strut', as well as giving the magnitude of the force it carries.

3.5 The method of sections

This method is most useful when the load in only one of the members is required. Instead of all, or even part, of the reciprocal diagram being drawn, the frame is divided into two sections by means of a line intersecting only three members, one of which is the member under investigation, and the equilibrium of one of these sections is considered.

Consider, for example, the simple framework of Fig. 3.5a. Suppose the load carried by the member BE is required. The frame is 'cut' by the line X–X, and that portion of the frame to the left (or, alternatively, to the right) of the cutting line is 'removed'. The 'collapse' of the remaining portion is prevented by applying to the cut members the forces which those members were originally carrying. The magnitude and sense of each of these forces are, of course, unknown, but it is usual to assume that they are all positive, i.e., tensile, as shown in Fig. 3.5b. Since the system of Fig. 3.5b is in equilibrium, the conditions of equilibrium for coplanar forces, and in particular the principle of moments, will be sufficient to determine the three unknowns F_{BE}, F_{BC}, and F_{AE}, In this case, since only F_{BE} is required, it is merely necessary to take moments about the point of intersection of the other unknowns F_{BC} and F_{AE}. This is the point D.

Thus, taking moments about D,

$$F_{BE} \times 1{\cdot}6 = 2 \text{ kN} \times 1{\cdot}7$$

from which

$$F_{BE} = +2{\cdot}125 \text{ kN}$$

F_{AE} may similarly be found by taking moments about B, the point of intersection of F_{BE} and F_{BC}; and F_{BC} by taking moments about E.

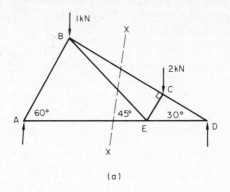

(a)

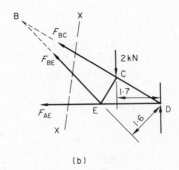

(b)

Figure 3.5

Worked examples

1. A simple framework ABCD, consisting of five members, is shown in Fig.3.6a. The frame is hinged at A, and supported on rollers at D, thereby ensuring a vertical reaction there. Vertical loads of 3 kN and 2 kN are supported at B and C, respectively.

Draw the reciprocal diagram for the framework, and hence determine the load carried by each member. Complete a Table showing the magnitudes of the loads, and the function of each member.

The space diagram of Fig. 3.6a is lettered in accordance with Bow's notation.

Consider first the equilibrium of the framework under the action of the four external forces. Because the point is supported on rollers, no horizontal component of force can be reacted at D, so that the reaction at D must be vertical. Furthermore, since the loads at B and C are also vertical, the reaction at A will be vertical, there being no horizontal component of any external force for this hinge to react.

The joint C is the only one at which there are no more than two forces

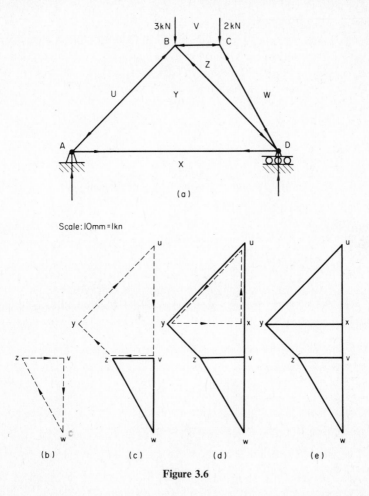

Figure 3.6

unknown in magnitude. The force polygon demonstrating the equilibrium of the forces acting on the pin at C is therefore drawn, and this is shown dotted in Fig. 3.6b. The sense of these forces is immediately transferred to the members in the space diagram at C. Equal and opposite forces may then be indicated at the other ends of members CB and CD.

The force polygon for joint B may then be added, and this is shown

4

dotted in Fig. 3.6c. Again, the sense of each force is transferred to the space diagram at B, and forces of opposite sense indicated at the other ends of members BA and BD.

The force polygon for joint A may then be added, as indicated by the dotted lines in Fig. 3.6d, and again the appropriate sense of the forces indicated in the space diagram.

Figures 3.6b, c, and d are, of course, only given for explanatory purposes. In practice, only the complete reciprocal diagram (Fig. 3.6e) need be drawn. From the reciprocal diagram, and the arrows on the space diagram, the following Table may be drawn up:

Member	Type	Force (kN)
AB	strut	3·0
BC	strut	1·2
CD	strut	2·3
DA	tie	2·1
BD	strut	1·3

2. Figure 3.7 shows the space and reciprocal diagrams for a simple framework. From the reciprocal diagram, deduce the magnitude of the forces in members EF, FG, and GH, and whether they are ties or struts.

Since Bow's notation has been used, it is clear that the vertical *downward* load of 2 kN is represented by vector **ab**. This establishes the scale of the diagram and also the fact that the letters in the space diagram have been read in a *clockwise* sense.

Consider the forces acting on the pin at the junction marked O. Reading the letters clockwise around this joint,

force exerted on O by the member EF = **ef** = 1·414 kN

The sense of this force shows the member to be pushing down on O, so that EF is a strut.

Force exerted on O by the member FG = **fg** = 1·0 kN

The sense of this force shows the member to be pulling upwards on O, so that FG is a tie.

Force exerted on O by member GH = **gh** = 0 (since **g** and **h** coincide)

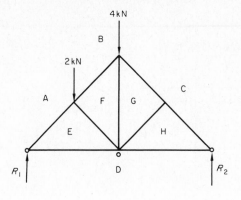

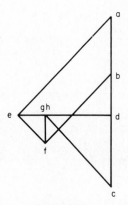

Figure 3.7

3. Draw the force diagram for the cantilever frame shown in Fig. 3.8a. Tabulate the magnitudes of the forces in each member, at the same time stating whether they are ties or struts. Find also the magnitude and direction of the reactions at the wall.

Bow's notation is first applied, in the usual way. The joint B must be considered first, since this is the only one at which there are no more than two unknown forces.

By considering the equilibrium of the forces at B, the force polygon **wx, xz, zw** may be drawn. This may be followed by the force polygon for joint C (**zx, xy, yz**). Note that, until the force polygon for joint C has been drawn, there are *three* unknowns at A: the magnitude of the force in AC; the magnitude of the reaction R_A; and the *direction* of the reaction R_A. The completed reciprocal diagram is shown in Fig. 3.8b.

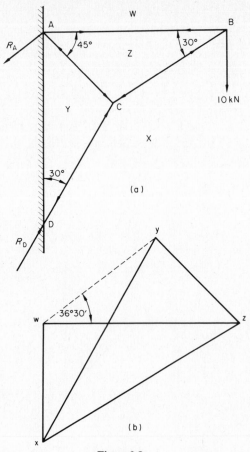

Figure 3.8

The required information may be obtained from this diagram, and is tabulated below.

Member	Type	Force (kN)
AB	tie	17·3
BC	strut	20·0
CD	strut	20·0
AC	strut	10·4

The reaction at A = R_A = **yw** = 12·2 kN at 36° 30′ to the horizontal.
The reaction at D = R_D = **xy** = 20·0 kN at 30° to the vertical.

4. The simple framework of Fig. 3.9 is supported on rollers at A and hinged at F, and loads are applied as shown.

Calculate the magnitude and direction of the reactions at A and F, and the magnitude and nature of the forces in the members CD, CG, and AG.

Consider the equilibrium of the frame as a whole. The support at A offers no resistance to horizontal forces and, in consequence, the reaction there can only be vertical. All horizontal components of the loading must, therefore, be reacted at the hinge F. Let H and V be the horizontal and vertical components of the reaction at F.

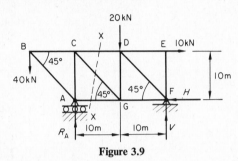

Figure 3.9

Resolving forces horizontally: $H = 10$ kN

Taking moments about F: $(R_A \times 20) + (10 \times 10) = (40 \times 30) +$
$$(20 \times 10)$$
$$20R_A + 100 = 1200 + 200$$
$$R_A = 1300/20 = 65 \text{ kN} \quad \text{(vertically upwards)}$$

Resolving forces vertically: $R_A + V = 40 + 20$
$$65 + V = 60$$
$$V = 60 - 65 = -5 \text{ kN}$$

The negative sign shows that the hinge is applying a downward load to the frame, not upward as originally assumed. The resultant reaction at F is the vector sum of H and V (Fig. 3.10).

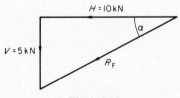

Figure 3.10

Resultant reaction at F $= R_F = \sqrt{(H^2 + V^2)} = \sqrt{(10^2 + 5^2)}$ kN
$$= 11 \cdot 18 \text{ kN}$$

This acts downwards, making an angle α with the horizontal where $\tan \alpha = 5/10 = 0 \cdot 5$; $\alpha = 26° \, 34'$.

Let the frame be 'cut' by the line X–X, and let the forces in the cut members be F_{CD}, F_{CG}, and F_{AG}, as shown in Fig. 3.11. Consider the equilibrium of that portion of the frame to the left of X–X.

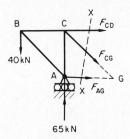

65 kN

Figure 3.11

Taking moments about G: $(F_{CD} \times 10) + (65 \times 10) = (40 \times 20)$
$$F_{CD} = + 15 \text{ kN}$$
Taking moments about C: $(F_{AG} \times 10) + (40 \times 10) = 0$
$$F_{AG} = -40 \text{ kN}$$
Taking moments about A: $(F_{CG} \times 7 \cdot 07) + (F_{CD} \times 10) = (40 \times 10)$
$$7 \cdot 07 F_{CG} = 400 - (F_{CD} \times 10)$$
$$= 400 - 150 = 250$$
$$F_{CG} = +35 \cdot 35 \text{ kN}$$

In Fig. 3.11, all these forces have been assumed tensile. The positive result obtained for F_{CD} and F_{CG} confirms this assumption. In the case of F_{AG}, however, the negative result shows this member to be in compression.

5. A pin-jointed structure is loaded and supported as shown in Fig. 3.12a. Draw the reciprocal diagram, and hence find the nature and magnitude of the forces in members AB, BC, and CD.

In this case, there are more than two unknown forces at every joint. It is necessary, therefore, to determine one of the reactions by considering, first, the equilibrium of the frame as a whole.

Taking moments about E: $R_D \times 20 = (60 \times 10) + (10 \times 15) +$
$$(40 \times 7 \cdot 5)$$
$$R_D = (600 + 150 + 300)/20 = 52 \cdot 5 \text{ kN}$$

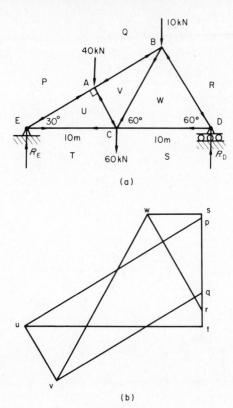

(b)

Figure 3.12

The force polygon for joint D may now be drawn (**rs, sw, wr**). This is followed by the force polygon for joint B (**qr, rw, wv, vq**), the force polygons for joint A and joint C, and, finally, the force polygon for joint E. The completed reciprocal diagram is shown in Fig. 3.12b. From the reciprocal diagram:

$$\text{compressive force in AB} = \mathbf{qv} = 94 \text{ kN}$$
$$\text{tensile force in BC} = \mathbf{vw} = 103 \text{ kN}$$
$$\text{tensile force in CD} = \mathbf{ws} = 30 \cdot 3 \text{ kN}$$

Problems

1. Draw the reciprocal diagram for the simple framework of Fig. 3.13, and hence determine the magnitudes of the forces in all the members, and the function fulfilled by each member. Tabulate your results. What are the magnitudes and directions of the support reactions?

(*Answer.* $F_{AB} = 8\cdot66$ kN, $F_{BC} = F_{CD} = 10$ kN, all ties;
$F_{AE} = 4\cdot33$ kN, $F_{BE} = 5$ kN, $F_{CE} = F_{DE} = 10$ kN, all struts;
$R_A = 7\cdot5$ kN, vertically downwards; $R_E = 17\cdot5$ kN, vertically
upwards.)

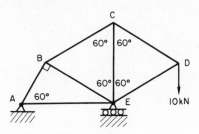

Figure 3.13

2. Figure 3.14 shows a pin-jointed structure carrying vertical loads of
2 kN and 4 kN, respectively, at B and C. Assuming the reactions at A
and E to be vertical, determine the nature and magnitude of the forces
in FC, CG, and GD.

(*Answer.* $F_{FC} = 2\cdot12$ kN, compression; $F_{CG} = 2\cdot5$ kN, compression;
$F_{GD} = 3\cdot535$ kN, tension.)

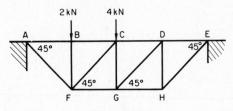

Figure 3.14

3. Draw the reciprocal diagram for the simple framework of Fig.
3.5a and hence verify that the forces in members BC, BE, and AE, are
2·554 kN (compression), 2·125 kN (tension), and 0·708 kN (tension).

4. Using the method of sections, verify that the members AB, BD,
and CD, of the simple framework shown in Fig. 3.6a, are subjected to
loads of 3·0 kN compression, 1·3 kN compression, and 2·3 kN compression, respectively.

5. Draw the reciprocal diagram for the pin-jointed frame shown in
Fig. 3.9, and hence verify the results obtained in worked example 4.

6. The cantilever framework of Fig. 3.15 carries equal loads of 10 kN at B and C. Assuming pin-joints throughout, find the nature and magnitude of the forces in members AB, BE, and ED, by means of (a) the method of sections (b) the reciprocal diagram. Find, also, the magnitude and direction of the reactions at A and F.

(*Answer.* $F_{AB} = 17 \cdot 32$ kN, tension; $F_{BE} = 17 \cdot 32$ kN, compression;
$\quad F_{ED} = 10$ kN, compression;
$\quad R_A = 22 \cdot 91$ kN, upwards and to the left, at 19° 6′ to the horizontal;

$\quad R_F = 25$ kN, upwards and to the right, at 30° to the horizontal.)

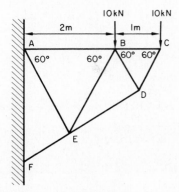

Figure 3.15

7. The roof truss of Fig. 3.16 is hinged at A and supported on rollers at E. Loads due to gravity and to the prevailing winds are applied to the frame as shown.

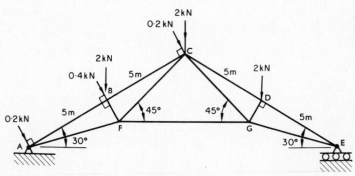

Figure 3.16

Determine the magnitude and direction of the reactions at the supports and the magnitude and nature of the loads in members BC, FC, and GF.

(*Answer.* $R_A = 3.485$ kN, at 6° 35′ to the vertical;
$\qquad R_E = 3.231$ kN, vertical;
$\qquad F_{BC} = 11.56$ kN, compression; $F_{FC} = 6.84$ kN, tension;
$\qquad F_{FG} = 5.28$ kN, tension.)

8. Determine the nature and magnitude of the forces in the members AB, BF, and FE, of the simple framework shown in Fig. 3.17. Find also the magnitude and direction of the support reactions.

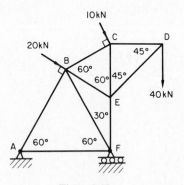

Figure 3.17

(*Answer.* $F_{AB} = 45$ kN, tension; $F_{BF} = 0$; $F_{FE} = 98$ kN, compression;
$\qquad R_A = 45$ kN, downwards and in the direction of BA;
$\qquad R_F = 98$ kN, vertically upwards.)

4. Stress and strain

4.1 Direct stress

In the previous chapter, section 3.2, a direct load is defined as a force
which tends to stretch or compress a member, and which has no transverse
component. In the context of section 3.2, this definition refers to a straight
member such as those of Fig. 4.1. A more general definition, referring to
a body of any shape, would describe a direct load as one whose direction
was perpendicular to the cross-sectional area (c.s.a.) resisting fracture.

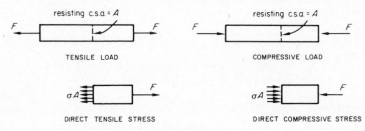

resisting c.s.a. = A resisting c.s.a. = A

TENSILE LOAD   COMPRESSIVE LOAD

DIRECT TENSILE STRESS   DIRECT COMPRESSIVE STRESS

Figure 4.1

For example, the tensile load of Fig. 4.1 is tending to pull apart the
two ends of the member. This is prevented by the molecular bond along
all planes at right-angles to the applied load. A typical plane resisting
fracture is indicated by the dotted line. Such a plane divides the body
into two parts, which are evidently held together by forces of attachment
distributed in some way across the section. These internal forces
constitute a state of *stress*, which, in this case, is a direct stress since their
direction is perpendicular to the section.

The way in which the forces of attachment are distributed across a
transverse plane may, in general, vary depending on how the load is
applied. However, for the cases of simple tension and compression,
shown in Fig. 4.1, it is reasonable to assume a uniform distribution of
these forces, provided the line of action of the applied load coincides
with the centre of area of the cross-section. This assumption is borne
out in practice, except perhaps at sections near the ends of the member.

45

Thus, each unit of area of the section carries an equal share of the load, and it is useful to define this as the *intensity of stress*:

intensity of stress, $\sigma =$ force per unit area of section $= F/A$ (4.1)

and therefore has the units N/m^2.

The intensity of stress, more often referred to as simply 'the stress', does not necessarily mean 'total load/total area' (which would be described as average stress) but can refer to a very small area of the section. Thus, even in cases where the stress varies in intensity across the section, a value for the 'force/unit area' may be quoted for any given point.

A direct stress may be either tensile or compressive depending on the sense of the applied load. The usual convention is to regard a tensile stress as positive and a compressive stress as negative. The magnitude and sense of a direct stress may normally be found by imagining the body to be 'cut' by a transverse plane, as in Fig. 4.1, and considering the equilibrium of one part of the body. With reference to Fig. 4.1,

total force on cut face due to stress = the applied load
$$\sigma A = F$$

which is only another form of eq. 4.1.

4.2 Direct strain

When the material of a body is in a state of stress, deformation takes place and the size and shape of the body is changed. The manner of deformation will depend on how the body is loaded, but a simple tension member tends to stretch and a simple compression member tends to contract. If the member has a uniform cross-sectional area, the intensity of stress will be the same throughout its length, so that each unit of length will extend or contract by the same amount. The total change in length, corresponding to a given stress, will thus depend on the original length of the member.

Deformation due to an internal state of stress is called *strain*. Any measurement of strain must be related to the original dimension involved, e.g., length. In general,

intensity of strain, $\epsilon =$ deformation/unit of original dimension (4.2)

For simple tension or compression (Fig. 4.2), this becomes

intensity of strain, $\epsilon =$ change in length/original length $= x/L$

(4.3)

where x is the extension or compression of the member.

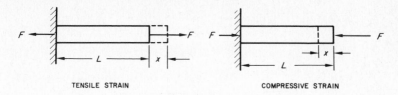

TENSILE STRAIN   COMPRESSIVE STRAIN

Figure 4.2

Again, this is usually referred to as simply 'the strain'. Since strain is the ratio between two lengths, it is dimensionless: it is, however, often expressed as a percentage.

4.3 Hooke's law

Engineering materials must, of necessity, possess the property of *elasticity*. This is the property which allows a piece of the material to regain its original size and shape when the forces producing a state of strain are removed. If a bar of elastic material, of uniform cross-section, is loaded progressively in tension, it will be found that, up to a point, the corresponding extensions will be proportional to the applied loads. This is Hooke's law. However, to be meaningful, loads and extensions must be related to a particular bar of known cross-sectional area and length. A more general statement of this law may be made in terms of the stress and strain in the material of the bar.

Within the limit of proportionality, the strain is directly proportional to the stress producing it.

The graph of stress against strain will thus be a straight line passing through the origin, as shown in Fig. 4.3.

The slope of this graph = stress/strain = a constant for a given material. This constant is known as *Young's modulus of elasticity* and is always denoted by E.

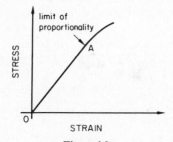

Figure 4.3

Young's modulus of elasticity

$$= E = \frac{\text{stress}}{\text{strain}} = \text{the slope of the stress–strain graph} \qquad (4.4)$$

The value of E for any given material can only be obtained by carrying out tests on specimens of the material.

For mild steel, $E = 200 \times 10^9 \text{ N/m}^2 = 200 \text{ GN/m}^2$.

For aluminium, $E = 70 \times 10^9 \text{ N/m}^2 = 70 \text{ GN/m}^2$.

Notice that, since strain is a dimensionless quantity, E has the same units as stress. E could in fact be defined as the stress required to produce unit strain, but the concept is unreal, since such a stress would exceed both the limit of proportionality and the ultimate strength of the material by some considerable margin.

Hooke's law provides a means by which the extension, or compression, of a member may be calculated. From eq. 4.4,

$$\text{strain} = \frac{\text{stress}}{E}$$

Substituting for stress and strain from eq. 4.1 and 4.3, we get

$$\frac{x}{L} = \frac{F/A}{E}$$

$$x = \frac{FL}{EA} \qquad (4.5)$$

4.4 Load-extension diagrams

It is obviously necessary, for design purposes, to know the value of Young's modulus for any material which is to be used for engineering purposes. Other properties of the material are also important; these include the greatest stress the material can withstand without fracturing, and the stress corresponding to the limit of proportionality.

To obtain this, and other information, a specimen of the material is produced in the form shown in Fig. 4.4. The working length of such a specimen is called 'the gauge length', and to this is attached an instrument capable of measuring small variations in this length. This instrument

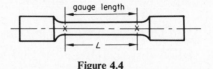

Figure 4.4

is called an extensometer. The enlarged ends of the specimen are clamped in the jaws of a testing machine, which stretches the specimen at a controlled rate. For progressively increasing amounts of extension, as indicated by the extensometer, the tensile load carried by the specimen is measured by means of a simple beam-balance technique, which is illustrated diagrammatically in Fig. 4.5. A tensile test of this nature may be continued until the specimen fractures, but it will be necessary to remove the extensometer (to avoid damaging it) soon after the limit of proportionality is reached, and thereafter to use a less sophisticated method of measuring the extension. The results obtained from such a test

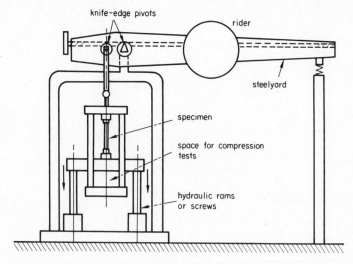

Figure 4.5

may then be used to plot a graph showing the variation of load with extension.

If a mild steel specimen is tested in this way, the resulting graph will be similar to that of Fig. 4.6. From O to A the graph is linear, showing that Hooke's law applies, so that A is the *limit of proportionality*. Soon afterwards, a point B is reached called the *elastic limit*, which represents the maximum elastic deformation of which the material is capable. Up to this point, the extension will completely disappear when the load is removed. If, however, the elastic limit is exceeded, the material experiences *plastic** deformation, which means that when the load is removed

* Plasticity is the ability to retain a deformation after the load producing it has been removed. In fact, it is the opposite of elasticity.

the extension does not completely disappear and the specimen is left with a 'permanent set'. At C, the specimen undergoes a sudden, and relatively appreciable, increase in length without any corresponding increase in load, and this is known as the *yield point*. This phenomenon of 'yielding' is peculiar to ferrous materials, particularly soft iron and low carbon steels, and is not exhibited by non-ferrous metals such as copper or brass. In practice, the points A, B, and C are very close together, and in commercial tests on mild steel the yield point, which is

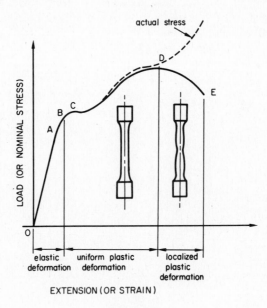

Figure 4.6

clearly defined, is taken to represent the elastic and proportional limits as well. After yielding, the specimen offers further resistance to deformation, although not as great as before, and further extension causes the load to rise until the point D is reached. This point marks the end of uniform extension over the whole length of the specimen, and a local extension, accompanied by a narrowing or 'necking' of the section, begins at some point along its length. This reduction in cross-sectional area causes the load to fall even though the actual stress is still rising, and the breaking load at E is in fact less than that at D. The load at D is called the *ultimate* load, since it is the maximum, and the corresponding stress is called the *ultimate tensile stress*.

Some clarification of the term 'stress' is required at this point. Normally, the stress, as defined by eq. 4.1, is based on the original cross-sectional area, which is assumed to remain unchanged. In fact, as the specimen extends, its cross-section reduces, so that the actual stress is higher than the nominal value, which is defined thus:

$$\text{nominal stress} = \text{load}/original \text{ c.s.a.} \qquad (4.6)$$

However, until the ultimate load is exceeded, the difference between the actual and nominal stresses is negligible; this is indicated by the dotted line in Fig. 4.6. The important values of the ultimate tensile stress and the yield stress are always based on the original cross-sectional area, and are calculated by means of eq. 4.6. Note also that, since nominal stress is proportional to load and strain is proportional to extension, the load-extension graph may be converted to a nominal stress-strain graph simply by multiplying the scales used by an appropriate factor.

To determine Young's modulus, E, from the load-extension diagram, eq. 4.5 may be re-arranged as follows:

$$E = \frac{FL}{xA} = \frac{\text{load}}{\text{extension}} \times \frac{L}{A} = \text{slope of OA} \times \frac{L}{A} \qquad (4.7)$$

In addition

$$\text{ultimate tensile stress} = \frac{\text{ultimate load}}{\text{original c.s.a.}} \qquad (4.8)$$

and

$$\text{yield stress} = \frac{\text{load at yield point}}{\text{original c.s.a.}} \qquad (4.9)$$

For materials with no clearly defined yield point, some substitute for yield stress must be provided. This is done by finding the load corresponding to a given non-proportional extension, usually expressed as a percentage. This is called the *proof load* and the corresponding stress is the *proof stress*. A typical load-extension diagram for a non-ferrous metal is shown in Fig. 4.7, which also makes clear the method of determining the 0·1% proof load.

Consideration of the total extension of the specimen at fracture in relation to the original gauge length is a good criterion of the ductility of the material. This is its ability to be drawn out, and is important in forming processes; it also may be obtained from the load-extension diagram.

$$\text{percentage elongation at fracture} = \frac{\text{final extension}}{\text{original length}} \times 100\%$$

$$(4.10)$$

5

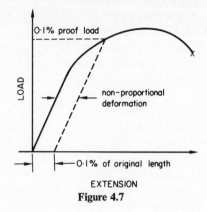

Figure 4.7

Another guide to the ductility of the material is obtained by considering reduction in cross-sectional area at the point of fracture. This, of course, must be obtained from the fractured specimen itself.

percentage reduction in area

$$= \frac{\text{original c.s.a.} - \text{c.s.a. at fracture}}{\text{original c.s.a.}} \times 100\% \qquad (4.11)$$

4.5 Factor of safety

The designer of a machine component or structural member will seek to ensure not only that it will not fracture under the applied loads but also that no permanent change in its dimensions takes place. To attain the latter object, the stress in the component must never be allowed to exceed the elastic limit stress for the material. Furthermore, since the value of the stress in the member must be calculated by using Hooke's law, the stress at the limit of proportionality should not be exceeded, as such calculations must otherwise be inaccurate.

Because of the greater precision being achieved in the calculation and prediction of stresses in engineering components, the practice of basing design, for ductile materials, on the yield point or proof stress has become more common in recent times. However, because it can be determined with greater accuracy, it is traditionally correct to use the ultimate tensile stress as the basis for design. A *factor of safety* is therefore defined, which enables a safe working stress to be calculated.

$$\text{factor of safety} = \frac{\text{ultimate tensile stress}}{\text{safe working stress}} \qquad (4.12)$$

The factor of safety used in any particular case will depend on the circumstances. For steel, factors of safety may vary from 3 for simple static loads, up to perhaps 15 for shock loads. Higher factors of safety, up to about 20, will probably be used where there are alternating stresses and a danger of metal fatigue.

The factor of safety should be chosen to ensure that the safe working stress never exceeds the stress at the limit of proportionality for the material, but, in general, other considerations will affect its value. These include:

the nature of the material, and the dependability of its specifications; the nature of the loading, i.e., whether statically or dynamically applied or whether there is a possibility of an overload; the likely rate of deterioration due to wear or corrosion; the possibility of defects in manufacture; the consequences of failure.

4.6 Shear stress

Figure 4.8a shows a member, fixed at one end and carrying at its free end a vertical downward load F. This force would be described as a *shearing force*, since it tends to make the material fail as in Fig. 4.8b. Severance

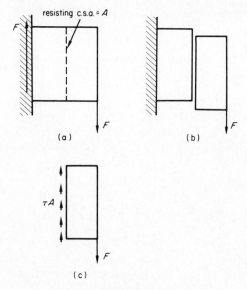

Figure 4.8

would occur along a plane which is parallel to the applied force, so that the portion to the right of the plane slides downwards relative to the portion to the left. Normally, shear failure will be resisted by forces of attachment along the plane and tangential to it, as shown in Fig. 4.8c, and the presence of these internal forces constitutes a state of stress. This type of stress is called *shear stress*. The distinguishing feature of shear loading, and the resulting shear stress, is that its direction is *parallel* to the cross-sectional area resisting fracture.

$$\text{shear stress, } \tau = \text{shear force/unit area of resistance} = F/A \quad (4.13)$$

For design purposes, a maximum allowable shear stress may be calculated by using a safety factor, in the manner of eq. 4.12, and based

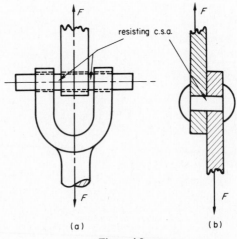

resisting c.s.a.

(a) (b)

Figure 4.9

on the *ultimate shear stress* for the material. This, of course, must be determined by applying shear loads to a specimen of the material and testing it to destruction. As in a tensile test, the ultimate shear stress is the maximum recorded value before fracture.

Figure 4.9a shows a pin subjected to shear loading. To cause the pin to fail, the shearing force F must fracture it at *two* places. The pin, thus, has twice the area of resistance to shear, and the shear stress will be given by $\tau = F/2A$, where A is the cross-sectional area of the pin.

Such a pin is said to be in *double shear*, as opposed to the *single shear* of the rivet of Fig. 4.9b. In theory, the strength of a pin in double shear is twice that of the same pin in single shear, but in practice this benefit is seldom achieved in full owing to bending effects.

4.7 Shear strain

The elastic deformation produced by a shear stress may be visualized by imagining the member of Fig. 4.8a to consist of a large number of laminations, parallel to the shearing force F. Since each lamina carries the same load, $\tau A = F$, each lamina will slip by the same amount relative to the adjacent lamina, and the net result is that the member will assume the shape of Fig. 4.10. The total deflection due to shear at the load point

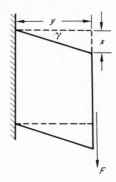

Figure 4.10

is x, and this will depend on the length of the member y. A measure of the shear strain is, therefore, the shear deflection per unit length of the member.

$$\text{shear strain} = \frac{\text{deformation}}{\text{unit of original dimension}} = \frac{x}{y} = \gamma \qquad (4.14)$$

since x will, in general, be small. Thus, the measure of shear strain is the rotation of the planes perpendicular to the applied shear force.

4.8 Relation between shear stress and shear strain

Hooke's law applies equally well to shear loading as to direct loading, so that Fig. 4.3 is relevant to the problem of relating shear stress and shear strain. The main difference lies in the fact that the resistance to shear deformation is less than that due to direct loading, so that the slope of the graph is smaller. Thus,

$$\text{the slope of the graph} = \frac{\text{shear stress}}{\text{shear strain}} = \text{a constant for a given material.}$$

This constant is called the modulus of rigidity and is denoted by G. For any given material, G must be found by means of a shear test.

$$\text{modulus of rigidity} = G = \frac{\tau}{\gamma} \tag{4.15}$$

$$\tau = G\gamma$$

For mild steel, $G = 80 \times 10^9 \text{ N/m}^2 = 80 \text{ GN/m}^2$.
For aluminium, $G = 25 \times 10^9 \text{ N/m}^2 = 25 \text{ GN/m}^2$.

Worked examples

1. A mild steel tie-bar is 10 mm diameter and 2 m long. Using a factor of safety of 3, calculate the maximum load it may be permitted to carry if the ultimate tensile stress of the steel is 540 MN/m². If $E = 200 \text{ GN/m}^2$, what will be the extension of the tie-bar when carrying its maximum load?

From eq. 4.12, the safe working stress $= 540/3 = 180 \text{ MN/m}^2$
cross-sectional area $= A = \pi(0 \cdot 010)^2/4 = 78 \cdot 54 \times 10^{-6} \text{ m}^2$

From eq. 4.1, maximum safe load $= \sigma A$
$= (180 \times 10^6)(78 \cdot 54 \times 10^{-6}) \text{ N}$
$= 14\ 140 \text{ N} = 14 \cdot 14 \text{ kN}$

From Hooke's law, maximum strain $= \dfrac{\text{maximum stress}}{E}$

$$= \frac{180 \times 10^6}{200 \times 10^9} = 0 \cdot 9 \times 10^{-3}$$

maximum extension $=$ maximum strain $\times$ length
$= (0 \cdot 9 \times 10^{-3}) \times 2 \text{ m}$
$= 1 \cdot 8 \text{ mm}$

2. An aluminium rod, ABC, is 1·0 m long and AB = BC. AB is 10 mm in diameter, and BC is 5 mm in diameter. The rod is subjected to a tensile load of 0·20 kN applied axially. For aluminium, $E = 70 \text{ GN/m}^2$.
Calculate the maximum stress in the bar, and its total extension.

For a 10 mm diameter rod, the cross-sectional area,

$$A = 78 \cdot 54 \times 10^{-6} \text{ m}^2$$

For a 5 mm diameter rod, the cross-sectional area,

$$A = 19.64 \times 10^{-6} \text{ m}^2$$

The maximum stress will occur in that part of the rod with the smaller diameter.

Maximum stress =

$$\sigma_{BC} = \frac{200}{19.64 \times 10^{-6}} = 10.2 \times 10^6 \text{ N/m}^2 = 10.2 \text{ MN/m}^2$$

From eq. 4.5,

$$x_{AB} = \frac{200 \times 0.5}{70 \times 10^9 \times 78.54 \times 10^{-6}} = 0.182 \times 10^{-4} \text{ m}$$

$$= 0.0182 \text{ mm}$$

$$x_{BC} = \frac{200 \times 0.5}{70 \times 10^9 \times 19.64 \times 10^{-6}} = 0.728 \times 10^{-4} \text{ m}$$

$$= 0.0728 \text{ mm}$$

Total extension $= x_{AB} + x_{BC} = 0.0182 + 0.0728 = 0.091 \text{ mm} = 91$ micron

3. A standard mild steel tensile test specimen has a diameter of 16 mm and a gauge length of 80 mm. Such a specimen was tested to destruction, and the following results obtained:

load at yield point = 87 kN; extension at yield point = 173 μm;
ultimate load = 124 kN; total extension at fracture = 24 mm;
diameter of specimen at fracture = 9.8 mm.

Calculate the modulus of elasticity of the steel, the ultimate tensile stress, the yield stress, the percentage elongation, and the percentage reduction in area.

Note that dimensions of standard tensile test specimens are given in BS18.

For a 16 mm diameter specimen, the cross-sectional area, $A = 200 \text{ mm}^2$,

$$\text{yield stress} = \frac{\text{yield load}}{A} = \frac{87 \times 10^3}{200 \times 10^{-6}} = 435 \times 10^6 \text{ N/m}^2 = 435 \text{ MN/m}^2$$

Since the load at the limit of proportionality is not given, the yield stress must be used to *estimate* the value of E,

$$\text{strain at the yield point} = \frac{x}{L} = \frac{173 \times 10^{-6}}{80 \times 10^{-3}} = 2.16 \times 10^{-3}$$

$$E = \frac{\text{stress}}{\text{strain}} = \frac{435 \times 10^6}{2 \cdot 16 \times 10^{-3}} = 201 \cdot 4 \times 10^9 \text{ N/m}^2 = 201 \cdot 4 \text{ GN/m}^2$$

$$\text{ultimate tensile stress} = \frac{\text{ultimate load}}{A} = \frac{124 \times 10^3}{200 \times 10^{-6}} = 620 \times 10^6 \text{ N/m}^2$$

$$= 620 \text{ MN/m}^2$$

$$\text{percentage elongation} = \frac{\text{final extension at fracture}}{\text{original length, } L} \times 100\%$$

$$= \frac{24 \times 10^{-3}}{80 \times 10^{-3}} \times 100 = 30\%$$

$$\text{cross-sectional area at fracture} = \pi(9 \cdot 8 \times 10^{-3})^2/4 = 75 \cdot 4 \times 10^{-6} \text{ m}^2$$

$$\text{percentage reduction in area} = \frac{\text{reduction in area}}{A} \times 100\%$$

$$= \frac{200 - 75 \cdot 4}{200} \times 100\% = 62\%$$

4. An aluminium alloy test specimen is made to standard specifications, with a diameter of 22·6 mm and a gauge length of 113 mm. A tensile test on this specimen produced the following results:

Load (kN)	0	24	48	70	96	115	124	128	133	136
Extension (mm)	0	0·09	0·17	0·25	0·34	0·44	0·55	0·68	0·90	1·11

Draw the load-extension graph, and hence deduce, for the material, the modulus of elasticity, the stress at the limit of proportionality, and the 0·1 % proof stress.

The load-extension graph is plotted in Fig. 4.11.
For a 22·6 mm diameter specimen, $A = 400 \text{ mm}^2$.
From eq. 4.7,

$$E = \text{the slope of the straight-line portion} \times \frac{L}{A}$$

$$= \frac{100 \times 10^3}{0 \cdot 355 \times 10^{-3}} \times \frac{113 \times 10^{-3}}{400 \times 10^{-6}} \text{ N/m}^2$$

$$= 79 \cdot 6 \times 10^9 \text{ N/m}^2 = 79 \cdot 6 \text{ GN/m}^2$$

The load at the limit of proportionality = 100 kN,

$$\text{proportional limit stress} = \frac{100 \times 10^3}{400 \times 10^{-6}} \text{ N/m}^2 = 250 \text{ MN/m}^2$$

Extension corresponding to 0·1 % strain = $113 \times 0·1/100 = 0·113$ mm.

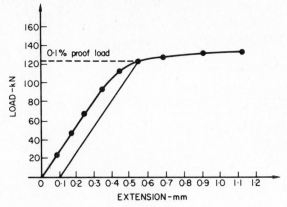

Figure 4.11

The load, corresponding to a non-proportional extension of this amount, may be found by drawing a line parallel to the straight-line portion of the graph and displaced 0·113 mm from it, as shown in Fig. 4.11.

From the graph, 0·1 % proof load = 124 kN

$$0\cdot1 \% \text{ proof stress} = \frac{124 \times 10^3}{400 \times 10^{-6}} \text{ N/m}^2 = 320 \text{ MN/m}^2$$

5. Calculate the force required to punch a circular hole, 50 mm in diameter, in a steel plate 5 mm thick. The ultimate shear stress of the steel is 200 MN/m².

The circular punch must shear through the material all around the edge of the hole.

area to be sheared = circumference × thickness = $\pi d \times t$
$$= \pi \times 50 \times 5 = 785\cdot4 \text{ mm}^2 = 785\cdot4 \times 10^{-6} \text{ m}^2$$
punching force = shear stress × shear area
$$= (200 \times 10^6) \times (785\cdot4 \times 10^{-6}) \text{ N} = 157 \text{ kN}$$

6. A rectangular block of rubber, measuring 200 × 300 × 5 mm, is rigidly fastened to a vertical wall, in the manner of Fig. 4.8a, so that it projects a distance of 200 mm from the wall. The modulus of rigidity of the rubber is 1·04 MN/m².

Calculate the vertical deflection due to shear of the free vertical edge when a downward load of 100 N is applied to it.

Area of section resisting shear = 300 × 5 = 1500 mm²

$$\text{shear stress in rubber} = \frac{100}{1500 \times 10^{-6}} \text{ N/m}^2 = \frac{1}{15} \text{ MN/m}^2$$

From Hooke's law,

$$\text{shear strain} = \frac{\tau}{G} = \frac{(1/15) \text{ MN/m}^2}{1 \cdot 04 \text{ MN/m}^2} = 0 \cdot 0641$$

But, if the vertical deflection is x mm,

$$\text{shear strain} = \frac{x}{200} \text{ (see Fig. 4.10)}$$

$$\frac{x}{200} = 0 \cdot 0641, \text{ so that } x = 200 \times 0 \cdot 0641 = 12 \cdot 82 \text{ mm}$$

7. A pin-joint is to be made in the manner of Fig. 4.9. Find a suitable diameter for the steel pin, if the force F carried by the pin is 20 kN. The ultimate shear stress for the steel is 200 MN/m², and a factor of safety of 4 is to be used.

$$\text{Safe working stress} = \frac{200}{4} = 50 \text{ MN/m}^2$$

With reference to Fig. 4.9, the pin is in double-shear, so that, if A is the cross-sectional area of the pin, the area resisting shear is $2A$. Thus,

$$\text{safe load} = 2A \times \text{safe working stress}$$
$$20 \times 10^3 = 2A \times 50 \times 10^6$$
$$A = 200 \times 10^{-6} \text{ m}^2 = 200 \text{ mm}^2$$

A 16 mm diameter rod has a sectional area of 200 mm², so that

$$\text{suitable diameter for the pin} = 16 \text{ mm}$$

Problems

1. A 14 mm diameter steel rod carries a load of 3·08 kN in tension. Calculate the stress in the material. If the rod is 2·5 m long and the modulus of elasticity is 200 GN/m², by how much will it extend?

(*Answer.* 20 MN/m², 0·25 mm.)

2. A brass rod measures 10 mm in diameter and 150 mm in length. The rod extends 0·3 mm when subjected to a tensile load. Given that for the brass, $E = 85$ GN/m², calculate the stress in the material and the magnitude of the load.

(*Answer.* 170 MN/m², 13·36 kN.)

3. A cast iron column, 3 m long, is in the form of a tube of 200 mm external diameter and 150 mm internal diameter. The lower end is firmly based on a horizontal floor, which may be assumed rigid, and its

upper end is used to support a mass of 1 tonne against the pull of gravity. If $g = 9.81$ m/s², calculate the stress induced in the tube.

Under this load, the tube is observed to contract by 17·3 microns. Determine Young's modulus for cast iron.

(*Answer.* 714 kN/m², 124 GN/m².)

4. A copper rod is 0·25 m long, and is 30 mm diameter for 150 mm of its length and 20 mm diameter for the remainder. A tensile load is applied to the rod so that the maximum stress induced in the material is 50 MN/m².

Determine the magnitude of the load, and calculate the total extension of the rod. For copper, $E = 103$ GN/m².

(*Answer.* 15·7 kN, 81 micron.)

5. A tie-bar is to carry a maximum load of 10 kN and is to be made from a mild steel with an ultimate tensile stress of 700 MN/m². If a factor of safety of 3 is specified, what is the minimum diameter of bar, to the nearest millimetre, which may be used?

Determine the percentage strain in the material when a bar of this diameter carries the maximum load. For steel, $E = 200$ GN/m².

(*Answer.* 8 mm, 0·1 %.)

6. A light alloy specimen has a diameter of 16 mm and a gauge length of 80 mm. When tested in tension, the load-extension graph proved linear up to a load of 6 kN, at which point the extension was 0·034 mm.

Determine the limit of proportionality stress and the modulus of elasticity for the material.

(*Answer.* 30 MN/m², 70·5 GN/m².)

7. A specimen of mild steel, with a diameter of 20 mm and a gauge length of 100 mm, is tested to destruction and the following readings obtained:

Load (kN)	Ext. (mm)	Load (kN)	Ext. (mm)	Load (kN)	Ext. (mm)	Load (kN)	Ext. (mm)
30	0·045	124	0·195	143	0·450	198	15·8
58	0·090	132	0·210	142	0·900	204	20·0
80	0·125	138	0·225	154	4·0	199	24·6
110	0·175	141	0·240	179	9·7	185	28·0

The breaking load was 160 kN and the final elongation 31·0 mm. The diameter at the point of fracture after testing was 12·6 mm. Plot load-extension graphs, using different scales for the elastic and plastic ranges, and hence estimate (a) Young's modulus (b) the stress at the limit of proportionality (c) the yield stress (d) the ultimate tensile stress (e) the percentage elongation (f) the percentage reduction in area.

(*Answer.* (a) 208 GN/m² (b) 398 MN/m² (c) 455 MN/m² (d) 650 MN/m² (e) 31 % (f) 60·3 %.)

8. The following results were obtained from a tensile test on an aluminium alloy specimen, whose diameter was 8 mm and whose gauge length was 40 mm.

Load (kN)	0	4	6	9	12	14	15	16	17	17·4
Extension (mm)	0	0·036	0·054	0·08	0·108	0·128	0·148	0·18	0·232	0·280

Plot a graph of load against extension and use it to estimate Young's modulus and the 0·2 % proof stress for the material.

(*Answer.* 90 GN/m², 340 MN/m².)

9. The compressive stress in a circular punch of 50 mm diameter is not to exceed 40 MN/m². What is the maximum thickness of steel plate in which a hole may be punched if the ultimate shear stress of the material is 200 MN/m²?

(*Answer.* 2·5 mm.)

10. Explain the meaning of the term 'double shear' and, in particular, state what advantage is to be gained by adopting such an arrangement. A bolt is 25 mm in diameter and is made from mild steel with an ultimate shear stress of 200 MN/m². Using a factor of safety of 4, calculate the maximum safe load which the bolt can carry in double shear.

(*Answer.* 49·1 kN.)

11. A short cantilever beam is 0·5 m long and 0·25 m deep, and carries a load of 100 kN at its free end, in the manner of Fig. 4.8a. The width of the section, which is rectangular, is 50 mm, and the material is mild steel for which G = 80 GN/m².

Assuming the shear stress in the material is uniformly distributed, and neglecting deformation due to other causes, calculate the deflection of the load due to shear.

(*Answer.* 0·05 mm.)

12. A coupling between two shafts is made by bolting together the flanged ends of the shafts. Six 20 mm diameter bolts are used, equally spaced around a pitch circle of 150 mm diameter. The ultimate shear stress of the material of the bolts is 240 MN/m², and a safety factor of 4 is specified.

Calculate the maximum torque which may be transmitted through the coupling.

(*Answer.* 8·48 kN m.)

5. Linear and angular motion

5.1 Displacement, velocity, and acceleration

When a point moves, it changes its position in space. The measure of this change is the straight line connecting the initial and final positions of the point in space. This straight line is known as its *linear displacement*. Displacement is a vector quantity, and its sense is always taken to be from the initial to the final position.

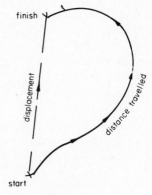

Figure 5.1

It is important to distinguish between 'linear displacement' and 'distance travelled' along a path which is not necessarily straight; this is made clear by Fig. 5.1. 'Linear displacement' and 'distance travelled' only coincide when the path of the latter is a straight line. However, the same symbol s is, on occasions, used to denote both quantities, so that care must be taken to read the symbol in its correct context.

When a body undergoes angular motion, its position in space may remain unaltered. Its orientation in space will, however, change, and the measure of this change is its *angular displacement*, which is the angle through which it turns relative to some datum. This is normally denoted by the symbol θ, and the unit of its measurement is the radian (see section

64

5.8). Angular displacement is also a vector quantity, its direction being indicated by the axis of rotation and its sense being described either as clockwise or anticlockwise. Problems involving changes in the axis of rotation will not, however, be encountered at the level for which this text is intended, so that only the magnitude and sense of an angular displacement need be considered here.

The motion of a body may be linear, or angular, or a combination of both. Linear motion is known as 'translation', and angular motion as 'rotation'. A disc which rolls along a plane, for example, has both translation and rotation. If the disc rolls without slipping, a relationship will exist between the linear and angular displacements (section 5.8).

The *linear velocity* of a point is the rate of change of its displacement with time.

For uniform motion in a straight line, the rate of displacement is constant and its measurement is quite straightforward. All that is necessary is to measure the time taken for a given displacement. For instance, if the displacement of a point over a distance of 20 m takes 5 s, the rate of displacement must be 4 m every second, or 4 m/s. This assumes that the rate of displacement does not vary over the 5 s period.

Thus, for uniform motion in a straight line,

$$\text{linear velocity at } every \text{ instant} = v = \frac{\text{displacement}}{\text{time taken}} \qquad (5.1)$$

In general, the rate of displacement will not remain constant, and to determine its value at any particular instant in time is more difficult. With non-uniform motion, it becomes necessary to envisage measuring the time taken for a very small displacement, δs. The prefix δ, by convention, means that the quantity it precedes is very small, so that the correspondingly small time taken would logically be δt. Little error is incurred by assuming that over this very short period the rate of displacement is constant, so that:

$$\text{linear velocity 'when' } \delta t \text{ is measured} = v \fallingdotseq \delta s/\delta t \qquad (5.2)$$

In the mathematical process, known as 'differentiation', eq. 5.2 becomes exactly true if the small period of time, δt, is allowed to become *infinitely* small, i.e., δt tends to zero. In this case, eq. 5.2 becomes:

$$\text{linear velocity at a } particular \text{ instant} = v = ds/dt \qquad (5.3)$$

This definition gives the *instantaneous* value of the velocity. Velocity is a vector quantity, and as such may be altered by changing its direction, as well as by changing its magnitude, (see chapter 8).

The expression 'speed' refers only to the magnitude of a linear velocity, and takes no account of its direction. Thus, it is possible for a point to travel at constant speed along a curved path, while, obviously, its velocity is constantly changing in direction. Here again, the same symbol v tends to be used for both speed and velocity, so that, in any particular instance, the meaning of the symbol should be carefully defined.

The term *average velocity* relates to a measurement taken over a finite period of time, and is defined thus:

$$\text{average velocity over the period} = \frac{\text{total displacement}}{\text{total time period}} \quad (5.4)$$

It should be appreciated that, throughout the period of time over which the total displacement is measured, the linear velocity, as given by eq. 5.3, may vary continuously. The exception, of course, is the case of uniform motion in a straight line, for which eq. 5.1 and 5.4 are identical.

In the same way, *average speed* is defined as follows:

$$\text{average speed over a period} = \frac{\text{total distance travelled}}{\text{total time period}} \quad (5.5)$$

Reference to Fig. 5.1 should make it clear that, for any given translation, the average speed and the average velocity may differ.

Similar definitions may be quoted for angular velocity and angular speed. The distinction between these two quantities again lies in the fact that the former takes into account the direction, i.e., the axis of rotation, of the motion. This book will restrict itself to problems in which the direction of the axis remains unchanged, so that this distinction need not be of concern.

The symbol ω is used to represent angular velocity, when measured in radian/second, so that, in general,

$$\text{angular velocity at a } \textit{particular} \text{ instant} = \omega = d\theta/dt \quad (5.6)$$

When the velocity of a body changes with time, it is said to possess an *acceleration*. An acceleration, in any given direction, may be either positive or negative. A negative acceleration, otherwise known as a 'deceleration' or 'retardation', implies that the speed of the body reduces with time. However, being a vector quantity, acceleration may be changed in direction as well as in magnitude.

The acceleration of a body may be defined as the rate at which its velocity is changing with time. This definition is true for both linear and angular motion, so that:

$$\text{linear acceleration at a } \textit{particular} \text{ instant} = a = dv/dt \quad (5.7)$$

$$\text{angular acceleration at a } \textit{particular} \text{ instant} = \alpha = d\omega/dt \quad (5.8)$$

Equations 5.7 and 5.8, again, use the calculus notation in which infinitely small changes in velocity are compared with infinitely small periods of time. These are the general expressions for acceleration.

For the particular case of uniform acceleration in a straight line, the rate at which the speed or velocity changes does not vary, in which case:

$$\text{acceleration at } every \text{ instant} = \frac{\text{change in velocity}}{\text{time taken}} \tag{5.9}$$

Equation 5.9 is applicable to both linear and angular motion.

5.2 Space-time graph

Figure 5.2 shows a graph in which the distance travelled by a body is plotted as a function of time.

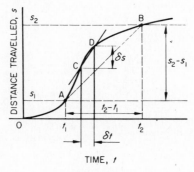

TIME, t

Figure 5.2

At time t_1, the distance travelled is s_1, and this condition is represented by point A. At time t_2, the distance travelled is s_2, and this condition is represented by point B. From eq. 5.5, the average speed over the period between these two times is given by:

$$\text{average speed} = (s_2 - s_1)/(t_2 - t_1) = \text{slope of the chord AB}$$

Suppose now that the period of time $(t_2 - t_1)$ is reduced to a very small period δt, as shown. Again, from eq. 5.5,

$$\text{average speed over the period } \delta t = \delta s/\delta t = \text{slope of chord CD}$$

If now δt is made infinitely small the chord CD becomes a tangent to the curve at a point corresponding to a particular instant in time:

$$\text{speed at this instant} = ds/dt = \text{slope of the tangent} \tag{5.10}$$

6

For straight line motion, in which there is no distinction between speed and velocity, eq. 5.10 is the same as eq. 5.3.

If s is replaced by θ, Fig. 5.2 and the above remarks also apply to angular motion.

5.3 Speed-time graph

Consider, now, the graph of Fig. 5.3, which shows the variation of speed with time. Equation 5.10 shows that a relationship exists between this graph and the space-time graph of Fig. 5.2. This relationship is that, at any particular instant in time, the slope of the space-time graph is equal to the value of the speed given by the speed-time graph.

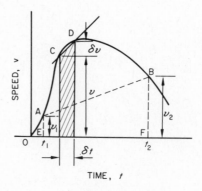

Figure 5.3

With reference to Fig. 5.3, suppose at time t_1 the speed is v_1, as indicated by point A, and at time t_2 the speed is v_2, as indicated by point B. The *average* acceleration over the time period $(t_2 - t_1)$ may be defined as:

$$\text{average acceleration} = \text{total change of speed/total time period}$$
$$= (v_2 - v_1)/(t_2 - t_1)$$
$$= \text{the slope of the chord AB}$$

Suppose, as before, the time period is reduced to δt, then:

$$\text{acceleration during the period } \delta t = \delta v/\delta t = \text{the slope of chord CD}$$

If δt now becomes infinitely small, this chord CD becomes a tangent to the curve at a point corresponding to a particular instant in time. Then,

$$\text{acceleration at this instant} = dv/dt = \text{the slope of the tangent} \qquad (5.11)$$

Since δt is very small (and in the limit infinitely small), the speed during this period may be assumed constant, the difference between v and $v + \delta v$ being negligible compared with v.

$$\text{Distance travelled during time } \delta t = \text{speed} \times \text{time}$$
$$= v\,\delta t$$
$$= \text{the area of shaded}$$
$$\text{strip (Fig. 5.3)}$$

If the areas of all similar strips between AE and BF are summated, the result will be the total distance travelled from time t_1 to time t_2. Thus, *the area under the speed-time graph represents the distance travelled.*

This corresponds to the mathematical process of 'integration', and the relationship may be expressed as follows:

$$\begin{array}{l}\text{total distance travelled} \\ \text{between time } t_1 \text{ and time } t_2\end{array} = \int_{t_1}^{t_2} v\,\mathrm{d}t = \text{area EACDBF} \qquad (5.12)$$

The speed-time graph is a very valuable tool in the solution of problems concerning motion (kinematics), since, in addition to *speed* and *time* values which may be read directly, measurement of its slope at any point gives the *acceleration* and the area beneath it gives the *distance travelled.*

A speed-time graph may similarly be drawn to represent angular motion, the vertical ordinate recording ω instead of v. In the same way, the slope of such a graph would represent angular acceleration, while the area beneath it would represent the angular displacement.

5.4 Acceleration-time graph

The variation of acceleration may likewise be plotted as a function of time. This is shown in Fig. 5.4, and this diagram will be related to the speed-time graph, by eq. 5.11, in the same way as the speed-time graph was related to the space-time graph. Each ordinate of the acceleration-time graph is equal to the slope of the speed-time graph at corresponding instants of time.

Conversely, and by the same arguments that were used in the preceding section, the total change in speed between times t_1 and t_2 will be given by the area under the acceleration-time curve:

$$\text{total speed change between times } t_1 \text{ and } t_2 = \int_{t_1}^{t_2} a\,\mathrm{d}t \qquad (5.13)$$
$$= \text{area ABCD}$$

Again, Fig. 5.4 may apply equally well to angular motion, a being replaced by α.

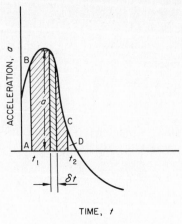

TIME, t

Figure 5.4

Worked examples

1. A man walks a distance of 1 km, due East, in a time of 10 min; and then a distance of 2 km, due North, in a time of 12 min.

Find (a) the total distance travelled (b) the total displacement (c) the average speed for the whole journey (d) the average velocity for the whole journey.

Figure 5.5 illustrates the man's journey.

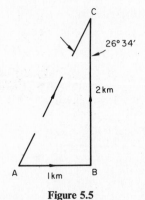

Figure 5.5

(a) Total distance travelled = 1 km + 2 km = 3 km.
(b) Total displacement = AC = $\sqrt{(1^2 + 2^2)} = \sqrt{(5)} = 2 \cdot 236$ km.
(c) Total time for the journey = 22 min = 1320 s.

From eq. 5.5,

average speed for the whole journey = 3000 m/1320 s
$$= 2{\cdot}273 \text{ m/s} = 8{\cdot}18 \text{ km/h}$$

(d) From eq. 5.4,

average velocity for the whole journey = 2236m/1320 s
$$= 1{\cdot}694 \text{ m/s} = 6{\cdot}10 \text{ km/h}$$

(in direction AC, i.e., 26° 34′ E of N).

2. A counter recording the revolutions of a flywheel was read at 30 s intervals over a 4·5 min period, and the figures recorded were as follows:

0, 603, 2340, 5000, 8264, 11 736, 15 000, 17 660, 19 397, 20 000

Draw the space-time graph for the motion, and hence estimate the greatest and least speeds of rotation of the flywheel, and the times at which they occur.

What is the average speed of the flywheel over the 4·5 min period?

The space-time diagram is shown plotted in Fig. 5.6. From eq. 5.10, the speed at any instant is given by the slope of this graph. By inspection, the greatest slope occurs half-way through the time period, i.e., at 2·25 min, when:

greatest speed = maximum slope = 17 500/2·5 = 7000 rev/min

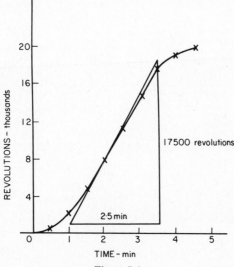

Figure 5.6

The least slope is seen to be zero, at the beginning, and at the end of the time period, i.e., least speed = 0, at zero time and at 4·5 min.

average speed of flywheel = total revs/total time = 20 000/4·5
= 4444 rev/min

3. A motor car is driven along a road and its speed is recorded at 30 s intervals. The speedometer readings, in km/h, are:

$$0, \quad 18, \quad 28, \quad 36, \quad 42, \quad 45, \quad 46, \quad 42, \quad 27, \quad 15, \quad 0$$

Plot the speed-time diagram, and hence estimate (a) the maximum acceleration and deceleration of the car (b) the total distance travelled (c) the average speed of the car.

The speedometer readings are first converted into m/s:

$$0, \quad 5, \quad 7·8, \quad 10, \quad 11·67, \quad 12·5, \quad 12·78, \quad 11·67, \quad 7·5, \quad 4·17, \quad 0$$

The speed-time graph is shown plotted in Fig. 5.7.

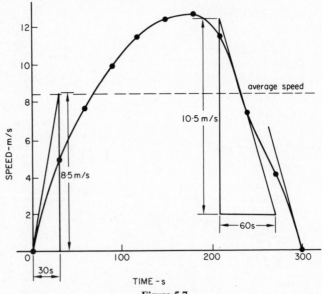

Figure 5.7

(a) The acceleration is given by the slope of this graph. By inspection, this is estimated to be a maximum at the start of the journey, i.e., $t = 0$,

maximum acceleration = 8·5/30 = 0·283 m/s²

The maximum deceleration, or maximum negative slope, is estimated to occur at $t = 230$ s, and also at the end of the journey, $t = 300$ s,

$$\text{maximum deceleration} = 10\cdot5/60 = 0\cdot175 \text{ m/s}^2$$

(b) Total distance travelled = total area under speed-time graph
$$= 2530 \text{ m} = 2\cdot53 \text{ km}$$

This area may be obtained by planimeter, mid-ordinate rule, or by any other accepted method.

(c) The average speed = total distance travelled/total time period
$$= \text{total area/base} = \text{mean height of the diagram}$$
$$= 2530/300 = 8\cdot43 \text{ m/s or } 30\cdot36 \text{ km/h}$$

4. A body accelerates uniformly from rest at the rate of 24 m/s² for a period of 0·6 s, and then at the rate of 5 m/s² for a period of 0·5 s. This is immediately followed by a period of uniform deceleration at the rate of 12 m/s², which brings the body to rest once more.

Sketch the acceleration-time diagram for the motion, derive from it the speed-time diagram, and hence determine: (a) the maximum speed of the body (b) the period of time for which the deceleration lasts (c) the total distance travelled.

Let $t = $ the period of time for the deceleration.

The acceleration-time diagram is shown in Fig. 5.8b. Each acceleration is represented by the horizontal lines BC, EF, and HJ, and the motion is seen to be divided into three distinct parts. In each part, the acceleration has a constant value, and it follows from eq. 5.11 that the slope of the speed-time graph is a constant in each part.

The speed-time graph is shown in Fig. 5.8a. Since the body is initially at rest, the graph starts at the origin and rises at the constant rate of 24 m/s each second (straight line LM). After 0·6 s, the slope, i.e., the acceleration, suddenly reduces to 5 m/s each second (straight line MN). After this, the slope of the graph is negative, since the acceleration is negative, the speed reducing to zero at the rate of 12 m/s each second (straight line NP).

(a) The maximum speed is seen to occur at N, i.e., after 1·1 s, and from eq. 5.13:

change in speed during the first 1·1 s = area ABCD + area DEFG
$$= (24 \times 0\cdot6) + (5 \times 0\cdot5)$$
$$= 14\cdot4 + 2\cdot5 = 16\cdot9 \text{ m/s}$$

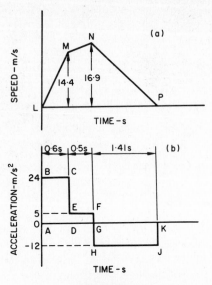

Figure 5.8

Since the initial speed was zero, this is the maximum speed. Thus, maximum speed = 16·9 m/s, and occurs at $t = 1\cdot1$ s.

(b) During the last part of the motion, the body must lose a speed of 16·9 m/s at the rate of 12 m/s each second. Therefore, the time required = $16\cdot9/12 = 1\cdot41$ s. Alternatively, if the total change in speed from beginning to end is to be zero, then the total area of the acceleration-time graph must be zero (eq. 5.13). Thus:

$$\text{negative area GHJK} = \text{area ABCD} + \text{area DEFG}$$
$$12 \times t = 16\cdot9 \text{ m/s}$$
$$t = 16\cdot9/12 = 1\cdot41 \text{ s}$$

(c) Total distance travelled = total area under speed-time graph

$$= \tfrac{1}{2}(0\cdot6)(14\cdot4) + \tfrac{1}{2}(14\cdot4 + 16\cdot9)(0\cdot5)$$
$$+ \tfrac{1}{2}(1\cdot41)(16\cdot9)$$
$$= 4\cdot32 + 7\cdot83 + 11\cdot90$$
$$= 24\cdot05 \text{ m}$$

5. A body accelerates uniformly from rest with a constant acceleration of 0·5 m/s² for a period of 8 s, and then continues to move at a constant speed.

Sketch the speed-time graph, and hence determine the time taken for the body to travel 25 m from the rest position.

The speed-time diagram is shown in Fig. 5.9.

Let V = the maximum speed. Then, since the acceleration is given by the slope of this graph,

$$\text{acceleration} = 0\cdot5 = V/8$$
$$V = 8 \times 0\cdot5 = 4 \text{ m/s}$$

Let t = the time taken for the body to travel 25 m from the rest position,

$$\text{shaded area of the diagram} = 25 \text{ m} = \tfrac{1}{2}(t + t - 8)\,4$$
$$25 = (t - 4)\,4$$
$$t = 4 + 6\cdot25 = 10\cdot25 \text{ s}$$

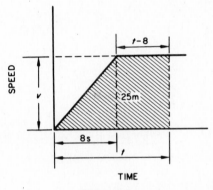

TIME

Figure 5.9

6. A poppet valve is operated by means of a cam, which is designed to impart to the valve uniform velocity during both the opening and the closing operations. The total lift of the valve is 6 mm, and the time taken for the valve to move from the fully closed to the fully open position is 1 millisecond (ms). The valve remains fully open for 0·5 ms, before dropping to the fully closed position during a further 0·75 ms. The valve remains fully closed for 0·75 ms before the cycle of operations is repeated.

Draw the velocity-time graph for the complete cycle of operations, and hence deduce the displacement-time and acceleration-time graphs. What must be the speed of rotation of the cam?

Each part of the motion is uniform, and therefore eq. 5.1 is applicable,

$$\text{speed rising} = \frac{6 \times 10^{-3}}{1 \times 10^{-3}} = 6 \text{ m/s}$$

$$\text{speed falling} = \frac{6 \times 10^{-3}}{0\cdot75 \times 10^{-3}} = 8 \text{ m/s}$$

Since the sequence of operations is periodic, it does not matter at which point in the cycle of events that time begins to be measured. It is convenient, here, to start the cycle with the 0·75 ms period when the valve is fully closed.

The velocity-time diagram is shown in Fig. 5.10b, and requires no explanation.

The displacement-time diagram is shown in Fig. 5.10a. The constant slope from $t = 0.75$ ms to $t = 1.75$ ms is equal to the velocity of 6 m/s, in accordance with eq. 5.10. From $t = 1.75$ ms to $t = 2.25$ ms, the slope is

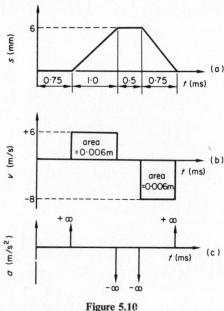

Figure 5.10

zero (since the velocity is zero), and from $t = 2.25$ ms to $t = 3.0$ ms the slope has the constant value of -8 m/s.

The acceleration-time diagram is shown in Fig. 5.10c. Acceleration is given by the slope of the velocity-time diagram (eq. 5.11), and Fig. 5.10b shows that, during each part of the motion, the slope is zero. However, sudden changes occur at $t = 0.75$ ms, $t = 1.75$ ms, $t = 2.25$ ms, and $t = 3.0$ ms, all of which correspond to *infinite* slopes, either positive or negative depending on the sense of the change. In practice, no change can be instantaneous, and the accelerations would not be infinite, as suggested by Fig. 5.10c: they would, however, be very large, leading to large inertia forces (see chapter 6), and such a situation would be undesirable.

From the diagram, the time for one complete cycle $= 3 \cdot 0 \times 10^{-3}$ s, so that, in $1 \cdot 0$ s, the cam must rotate through $1/(3 \times 10^{-3})$ revolutions.

speed of rotation of cam $= (\tfrac{1}{3}) \times 1000 \times 60 = 20\ 000$ rev/min

7. The displacement of a point, in metres, at any time t seconds, is given by the equation: $s = 8t + 15t^2 - t^3$.

Calculate the displacement, velocity, and acceleration of the point when $t = 4$ s.

$$\text{Displacement} = s = 8t + 15t^2 - t^3$$
$$\text{velocity} = v = \mathrm{d}s/\mathrm{d}t = 8 + 30t - 3t^2$$
$$\text{acceleration} = a = \mathrm{d}v/\mathrm{d}t = 30 - 6t$$

Thus, when $t = 4$ s,

$$\text{displacement} = s = 8(4) + 15(4)^2 - (4)^3 = 208 \text{ m}$$
$$\text{velocity} = v = 8 + 30(4) - 3(4)^2 = 80 \text{ m/s}$$
$$\text{acceleration} = a = 30 - 6(4) = 6 \text{ m/s}^2$$

5.5 Formulae for constant acceleration

Figure 5.11 shows a speed-time graph which describes the motion of a body having constant acceleration. Because the acceleration does not vary in any way, the slope of the graph is constant, i.e., the graph is a straight line.

For the case shown, the body has an initial speed u, which increases to speed v during a period of time t. Section 5.3 shows that the distance

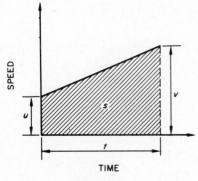

TIME

Figure 5.11

travelled, s, is represented by the area of the diagram (which is a trapezium) and the acceleration a is given by the slope of the graph.

$$s = \text{area of trapezium} = \tfrac{1}{2}(u + v)\, t \qquad (5.14)$$

$$a = \text{slope of graph} = (v - u)/t \qquad (5.15)$$

Note that, for constant acceleration, the average speed, which is equal to the mean height of the diagram, is $\tfrac{1}{2}(u + v)$. This is *only* true for the particular case of uniform acceleration. Equation 5.14 thus reads: total distance = average speed × time, which is only a re-statement of eq. 5.5. In the same way, eq. 5.15 may be expressed in words:

$$\text{acceleration} = \text{increase in speed/time taken,}$$

which is in accordance with the basic concept of acceleration.

These equations are a pair of simultaneous equations involving five variables, only four of which appear in any one equation. By eliminating each of the variables in turn, three further equations may be deduced. These are: $s = ut + \tfrac{1}{2}at^2$; $v^2 = u^2 + 2as$; $s = vt - \tfrac{1}{2}at^2$. Since in almost every case the initial speed u is known, there is little point in eliminating it from the equation. For this reason, the last equation is of little importance and may be discarded.

To sum up, although there are only two basic equations (5.14 and 5.15), two further equations may be deduced to provide four useful relationships for the solution of problems involving uniform acceleration:

$$\left.\begin{aligned}
s &= \tfrac{1}{2}(u + v)\, t \\
v &= u + at \\
s &= ut + \tfrac{1}{2}at^2 \\
v^2 &= u^2 + 2as
\end{aligned}\right\} \qquad (5.16)$$

Similar equations may be developed for angular motion. These are:

$$\left.\begin{aligned}
\theta &= \tfrac{1}{2}(\omega_1 + \omega_2)\, t \\
\omega_2 &= \omega_1 + \alpha t \\
\theta &= \omega_1 t + \tfrac{1}{2}\alpha t^2 \\
\omega_2^2 &= \omega_1^2 + 2\alpha\theta
\end{aligned}\right\} \qquad (5.17)$$

where ω_1 and ω_2 are the initial and final angular velocities.

On no account must eq. 5.16 and 5.17 be used where a change of acceleration occurs during the time period t.

5.6 Projectiles

When a body is projected into the air, its subsequent motion is controlled by gravity and will depend only on gravity and its initial velocity of projection.

This statement assumes that air resistance is negligible, and, since this may be appreciable at high velocities, the remarks made in this section should, strictly speaking, be applied only where velocities are limited to relatively low values. The consideration of air resistance, which is dependent on a number of factors (such as size and shape) in addition to velocity, would place the subject of motion under gravity outside the scope of this book. For this reason, it must be ignored, and the original statement will be held to be true. In many cases, however, the errors incurred will be small.

Thus, in the simplified theory of motion under gravity, the only acceleration the projectile possesses is that due to gravity (see sections 2.8 and 6.4). This is denoted by g, and any variation in its value, due to changes in position relative to the Earth, is very slight and may be neglected. The accepted mean value of g is 9·81 m/s^2. Motion under gravity is, therefore, a particular case of motion with uniform acceleration, and, as such, equations 5.16 are applicable.

The motion of a projectile may be in the vertical direction only or, as in the more general case, may have in addition a component in the horizontal direction. In the general case it is always convenient to resolve the motion into its horizontal and vertical components, as described in section 1.3. Since the force due to gravity is vertical, it is only the vertical component of the motion which is subject to the acceleration due to gravity.

It is necessary to adopt a sign convention for the vertical component of the motion. The *upward* direction will be considered *positive*. Consequent to this is the fact that the acceleration due to gravity must be considered negative. Thus, for any projectile,

$$\text{vertical component of acceleration} = -g \qquad (5.18)$$

$$\text{horizontal component of acceleration} = 0 \qquad (5.19)$$

(Note that the negative sign associated with g does not necessarily imply a deceleration. This will only be the case when the body has a positive, i.e., upward, velocity. When the body is falling, its speed will naturally increase, but both velocity and acceleration will then be negative.)

Consider, first, the case of a body which is projected vertically upwards with a velocity V. The body will subsequently rise to some vertical height

h, before falling back to its original position. The velocity-time diagram for the motion is shown in Fig. 5.12. This may be used to reduce the problem to one of simple geometry, as follows:

$$\text{slope} = -V/t_1 = -g \quad (\text{where } t_1 = \text{time to reach height } h)$$
$$\text{positive area} = \tfrac{1}{2}t_1 V = h$$

From which:

$$\text{time to reach greatest height} = t_1 = V/g$$
$$\text{greatest height reached} = h = \tfrac{1}{2}(V/g)\,V = V^2/2g$$
$$\text{total time of flight} = T = 2t_1 = 2V/g$$

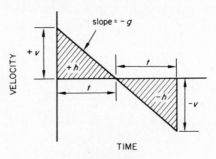

Figure 5.12

Alternatively, equations 5.16 may be used.
Considering the upward part of the motion only:

$$
\left.
\begin{aligned}
s &= +h \\
u &= +V \\
v &= 0 \\
a &= -g \\
t &= t_1
\end{aligned}
\right\}
\quad
\begin{aligned}
v^2 &= u^2 + 2as \\
0 &= V^2 - 2gh \\
h &= V^2/2g
\end{aligned}
\quad
\begin{aligned}
v &= u + at \\
0 &= V - gt_1 \\
t_1 &= V/g
\end{aligned}
$$

Considering the whole of the motion:

$$
\left.
\begin{aligned}
s &= 0 \\
u &= +V \\
v &= ? \\
a &= -g \\
t &= T
\end{aligned}
\right\}
\quad
\begin{aligned}
s &= ut + \tfrac{1}{2}at^2 \\
0 &= VT - \tfrac{1}{2}gT^2 \\
0 &= T(V - \tfrac{1}{2}gT) \\
&\text{Since } T \text{ is not zero} \\
V &- \tfrac{1}{2}gT = 0; \; T = 2V/g
\end{aligned}
\quad
\begin{aligned}
v &= u + at \\
v &= V - gT \\
&= V - g(2V/g) \\
v &= -V
\end{aligned}
$$

Suppose now that the initial velocity of projection has a magnitude V and a direction inclined at an angle α to the horizontal, as shown in Fig. 5.13. This diagram also shows the path of the projectile, and the total horizontal displacement, or range, is R, while the maximum vertical height reached is again h. The velocity of projection may be resolved into the horizontal and vertical components $V\cos\alpha$ and $V\sin\alpha$, respectively. Let the total time of flight be T, as before, and the time taken to reach the greatest height t_1.

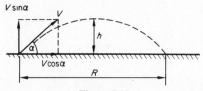

Figure 5.13

Consider the vertical component of the motion:

$$
\left.
\begin{array}{l}
s = 0 \\
u = +V\sin\alpha \\
a = -g \\
t = T
\end{array}
\right\}
\quad
\begin{array}{l}
s = ut + \tfrac{1}{2}at^2 \\
0 = (V\sin\alpha)T - \tfrac{1}{2}gT^2 \\
\text{from which,} \\
T = 2V\sin\alpha/g
\end{array}
\quad \text{(for the whole motion)}
$$

$$
\left.
\begin{array}{l}
s = +h \\
u = +V\sin\alpha \\
v = 0 \\
a = -g \\
t = t_1
\end{array}
\right\}
\quad
\begin{array}{l}
v^2 = u^2 + 2as \\
0 = (V\sin\alpha)^2 - 2gh \\
h = V^2\sin^2\alpha/2g
\end{array}
\quad
\begin{array}{l}
v = u + at \\
0 = V\sin\alpha - gt_1 \\
t_1 = V\sin\alpha/g
\end{array}
\quad
\begin{array}{l}
\text{(for the first} \\
\text{half of the} \\
\text{motion)}
\end{array}
$$

Consider the horizontal component of the motion:

$$
\left.
\begin{array}{l}
s = R \\
u = V\cos\alpha \\
a = 0 \\
t = T = 2V\sin\alpha/g
\end{array}
\right\}
\quad
\begin{array}{l}
s = ut + \tfrac{1}{2}at^2 \\
R = (V\cos\alpha)T + 0 = (V\cos\alpha)2V\sin\alpha/g \\
R = 2V^2\sin\alpha\cos\alpha/g = V^2\sin2\alpha/g
\end{array}
$$

Summary of formulae for the general case of Fig. 5.13:

$$\text{time taken to reach maximum height} = t_1 = V\sin\alpha/g \tag{5.20}$$

$$\text{maximum height reached} = h = V^2\sin^2\alpha/2g \tag{5.21}$$

$$\text{total time of flight} = T = 2V\sin\alpha/g \tag{5.22}$$

$$\text{horizontal displacement} = \text{range} = R = V^2\sin2\alpha/g \tag{5.23}$$

where V is the initial velocity of projection and α its inclination to the horizontal.

Worked examples

1. The armature of an electric motor normally rotates at 8000 rev/min. When the motor is switched on, a time period of 12 s elapses before the normal running speed is reached.

Assuming constant acceleration, calculate (a) the angular acceleration and (b) the number of revolutions made by the armature during this time period.

$$\left.\begin{array}{l} \omega_1 = 0 \\ \omega_2 = 8000 \times 2\pi/60 = 838 \text{ rad/s} \\ t = 12 \text{ s} \\ \alpha = ? \\ \theta = ? \end{array}\right\} \left[\begin{array}{l} \text{(a)} \quad \omega_2 = \omega_1 + \alpha t \\ \qquad 838 = 0 + \alpha 12 \\ \qquad \alpha = 69 \cdot 1 \text{ rad/s}^2 \\ \text{(b)} \quad \theta = \tfrac{1}{2}(\omega_1 + \omega_2) t \\ \qquad \theta = \tfrac{1}{2}(0 + 838)\, 12 \\ \qquad = 5028 \text{ rad} \\ \qquad n = 800 \text{ rev} \end{array}\right.$$

2. A body is projected vertically upwards with a velocity of 20 m/s. The point of projection is on the edge of a deep hole, so that, on returning to Earth, the body continues its descent to the bottom of the hole. The hole is 30 m deep. Assuming $g = 10$ m/s^2, determine: (a) the maximum height reached (b) the time taken to reach the maximum height (c) the total time of flight (d) the velocity with which the body strikes the bottom of the hole.

Consider the upward motion of the body:

$$\left.\begin{array}{l} s = h \\ u = 20 \text{ m/s} \\ v = 0 \\ a = -g \\ t = ? \end{array}\right\} \begin{array}{l} v^2 = u^2 + 2as \\ 0 = (20)^2 - 2gh \\ h = 400/(2 \times 10) \\ \quad = 20 \text{ m} \end{array} \qquad \begin{array}{l} v = u + at \\ 0 = 20 - gt \\ t = 20/10 \\ \quad = 2 \text{ s} \end{array}$$

(a) Maximum height reached above point of projection = 20 m.
(b) Time taken to reach maximum height = 2 s.
Consider the whole of the motion:

$$\left.\begin{array}{l} s = -30 \text{ m} \\ u = +20 \text{ m/s} \\ a = -g \\ v = ? \\ t = ? \end{array}\right\} \begin{array}{l} s = ut + \tfrac{1}{2}at^2 \\ -30 = 20t - \tfrac{1}{2}gt^2 \\ 5t^2 - 20t - 30 = 0 \\ t^2 - 4t - 6 = 0 \\ t = \dfrac{4 \pm \sqrt{(16 + 24)}}{2} \\ t = 2 + \sqrt{10}, \text{ or } 2 - \sqrt{10} \\ t = 2 + 3 \cdot 162 = 5 \cdot 162 \text{ s} \\ \text{(since the negative answer is impossible)} \\ v = u + at \\ v = 20 - gt = 20 - (10 \times 5 \cdot 162) \\ \quad = 20 - 51 \cdot 62 = -31 \cdot 62 \text{ m/s} \end{array}$$

(c) Total time of flight $= 5 \cdot 162$ s

(d) Velocity on reaching bottom of hole $= 31 \cdot 62$ m/s (downwards)

The velocity-time diagram for this motion is given in Fig. 5.14, from which the above answers may be deduced from simple geometry.

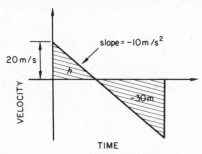

slope $= -10$ m/s^2

20 m/s

h

-30 m

VELOCITY

TIME

Figure 5.14

3. A jet of water issues from an orifice in the vertical side of a tank. In a horizontal distance of 0·5 m, the jet is observed to fall a vertical distance of 50 mm (Fig. 5.15).

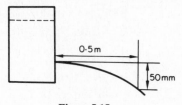

0·5 m

50 mm

Figure 5.15

Calculate the velocity of the jet as it leaves the orifice, assuming g to be 10 m/s^2.

Consider the vertical component of the motion:

$$\left. \begin{array}{l} s = -0 \cdot 050 \text{ m} \\ u = 0 \\ a = -g \\ t = \text{?} \end{array} \right\} \quad \begin{array}{l} s = ut + \tfrac{1}{2}at^2 \\ -0 \cdot 05 = 0 - \tfrac{1}{2}gt^2 \\ t^2 = 0 \cdot 05/5 = 0 \cdot 01 \text{ s}^2 \\ t = 0 \cdot 1 \text{ s} \end{array}$$

Consider the horizontal component of the motion:

$$\left. \begin{array}{l} s = 0 \cdot 5 \text{ m} \\ u = \text{?} \\ a = 0 \\ t = 0 \cdot 1 \text{ s} \end{array} \right\} \quad \begin{array}{l} s = ut + \tfrac{1}{2}at^2 \\ 0 \cdot 5 = u(0 \cdot 1) + 0 \\ u = 0 \cdot 5/0 \cdot 1 \\ \quad = 5 \cdot 0 \text{ m/s} \end{array}$$

The jet emerges from the orifice with a horizontal velocity of 5·0 m/s.

7

4. A shell is fired, from a position at sea level, at a target which stands on a horizontal plateau 420 m above sea level. The target is exactly 3 km from the firing position, measured horizontally. If the muzzle velocity of the shell is 500 m/s, determine the required elevation of the gun to the horizontal, and the time taken for the shell to reach the target. Take $g = 10$ m/s².

Let T be the total time of flight and α the required elevation.
Consider the horizontal component of the motion:

$$\left.\begin{array}{l} s = 3000 \text{ m} \\ u = 500 \cos \alpha \text{ m/s} \\ a = 0 \\ t = T \end{array}\right\} \begin{array}{l} s = ut + \tfrac{1}{2}at^2 \\ 3000 = (500 \cos \alpha)\,T + 0 \\ 6 = T \cos \alpha \\ T = 6 \sec \alpha \end{array}$$

Consider the vertical component of the motion:

$$\left.\begin{array}{l} s = +420 \text{ m} \\ u = +500 \sin \alpha \text{ m/s} \\ a = -g = -10 \text{ m/s}^2 \\ t = T = 6 \sec \alpha \end{array}\right\} \begin{array}{l} s = ut + \tfrac{1}{2}at^2 \\ 420 = (500 \sin \alpha)(6 \sec \alpha) - \tfrac{1}{2}(10)(6 \sec \alpha)^2 \\ 420 = 3000 \tan \alpha - 180 \sec^2 \alpha \\ 420 = 3000 \tan \alpha - 180(1 + \tan^2 \alpha) \\ 180 \tan^2 \alpha - 3000 \tan \alpha + 600 = 0 \\ 3 \tan^2 \alpha - 50 \tan \alpha + 10 = 0 \end{array}$$

This quadratic in $\tan \alpha$ may be solved to give:

$$\tan \alpha = 16\cdot47 \text{ or } 0\cdot2017$$
$$\alpha = 86° \; 30' \text{ or } 11° \; 24'$$

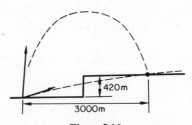

Figure 5.16

If the larger of these angles is used, the shell will descend on to the target, whereas if the smaller angle is used the shell will still be rising when it reaches the target (Fig. 5.16). This may be easily investigated by calculating the vertical component of velocity after a time corresponding to the smaller angle, and thus showing it to be still positive. Since the target is on a *horizontal* plateau, the shell must be made to drop on to it.

Therefore, the required angle of elevation = 86° 30′. The time taken for the shell to reach the target = T = 6 sec 86° 30′ = 98·3 s.

5.7   Relative velocity of unconnected bodies

By its very nature, all motion is relative. A body can only be said to 'move' if it changes its position in space relative to some other body. The whole concept of motion disappears when one supposes the existence of a single body in isolation. The displacement, velocity, and acceleration of a body may, therefore, be defined only in relation to some other body, or datum, which is usually regarded as 'fixed'.

It is most important to realize that the term 'fixed' is also a relative term. It is common practice, for example, to assume that the Earth is 'fixed', and velocities are accredited to bodies moving across its surface without any further reference being given. The Earth is by no means fixed, as everybody knows, but, for most purposes, it provides a very convenient datum from which to measure motion. In precisely the same way, other bodies, or points, may be used as reference datums from which motion may be measured. These points may then also be described as 'fixed', or 'at rest', and this description is just as valid for these points as it is for the Earth.

To be correct, therefore, the reference datum should always be given when specifying a velocity. This includes the state of rest, which, after all, is only the particular case of zero velocity. Thus, the velocity of a point P may be measured *relative to a point A*, or *relative to a point B*, or *relative to the Earth*. The choice of datum is purely a matter of convenience.

The velocity of a point P, relative to a point A, is defined as the velocity with which P appears to be moving to an observer situated at and moving with A. For convenience, the following notation will be used:

$$\text{velocity of P relative to A} = v_{PA}$$
$$\text{velocity of P relative to B} = v_{PB}$$
$$\text{velocity of A relative to B} = v_{AB}, \text{ etc.}$$

The letter O is normally reserved for use as a symbol representing the Earth. When the reference datum is the Earth, however, the fact is frequently taken for granted. Thus, one might write:

$$\text{velocity of P} = v_P$$

whereas, more precisely, this should be written:

$$\text{velocity of P relative to the Earth} = v_{PO}$$

Consider two points, A and B, with velocities v_A and v_B (relative to the Earth), as shown in Fig. 5.17. In order to visualize the velocity of B relative to A, it is necessary to place oneself in the position of 'an observer situated at and moving with A'. To the occupant of a moving motor car, the dashboard, interior, and all other visible parts of the vehicle appear stationary, while the road, houses, and trees appear to be in motion. The only effective way, therefore, of becoming such an observer is to bring A to rest, without disturbing the relative motion of A and B. This may be achieved by imposing on *both* A and B (and on all other bodies, including the Earth), the velocity $-v_A$. Then,

$$\text{total velocity of A} = v_A - v_A = 0$$
$$\text{total velocity of B} = v_B - v_A = v_{BA}$$
$$\text{total velocity of the Earth} = 0 - v_A = -v_A$$

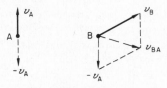

Figure 5.17

The point A is now 'fixed', and all other bodies are moving relative to it. Thus,

$$\text{velocity of B relative to A} = v_{BA} = v_B - v_A \qquad (5.24)$$

Note carefully that this is a *vector* difference. Figure 5.17 shows a possible method of combining the velocities v_B and $-v_A$ to give the resultant velocity v_{BA}, but reference should be made to chapter 1 (section 1.2 and Fig. 1.3) where a more general method of determining a vector difference is given. This method is used in the velocity vector diagram of Fig. 5.18, in which **oa** represents v_A, and **ob** represents v_B. The corresponding *small* letters **o**, **a**, and **b**, used in this vector diagram, are called *velocity images*

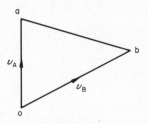

Figure 5.18

of the Earth, point A, and point B, respectively. The velocity image of the Earth, **o**, has special significance, and is known as the *pole* of the diagram. From eq. 5.24,

$$\text{velocity of B relative to A} = v_{BA} = v_B - v_A$$
$$= \mathbf{ob} - \mathbf{oa}$$
$$= \mathbf{ob} + \mathbf{ao} \text{ (since } -\mathbf{oa} = +\mathbf{ao}\text{)}$$
$$= \mathbf{ao} + \mathbf{ob}$$
$$= \mathbf{ab}$$

Note that the vector representing the velocity of B, relative to A, starts at **a** and finishes at **b**, just as the vector representing the velocity of B, relative to the Earth, starts at **o** and finishes at **b**. Thus, the general rule to remember is that, for any velocity vector diagram:

a velocity *relative to A*, is measured *from* **a**;
a velocity *relative to B*, is measured *from* **b**;
a velocity *relative to the Earth*, is measured *from* **o**;

or, in other words, the velocity image of the stated reference datum is the point *from* which all velocities are measured. If this rule is remembered, and understood, there should be no difficulty in reading a velocity vector diagram correctly to give the magnitude, direction, and sense of any velocity.

Velocity diagrams, such as that of Fig. 5.18, do not give any information regarding the relative *positions* of points in space. If such information is required, then a *space diagram*, or 'map' of the situation, is required. In many problems, both relative velocities and relative positions of bodies may be needed. For these problems, it is necessary to draw both a velocity diagram and a space diagram. In Fig. 5.19, the space diagram

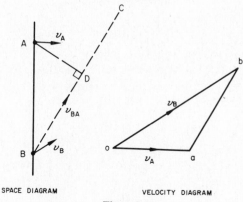

SPACE DIAGRAM   VELOCITY DIAGRAM

Figure 5.19

indicates the positions of two points, A and B, at a particular instant. A and B have velocities, relative to the Earth, as shown, and the velocity diagram gives their magnitudes, directions, and senses. If A is taken as the reference datum, i.e., assuming A is 'fixed', B will move with the velocity v_{BA} which is given by vector **ab**. Thus, if A is regarded as 'fixed', B will move along the path BC at speed v_{BA}. The shortest distance between A and B, at any time, will be AD, and the time taken for B to reach this position of closest approach is given by BD/v_{BA} (distance/velocity).

5.8 Relation between linear and angular motion

The distance travelled by a point which moves along a circular path, such as AB in Fig. 5.20b, is clearly related to the radius of the circle, r, and the angle θ subtended by the arc AB at its centre. In order to express this relationship simply, a unit of angular measure, called the 'radian', is defined.

One radian is the angle subtended at the centre of a circle by an arc whose length is equal to the radius of the circle. An angle of 1 rad is illustrated in Fig. 5.20a.

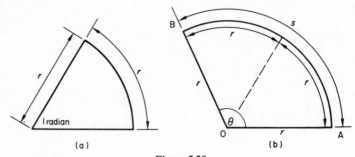

Figure 5.20

With reference to Fig. 5.20b, the number of radians subtended at the centre O by the arc AB, whose length is s, may be obtained by discovering how many lengths equal to the radius r are equivalent to the length s. For the case shown, the answer is obviously 2, but in general:

$$\theta = (s/r) \text{ rad} \tag{5.25}$$

Conversely, *provided θ is measured in radians*, the distance travelled along a circular arc of radius r may be calculated from eq. 5.25. Transposing, this becomes,

$$s = r\theta \tag{5.26}$$

Since the complete circumference of a circle subtends an angle of 360° at its centre, and the length of the circumference is $2\pi r$, the conversion factor relating degrees and radians is given by:

$$360° = (2\pi r/r) \text{ rad}$$
$$360° = 2\pi \text{ rad} \qquad (5.27)$$

The time taken for a point to travel along a circular arc, of length s, is of necessity the same as the time taken by the corresponding radial arm to rotate through the angle θ. If this time is t, then, from eq. 5.26,

$$(s/t) = r(\theta/t)$$
average linear speed $= r \times$ average angular speed

If θ is now made very small, the average linear speed, over the correspondingly very small time, becomes the instantaneous linear velocity and the average angular speed becomes the instantaneous angular velocity. This may be expressed mathematically, and more simply, by differentiating eq. 5.26 with respect to time:

$$ds/dt = r(d\theta/dt)$$

where r is a constant. Thus,

$$v = r\omega \qquad (5.28)$$

where v is the instantaneous value of the linear velocity, and ω is the instantaneous value of the angular velocity, *measured in radian/second*, and r is the radius of curvature of the path.

In a similar manner, an equation relating linear and angular acceleration may be deduced from eq. 5.28. By differentiation, this equation becomes:

$$dv/dt = r(d\omega/dt)$$
$$a = r\alpha \qquad (5.29)$$

In mechanical engineering science, the relationships expressed by eq. 5.26, 5.28, and 5.29 are constantly in use. For this reason, it is essential that they be memorized.

5.9 Relative velocity of points on a link

Two points on a rigid link are distinguished from two unconnected points by remaining, at all times, a constant distance apart. It follows that, if one point on a link is taken to be the reference datum—i.e., is regarded as being at rest—any other point on the link is constrained to move in a circle about it.

Figure 5.21 shows two such points, A and B, on a link. For convenience, two space diagrams are given, one indicating the motion of the points relative to the Earth, and the other their motion relative to A. In the latter space diagram, A is of course 'fixed' and, since AB is a constant length, v_{BA} must be perpendicular to AB. Instantaneously, B is rotating in a circle of radius AB about the centre A, with the velocity v_{BA}. Thus, from eq. 5.28,

$$\omega_{AB} = v_{BA}/AB = ab/AB \qquad (5.30)$$

The space diagram shows that this angular velocity is in the anticlockwise sense for the particular case considered. The vector **ab**, representing v_{BA}, is known as the velocity image of the link AB.

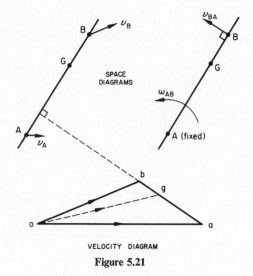

VELOCITY DIAGRAM

Figure 5.21

Suppose, now, that G is a third point on the link. For example, G might be the centre of gravity of the link. Since the link AGB is rigid, it is clear that $\omega_{AG} = \omega_{AB}$. Expressing this equality in the manner of eq. 5.30,

$$\frac{ag}{AG} = \frac{ab}{AB}$$

$$\frac{ag}{ab} = \frac{AG}{AB} \qquad (5.31)$$

The physical significance of this equation is stated below, and enables the velocity image of G to be inserted in the velocity diagram.

Three important facts have emerged from this discussion on the relative velocities of points on a rigid link. These are:

(a) *The velocity image of a rigid link is always perpendicular to the link.*

(b) *The angular velocity of the link is obtained by dividing its velocity image by the length of the link (eq. 5.30).*

(c) *The velocity image of any point on a rigid link divides the velocity image of the link in the same ratio as the point divides the link itself, (eq. 5.31).*

5.10 Velocity diagrams for simple mechanisms

If a number of rigid links are connected together, in a manner that permits constrained relative motion between them, a *kinematic chain* is formed. If one of the members of a kinematic chain is fixed, then it becomes a *mechanism*. By applying the rules deduced in the previous

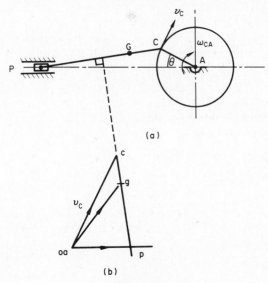

Figure 5.22

section, a velocity vector diagram may be drawn for any given position of the mechanism. This diagram is made up of the velocity images of all the links in the mechanism.

Consider the slider-crank mechanism shown in Fig. 5.22a. This is the mechanism used in reciprocating engines to convert the reciprocating motion of the piston into the rotary motion of the crankshaft. For this reason, it is often referred to as the 'simple engine mechanism'. Suppose the lengths of the crank AC, and the connecting-rod CP, are known, and that the angular velocity of the crank corresponding to a particular crank angle, θ, is given. It is then possible to calculate the velocity of the crank-pin, C, by using eq. 5.28: $v_C = AC\omega_{AC}$.

The velocity diagram is drawn by the following procedure.

(a) A pole o is selected to represent the velocity image of the Earth.

(b) The velocity images of any points which are fixed, relative to the Earth, will coincide with the pole. In this case, for example, the point A has zero velocity, and so the vector **oa** has zero length.

(c) The vector **oc** (or **ac**) is drawn, to some suitable scale, to represent the known velocity v_C in magnitude, direction, and sense. The velocity image of point C is, thus, obtained.

(d) *From* c a vector, of indeterminate length, but in a direction perpendicular to CP, is drawn to represent the velocity of P *relative to C* in direction only. The velocity image, **p**, must lie on this line.

(e) Since the point P is constrained, by fixed guides or a cylinder, to move parallel to the line of stroke, the velocity of P *relative to the Earth* must be horizontal (in this case). Therefore, a horizontal vector may be drawn *from* o to represent this velocity in direction, and which will locate the position of the velocity image **p** by intersection with the vector drawn previously (d).

(f) The velocity image of the point G, on the connecting-rod, is located by dividing **cp**, such that: (**cg**/**cp**) = (CG/CP).

The completed velocity diagram is shown in Fig. 5.22b.

From the velocity diagram, the following information may be extracted:

(a) the velocity of $P = v_P = $ **op**;

(b) the angular velocity of $CP = \omega_{CP} = $ **cp**/CP (this being anticlockwise since, if C is regarded as fixed, P has the velocity **cp** downwards);

(c) the velocity of $G = v_G = $ **og**.

Another basic mechanism is the *four-bar chain*, or *quadric cycle mechanism*, which is shown in Fig. 5.23a. The driver is the crank AB, and, if this is driven at (say) constant speed, the follower CD is made to perform some defined pattern of motion by virtue of the coupling rod BC.

If the angular velocity of AB is given, then v_B may be calculated: $v_B = AB\omega_{AB}$. This may be used to draw the velocity diagram, as shown in Fig. 5.23b. Again, the pole o is selected, and the velocity images of the fixed points A and D are shown coincident with it. Vector **ob** (or **ab**) is drawn, to some suitable scale, to represent v_B in magnitude, direction, and sense. By considering the velocity of C, first relative to B and then relative to D, the velocity images **bc** and **dc** may be drawn perpendicular to BC and DC, respectively, to locate the velocity image **c**.

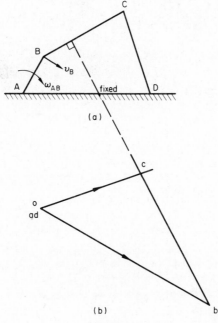

Figure 5.23

On completion of a velocity diagram for a mechanism, it is wise to check that all the velocity images are at right-angles to their corresponding links in the space diagram. In Fig. 5.23, **ab**, **bc**, and **dc** are at right-angles to the links AB, BC, and DC, respectively.

From Fig. 5.23b:

(a) velocity of C $= v_C = $ **oc**;

(b) angular velocity of the follower CD $= \omega_{CD} = $ **dc**$/$DC (which is clockwise, since D is fixed and **oc** is to the right);

(c) angular velocity of BC $= \omega_{BC} = $ **bc**$/$BC (which is anticlockwise, since, if B is regarded as fixed, C has the upward velocity **bc**).

Worked examples

1. Two motor cars, A and B, are travelling along straight roads towards cross-roads C. The angle ACB is 60°. At a particular instant, which,

for convenience, will be called zero time, car A is 5 km from C and is travelling at 100 km/h, while car B is 2 km from C and is travelling at 50 km/h.

Determine the shortest distance between the cars at any time, and the time at which this situation occurs.

The space and velocity diagrams are shown in Fig. 5.24. Let B be regarded as 'fixed'. Then:

velocity of A (relative to B) = **ba** = 86·6 km/h;
relative to B, A will move along the path AC', shown dotted in the space diagram, at the rate of 86·6 km/h;
shortest distance between the cars = BC' = 0·5 km;
time taken for A to move to C' = AC'/**ba**

$$= \frac{4\cdot33 \text{ km}}{86\cdot6 \text{ km/h}} = 0\cdot05 \text{ h} = 3 \text{ min}$$

Note that in this same time, the point C has moved, relative to B, with the velocity **bc** to the position C'.

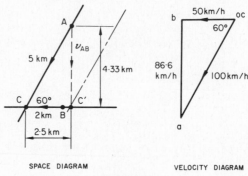

SPACE DIAGRAM   VELOCITY DIAGRAM

Figure 5.24

2. Figure 5.25 shows a velocity diagram, giving the velocities of points A, B, C, D, E, F, G, and H, relative to the Earth. The velocity of B is 10 m/s. From this diagram, determine the velocities of all the other points, including the Earth, relative to G.

Are all the points moving away from each other?

Velocities relative to G will be measured *from g* in the velocity diagram. Thus, relative to G,

velocity of A = **ga** = 20 m/s
velocity of B = **gb** = 22·36 m/s
velocity of C = **gc** = 28·28 m/s

velocity of D = **gd** = 22·36 m/s
velocity of E = **ge** = 20 m/s
velocity of F = **gf** = 10 m/s
velocity of H = **gh** = 10 m/s
velocity of the Earth = **go** = 14·14 m/s

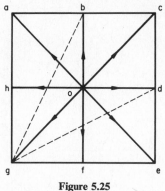

Figure 5.25

It is impossible to tell from the velocity diagram the relative *positions* of the points. Consequently, the points need not be moving apart.

3. A body is lowered at a constant velocity of 2 m/s by means of a rope wound round a drum, as shown in Fig. 5.26. The effective diameter of the drum is 0·2 m.

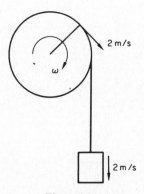

Figure 5.26

Calculate the angular velocity of the drum in rev/min, and the number of revolutions it makes while the body descends 15 m.

Assuming the rope does not stretch, each point on the rope has the same linear speed as the body. Thus, at any instant, linear velocity of a point on the circumference of the drum = 2 m/s. From eq. 5.28,

angular velocity of the drum $= \omega = v/r = 2/0 \cdot 1 = 20$ rad/s

If n is the speed of rotation in rev/min,

$$n = 20 \times 60/2\pi$$
$$= 191 \text{ rev/min}$$

As the body descends 15 m, this amount of rope is uncoiled from the drum.

From eq. 5.25,

$$\text{angle through which drum turns} = \theta = s/r$$
$$= 15/0 \cdot 1$$
$$= 150 \text{ rad}$$
$$\text{number of revolutions made} = 150/2\pi = 23 \cdot 9 \text{ rev}$$

4. A slider-crank mechanism is shown in Fig. 5.27a with the connecting-rod PC extended to B. $PC = 1 \cdot 0$ m; and $CB = AC = 0 \cdot 2$ m. For the

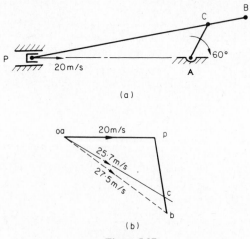

(a)

(b)

Figure 5.27

given configuration, draw the velocity diagram for the mechanism assuming that the instantaneous velocity of the piston is 20 m/s. Hence determine the velocity of B, and the angular velocity of the crank AC in rev/min.

The velocity diagram, shown in Fig. 5.27b, may be drawn as follows. Vector **op** is drawn, to a suitable scale, representing the given velocity of P. Since A is fixed, its velocity image will coincide with the pole **o**. The velocity of C, relative to A, is perpendicular to AC; the velocity of C, relative to P, is perpendicular to PC.

Vectors **ac** and **pc** are, therefore, drawn at right-angles to AC and PC, respectively, to locate the velocity image **c**.

Vector **pc** is produced to **b**, such that: **pc/pb** = PC/PB.

From the velocity diagram:

$$\text{velocity of B} = \mathbf{ob} = 27{\cdot}5 \text{ m/s}$$
$$\text{velocity of C} = \mathbf{oc} = \mathbf{ac} = 25{\cdot}7 \text{ m/s}$$
$$\text{angular velocity of AC} = (\mathbf{ac}/AC) = 25{\cdot}7/0{\cdot}2 = 128{\cdot}5 \text{ rad/s (clockwise)}$$
$$\text{speed of rotation of AC} = 128{\cdot}5 \times 60/2\pi = 1227 \text{ rev/min (clockwise)}$$

5. A four-bar chain mechanism, ABCD, is shown in Fig. 5.28. The crank AB is 0·25 m long, and rotates in an anticlockwise sense at 60 rad/s. The fixed link is 0·8 m long; the coupling rod is 1·1 m long; and the follower CD is 0·55 m long.

Draw the velocity diagram for the position shown, and hence find the angular velocities of CD and BC.

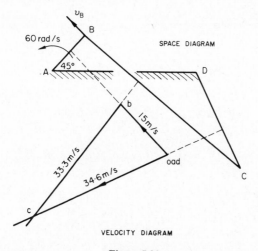

Figure 5.28

Since A and D are fixed, their velocity images coincide with the pole **o**,

$$\text{velocity of B} = AB\omega_{AB} = 0{\cdot}25 \times 60 = 15 \text{ m/s}$$

To a suitable scale, **ob** (or **ab**) is drawn to represent the velocity of B. The velocity images of the links BC and CD are perpendicular to their respective links. Thus, vectors **bc** and **dc** may be drawn to locate the velocity image **c**.

From the velocity diagram,

$$\mathbf{bc} = 33\cdot3 \text{ m/s}$$
$$\mathbf{dc} = 34\cdot6 \text{ m/s}$$

angular velocity of CD $= \omega_{CD} = \mathbf{dc}/DC = 34\cdot6/0\cdot55$
$$= 62\cdot9 \text{ rad/s (clockwise)}$$
angular velocity of BC $= \omega_{BC} = \mathbf{bc}/BC = 33\cdot3/1\cdot1$
$$= 30\cdot3 \text{ rad/s}$$

(This has a clockwise sense, since, if B is regarded as 'fixed', C has the velocity **bc**, which is downwards and to the left.)

Problems

1. An athlete runs 200 m in a time of 21·5 s. The first 150 m of the track is a semi-circle, and the remaining 50 m is straight.

Calculate (a) his total displacement in the given time (b) his average speed (c) his average velocity.

(*Answer.* (a) 107·8 m in a direction 117° 38′ to his initial direction of motion (b) 9·30 m/s (c) 5·02 m/s.)

2. An aircraft takes off from an airfield and flies 500 km due south in a time of 50 minutes, and then changes course to fly in a north-easterly direction for a further 30 min. The aircraft then lands at an aerodrome exactly 600 km from the point of take-off.

Determine (a) the total distance travelled (b) the average speed of the aircraft over the whole flight (c) the average velocity of the aircraft over the whole flight.

(*Answer.* (a) 1338 km (b) 1004 km/h (c) 450 km/h, 8° 54′ N of E.)

3. In a period of 25 s, the velocity of a body changes from 10 m/s due north to 20 m/s in a direction 30° west of north. Determine the average acceleration of the body over this period of time.

(*Answer.* 0·496 m/s², in a direction 53° 45′ west of north.)

4. The displacement of a body from a given point is recorded at 20 s intervals. Beginning with that corresponding to zero time, the displacements, in metres, are:

0, 4, 16, 36, 64, 100, 130, 140, 130, 110, 90

From these figures, deduce (a) the maximum speed of the body (b) the time at which it occurs (c) the times at which the velocity is zero (d) the average velocity over the whole period (e) the velocity at the end of this period.

(*Answer.* (a) 2 m/s (b) 100 s (c) 0 and 140 s (d) 0·45 m/s (e) −1 m/s.)

5. The wheels of a motor car have an effective diameter of 0·6 m. The speed of the vehicle, in m/s, was noted at intervals of 1 min during a journey lasting 12 min. The figures recorded were as follows:

0, 1·2, 4·8, 9·0, 12·0, 13·8, 14·4, 13·8, 12·0, 9·0, 4·8, 1·2, 0

From these figures, estimate (a) the total distance travelled by the vehicle (b) the average speed of the vehicle (c) the number of revolutions made by each of its wheels (d) the maximum angular velocity of each wheel (e) the maximum acceleration and deceleration of the vehicle, and the times when they occur.

(*Answer.* (a) 5·76 km (b) 8·0 m/s (c) 3056 (d) 48 rad/s (e) +0·08 m/s^2 at 2 min, −0·08 m/s^2 at 10 min.)

6. A cam is designed to raise a valve with a uniform acceleration of 100 m/s^2 lasting for 5 ms, followed immediately by a deceleration of 100 m/s^2 of similar duration. Draw the acceleration-time graph for the motion of the valve, and deduce from it the velocity-time graph. Hence find the maximum velocity of the valve and its total lift.

(*Answer.* 0·5 m/s, 2·5 mm.)

7. The armature of an electric motor requires 20 s to accelerate from rest to a speed of 1050 rev/min. After doing so, the motor is allowed to run at this speed for 2 min. The power is then switched off, and the armature turns through a further 700 rev before coming to rest.

Determine (a) the initial acceleration of the armature (b) the time taken for the armature to come to rest after the power is disconnected (c) the final deceleration of the armature (d) the total number of revolutions over the whole period.

(*Answer.* (a) 5·5 rad/s^2 (b) 80 s (c) 1·375 rad/s^2 (d) 2975.)

8

8. A rocket rises vertically with constant acceleration. After reaching a height of 1 km, the rocket is observed to rise from 1 km to 2 km in 1·3 s, and from 2 km to 3 km in 1·0 s.

Determine the acceleration of the rocket, and its velocity at the height of 3 km.

(*Answer.* 201 m/s^2, 1100 m/s.)

9. The angular position of a rotating body is given by the equation:

$$\theta = 10t + 6t^2 - 2t^3$$

where θ is measured in radians, and t is the time in seconds.

Determine the time when the body comes to rest, and find also the angular position and angular acceleration at this time.

(*Answer.* 2·633 s, 31·42 rad, or 5 rev, −19·6 rad/s^2.)

10. A car travelling at 25 km/h along a straight level road accelerates uniformly at 0·6 m/s^2 until its speed is 100 km/h. It maintains this speed for a period of time, and then decelerates uniformly at 2 m/s^2 until its velocity is zero. If the distance travelled by the car from the beginning of the acceleration period to finally coming to rest is 3 km, find the time of the constant velocity period.

(*Answer.* 79·4 s.)

11. A stone is projected vertically upwards with an initial velocity of 18 m/s. Assuming $g = 9·81$ m/s^2, and neglecting air resistance, find (a) the maximum height reached (b) the time taken to reach maximum height (c) the times at which the stone is at a height of 9 m.

(*Answer.* (a) 16·5 m (b) 1·835 s (c) 0·597 s and 3·072 s.)

12. A projectile is launched with an initial velocity of 300 m/s in a direction making an angle of 60° with the horizontal. Neglecting air resistance and assuming $g = 10$ m/s^2, find (a) the maximum vertical height reached (b) the range of the projectile (c) the total time of flight.

(*Answer.* (a) 3·375 km (b) 7·794 km (c) 52·0 s.)

13. The velocity of the jet leaving the nozzle of a fire hose is 50 m/s. At what angle of elevation must the nozzle be held if the water emerging from it is to strike the window of a blazing building in the shortest possible time? The height of the window above the ground is 25 m, and the nozzle is stationed 50 m from the foot of the building. Assume $g = 10$ m/s^2.

(*Answer.* 32° 40′.)

14. A and B are two points rotating in circles, at constant speeds, about the same axis O. The point A rotates at 15 rad/s in a circle of radius 20 mm, while B rotates in the same direction at 8 rad/s in a circle of 12 mm radius.

Find the velocity of A relative to B when the angle AOB is 60°.

(*Answer*. 0·265 m/s at 18° 16′ to the direction of motion of A.)

15. At noon, three ships, A, B, and C, lie on the same latitude. A is 100 km due west of B, and C is 200 km due east of B. The ship B is proceeding due north at 10 km/h, while A is sailing north-east at 20 km/h.

At what time will A and B lie on the same longitude, and what then will be the distance between them? What course and speed must the ship C maintain if it is to rendezvous with B at this time?

(*Answer*. 7·04 pm, A is 29·43 km due north of B, 70° 32′ west of north at 30 km/h.)

16. An engine mechanism, similar to that of Fig. 5.22a, has the following particulars: stroke 100 mm; length of connecting rod 220 mm; the centroid of the connecting rod is 60 mm from the crank-pin. Draw the velocity diagram for the mechanism when the crank angle, θ, is 25° past the inner dead-centre position, and the crank is rotating at 1050 rev/min. Hence, find (a) the instantaneous velocity of the piston (b) the instantaneous angular velocity of the connecting rod (c) the instantaneous velocity of the centroid of the connecting rod.

(*Answer*. (a) 2·85 m/s (b) 22·73 rad/s, anticlockwise if the piston is to the left of the crank (c) 4·4 m/s at 55° 45′ to the line of stroke.)

17. A four-bar chain, ABCD, has a fixed link AD, 0·2 m long, and B and C are on the same side of AD, in the manner of Fig. 5.23a. In this case, however, the angle BAD is 135° and AB rotates anticlockwise at 100 rad/s, i.e., in a direction tending to increase the angle BAD. AB = 0·1 m; CD = 0·3 m; and BC = 0·4 m.

Draw the velocity image of the mechanism for this particular configuration, and hence find the angular velocities of the follower CD and coupling rod BC, and the velocity of the mid-point of BC.

(*Answer*. 46 rad/s, 29·6 rad/s, both anticlockwise; 10·5 m/s, at 11° 45′ to AD.)

6. Force and acceleration

6.1 Recognition of a force by its effect

Although most people are familiar with the concept of force, it is a quantity not easy to define. It may be said that force is that which tends to alter the relative motion of, or to change the shape of, the body to which it is applied. A force can be recognized only by its effect on the body to which it is applied. A force must therefore be measured in terms of these effects.

The laws governing the effect of a force on the motion of a body have been set out by Sir Isaac Newton.

6.2 Newton's laws of motion

1. *A body continues in its present state of rest or uniform motion in a straight line unless acted upon by some external force.*
2. *The rate of change of momentum of a body is directly proportional to the resultant external force which is producing the change.*
3. *To every action there is an equal and opposite reaction.*

Newton's first law is a simple statement of the fact that if a force is applied to a body, the body will be affected in some way. If the force is unresisted, then the only effect possible is a change in its state of motion. The tendency of a body to continue in its present state of motion is called its *inertia*, and this property is found to be dependent on the mass of the body. The state of motion of the body is defined by its velocity, which is a vector quantity and may be changed in either magnitude or direction, or both. In considering the effect of a force on a body, therefore, the two quantities 'mass' and 'velocity' are very important, and it is convenient to define *momentum* as the product of mass and velocity. This is dealt with more fully in the next chapter.

Newton's second law postulates a relationship between the applied force and the change of momentum produced in a given time. This is a reasonable proposition, but one which requires verification by experiment.

102

Newton's third law is concerned with the resulting effects on the agency providing the external force. For example, a moving railway truck may be brought to rest by a pair of spring-loaded buffers. The buffers exert a force on the truck, thereby changing its momentum. This force may be detected and measured by observing its effect on the truck. However, it is also clear that the truck exerts a force on the buffers, as is evidenced by the compression of the buffer springs. These forces are equal and opposite.

6.3 Newton's second law of motion

This law is perhaps the most important of the three, since it provides a means of *measuring* a force.

Consider a body of mass m which is moving with a velocity u. Let an unresisted force F be applied to the body, so that a change of momentum will take place. Suppose that, after a time t, the body has a velocity v,

initial momentum of the body $= mu$

final momentum of the body $= mv$

change in momentum $=$ final momentum $-$ initial momentum

$$= mv - mu$$

(Note that this is a vector difference.)

Rate of change of momentum $= \dfrac{\text{change in momentum}}{\text{time taken}}$

$$= \frac{mv - mu}{t}$$

Then, according to Newton's second law,

$$F \propto \frac{mv - mu}{t}$$

If the mass, m, of the body remains constant, this may be written:

$$F \propto m\frac{(v - u)}{t}$$

But, from eq. 5.15,

$$\frac{(v - u)}{t} = a$$

where a is the acceleration of the body, so that:

$$F \propto ma \tag{6.1}$$

More precisely, using the calculus notation, Newton's second law states:

$$F \propto \frac{\mathrm{d}(mv)}{\mathrm{d}t}$$

If m is constant, this becomes:

$$F \propto m\frac{\mathrm{d}v}{\mathrm{d}t}$$

which is the same as eq. 6.1, since $\mathrm{d}v/\mathrm{d}t = a$ (eq. 5.7).

Equation 6.1 shows that the effect of a *force* on a body of constant mass, m, is to give it an *acceleration* in the same direction as the force. Furthermore, the equation also shows that force must have the dimensions of mass × acceleration,

$$\text{dimensions of force} = M\left(\frac{L}{T^2}\right) = MLT^{-2}$$

The unit of force may now be defined as the force required to give unit mass unit acceleration. In SI units, the unit of mass is the kilogramme (kg), and the unit of acceleration is the metre per second per second (m/s^2). The corresponding unit of force is called the *newton* (N).

1 *newton is defined as the force required to give a mass of* 1 *kg an acceleration of* 1 *m/s*^{2}. That is:

$$1 \text{ N} = 1 \text{ kg m/s}^2$$

With this system of units specified, the equation derived from Newton's second law may now be written:

$$F = ma \qquad\qquad (6.2)$$

6.4   The gravitational force on a body

The force of attraction between the Earth and a body is known as the force due to gravity. This force is proportional to the mass of the body (see section 2.8), and it follows that the acceleration due to gravity will be the same for all masses.

From Newton's second law,

$$a = \frac{F}{m} = \frac{\text{constant} \times m}{m} = \text{constant}$$

This constant acceleration is normally denoted by the symbol g, and has the value of 9·81 m/s^2,

$$\text{acceleration due to gravity} = g = 9\!\cdot\!81 \text{ m/s}^2 \qquad (6.3)$$

Newton's second law may now be used to express the force due to gravity which acts on a body:

gravitational force on a body = mass × gravitational acceleration
That is,

$$\text{gravitational force} = mg \qquad (6.4)$$

Thus, the force due to gravity on a mass of 10 kg will be 98·1 N. Note that arithmetic may be simplified by assuming that $g = 10$ m/s^2, in which case the force of gravity on a mass of 10 kg becomes 100 N. The error involved is less than 2%.

Worked examples

1. Calculate the force required to give a truck of mass 1000 kg (1 tonne) an acceleration of 2 m/s^2.

From Newton's second law,

$$
\begin{aligned}
\text{force} &= \text{mass} \times \text{acceleration} \\
&= 1000 \text{ kg} \times 2 \text{ m/s}^2 \\
&= 2000 \text{ kg m/s}^2 \\
&= 2000 \text{ N} = 2 \text{ kN}
\end{aligned}
$$

2. Calculate the acceleration given to a body of mass 50 kg by a force of 1 kN applied vertically upwards.

A diagram should first be drawn, as in Fig. 6.1, showing *all* the forces acting on the body.

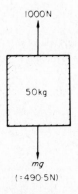

Figure 6.1

In this case, there are two forces acting on the body:
the vertical upward force of 1000 N;
the force due to gravity which acts vertically downwards.
Force due to gravity $= mg = 50(9{\cdot}81) = 490{\cdot}5$ N.
From Fig. 6.1, *resultant* force on the body $= 1000 - 490{\cdot}5 = 509{\cdot}5$ N
vertically upwards.
From Newton's second law,

$$F = ma$$

where F is the *resultant* force acting on the body.
Thus,

$$509{\cdot}5 = 50a$$

$$a = \frac{509{\cdot}5}{50} = 10{\cdot}19 \text{ m/s}^2, \text{ vertically upwards.}$$

3. A body lying on a smooth horizontal surface is subjected to the action of three horizontal forces whose magnitudes and directions are shown in Fig. 6.2a. If the acceleration of the body along the horizontal surface has a magnitude of 2 m/s², determine the direction of the acceleration and the mass of the body.

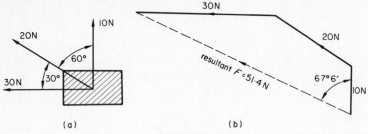

Figure 6.2

The resultant of the three forces must first be found by vector addition. From the force vector diagram of Fig. 6.2b,

resultant force $= F = 51{\cdot}4$ N, acting at $67°\ 6'$, to the 10 N force

Since the acceleration must always be in the same direction as the resultant force, this is also the direction of the acceleration.
From Newton's second law,

$$F = ma$$
$$51{\cdot}4 = m(2)$$
$$m = 51{\cdot}4/2 = 25{\cdot}7 \text{ kg}$$

4. Two masses of 10 kg and 20 kg lie on smooth planes inclined at 60°
and 30° to the horizontal, respectively, and are connected by a light,
inextensible, string which passes over a smooth cylinder at the top of the
planes, as shown in Fig. 6.3. Determine the acceleration of the system,
and the tension in the string.

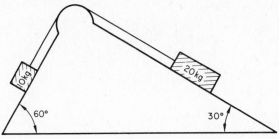

Figure 6.3

Where a number of bodies are involved in a problem, each body should
be considered separately.

A diagram should be drawn for each body, showing *all* the forces
acting on it, and an equation of motion for the body deduced from
Newton's second law.

Let F_T be the tension in the string, and a the acceleration of the system.
It will be assumed that the 10 kg mass accelerates *up* its plane, and the
20 kg mass accelerates *down* its plane. Should this assumption be
incorrect, a negative answer will be obtained for a.

Consider the 10 kg mass (Fig. 6.4). Three forces act on this mass: the
force due to the tension in the string, acting up the plane; the force due
to gravity, mg, acting vertically downwards; a normal reaction, R_1,
exerted by the plane on the mass.

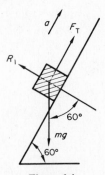

Figure 6.4

Since there can be no motion perpendicular to the plane, the effect of R_1 must be cancelled out by the component perpendicular to the plane of the force due to gravity. That is, resolving perpendicular to the plane, $R_1 = mg \cos 60°$.

The other component of the gravitational force, $mg \sin 60°$, acts parallel to the plane and opposes the force F_T, which is pulling the mass up the plane.

Resultant force in the direction of motion $= F_T - mg \sin 60°$.

From Newton's second law,

$$F_T - mg \sin 60° = ma$$
$$F_T - 10g \sin 60° = 10a \qquad (1)$$

This is the equation of motion for the 10 kg mass.

Consider the 20 kg mass (Fig. 6.5).

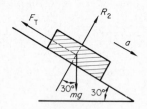

Figure 6.5

Again, since there can be no motion perpendicular to the plane:

$$R_2 = mg \cos 30°$$

Resultant force in the direction of motion $= mg \sin 30° - F_T$.

Note that, in this case, it is the tension F_T which opposes the gravitational force component pulling the mass down the plane.

From Newton's second law,

$$mg \sin 30° - F_T = ma$$
$$20g \sin 30° - F_T = 20a \qquad (2)$$

This is the equation of motion for the 20 kg mass.

Addition of eq. 1 and 2 gives:

$$20g \sin 30° - 10g \sin 60° = 20a + 10a$$

from which:

$$a = 1·34g/30 = 0·0447g = 0·438 \text{ m/s}^2$$

Substitution in eq. 1 gives:

$$F_T - 10g \sin 60° = 10(0·438)$$
$$F_T = 8·66g + 4·38 = 89·33 \text{ N}$$

5. A lorry and trailer, initially at rest, accelerate uniformly along a level road, and after travelling 1 km reach a speed of 54 km/h. The mass of the lorry is 3 tonnes, and that of the trailer 2 tonnes. Frictional resistances are equivalent to 0·2 N/kg. Calculate the tractive effort required, and the draw-bar pull, during the motion. (1 tonne = 1000 kg.)

The velocity-time diagram is shown in Fig. 6.6.

$$54 \text{ km/h} = 54\ 000/3600 = 15 \text{ m/s}$$

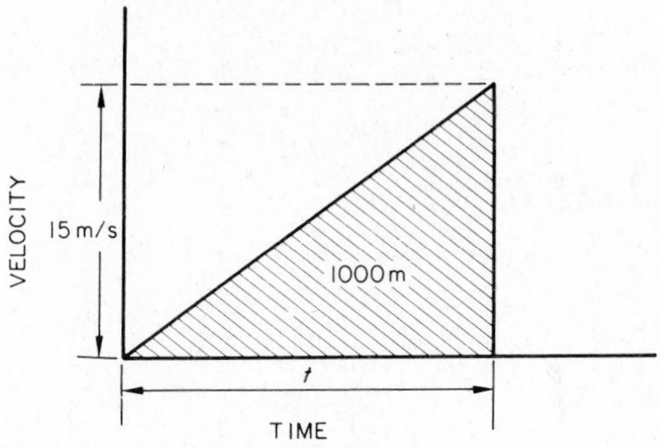

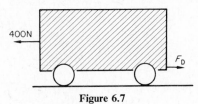

Figure 6.6

From this diagram,

$$\tfrac{1}{2}(t)\,15 = 1000 \text{ m}$$
$$t = 2000/15 = 133\cdot3 \text{ s}$$
$$\text{acceleration} = 15/133\cdot3 = 0\cdot1125 \text{ m/s}^2$$

Consider the trailer (Fig. 6.7).

Let the draw-bar pull $= F_D$
frictional resistance $= 0\cdot2(2000) = 400$ N
resultant force, $F = (F_D - 400)$ N

400N

F_D

Figure 6.7

From Newton's second law,

$$F = ma$$
$$F_D - 400 = 2000(0\cdot1125)$$
$$\text{draw-bar pull} = F_D = 400 + 225 = 625 \text{ N}$$

Consider the lorry (Fig. 6.8).

Let tractive effort $= F_E$
frictional resistance $= 0\cdot2(3000) = 600$ N
resultant force, $F = (F_E - F_D - 600)$ N

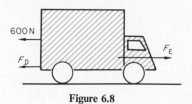

Figure 6.8

From Newton's second law,

$$F = ma$$
$$F_E - F_D - 600 = 3000(0\cdot1125)$$
$$\text{tractive effort} = F_E = F_D + 600 + 337\cdot5$$
$$= 625 + 600 + 337\cdot5 = 1562\cdot5 \text{ N}$$

Problems

1. A pit cage with a total mass of 1000 kg is at rest at the bottom of a mine shaft. The cage is raised with uniform acceleration, so that it rises 100 m in 20 s.

Calculate the tension in the cable.

(*Answer.* 10·3 kN.)

2. A body of mass 15 kg is at rest on a smooth plane inclined at 30° to the horizontal. When released, the body accelerates down the plane.

Calculate (a) the normal reaction between the body and the plane (b) the acceleration of the body (c) the distance travelled down the plane in 1 min.

(*Answer.* (a) 127·4 N (b) 4·905 m/s² (c) 8·829 km.)

3. A motor car, of total mass 1 tonne, is travelling at constant speed of 60 km/h up an incline of 1 in 30 against frictional resistances of 0·1 N/kg. Calculate the tractive effort required to maintain this constant speed.

If the engine is suddenly switched off, what will be the time taken for the car to come to rest?

(*Answer.* 427 N, 39 s.)

4. The table of a planing machine has a mass of 600 kg. The power is shut off during operation, and as a result the table comes to rest in 0·5 s after travelling a distance of 150 mm.

Estimate the force on the cutting tool, assuming this to be independent of speed. The coefficient of sliding friction between the table and the machine bed may be taken to be 0·1.

(*Answer*. 131·4 N.)

5. Masses of 12 kg and 18 kg are connected by a light inextensible string. The string is passed over a smooth peg, so that the masses hang down vertically on either side. If the system is then released, calculate its acceleration, and the tension in the string.

(*Answer*. 1·96 m/s², 141·3 N.)

6. A light inextensible string carrying masses of 5 kg and 4 kg, respectively, at each end is passed over a fixed steel pin of mass 1 kg. The axis of the pin is horizontal and the masses hang down vertically on either side. When the system is released, the larger mass is observed to fall from rest through a vertical height of 900 mm in 2 seconds. Calculate: (a) the total circumferential force of friction between pin and string, (b) the total vertical force required to support the pin during the motion.

(*Answer*. (*a*) 5·76 N (b) 97·65 N.)

7. A motor car has a mass of 1200 kg and is uniformly accelerated from rest to a speed of 72 km/h in a distance of 50 m on a level road. Assuming that the total resistances to motion amount to a force of 0·2 N/kg, determine: (a) the propulsive force of the vehicle, (b) the change in momentum.

(*Answer*. (a) 5·04 kN (b) 24 000 kg m/s.)

8. A locomotive of mass 100 tonne is used to draw a train of mass 400 tonne. Resistances to motion are equivalent to 0·1 N/kg for both locomotive and train. If the draw-bar pull between locomotive and train is not to exceed 200 kN, determine: (a) the maximum acceleration which can be achieved on a level track, (b) the maximum gradient which can be ascended at constant speed, (c) the tractive effort exerted by the locomotive in each of these cases.

(*Answer*. (a) 0·4 m/s² (b) 1/24·5 (c) 250 kN in both cases.)

7. Momentum

7.1 Definition

When a body has motion, there are two questions which an engineer must ask. What is the velocity of the body? How much matter is moving with this velocity? The answers to these questions are represented, respectively, by the velocity, v, and the mass, m, of the body. If either is increased, then so is the total 'quantity of motion' of the system. It follows that the product of mass and velocity is a measure of the 'quantity of motion' of the body, and this is called the *momentum* of the body,

$$\text{momentum of the body} = mv \qquad (7.1)$$

It should be clear from this definition that a small mass with a large velocity may have the same momentum, or quantity of motion, as a large mass with a small velocity.

Since velocity is a vector quantity, the product of mass and velocity must also be a vector quantity. Thus, momentum is a vector quantity, and consideration must always be given to its direction and sense, as well as its magnitude.

7.2 Impulsive forces

Newton's second law shows that the effect of a force on a body is to bring about a change in momentum *in a given time*. This provides a useful method of measuring a force, but such a measurement becomes difficult if the time taken for the change is very small. This would be the case if a body was subjected to a sudden blow, shock load, or impact. In such cases, it may well be possible to measure the change in momentum with reasonable accuracy, but the time duration of the impact force may be in doubt and, in the absence of special equipment, may have to be estimated. Forces of this type, having a short time duration, are called *impulsive forces*, and their effect on the body to which they are applied, that is the change of momentum produced, is called an *impulse*.

112

From Newton's second law,

$$\text{impulsive force, } F = \frac{\text{change in momentum}}{\text{time taken}} = \frac{\text{change in momentum}}{\delta t} \quad (7.2)$$

where the time taken, δt, is very small.

$$\text{impulse of the force} = F\delta t = \text{change in momentum} \quad (7.3)$$

These equations show that, for a given impulse or change in momentum, an impulsive force will be very large if the time duration is very small.

7.3 Impact of jets on fixed vanes

Figure 7.1 shows a curved vane, AB, which is fixed. A jet of fluid impinges on the vane, entering it tangentially at A with a velocity v_i, and leaving it at B with a velocity v_o. If there is no friction between the jet and the vane,

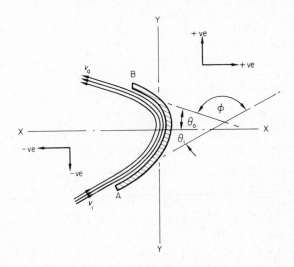

Figure 7.1

the speed, v, of the jet will remain unaltered, and the difference between v_i and v_o will be one of direction only. Consider a mass m of the fluid, which is deflected in this way. In general,

$$\text{change in momentum} = \text{final momentum} - \text{initial momentum}$$
$$= mv_0 - mv_i$$
$$= \mathbf{ob} - \mathbf{oa} = \mathbf{ab} \text{ (Fig. 7.2)}$$

If m is the mass of fluid passing over the vane in unit time, the vector **ab** will represent the change in momentum of the fluid per unit time, which by Newton's second law is the force acting on the fluid. By Newton's third law, the force on the vane will be equal and opposite, and is given by vector **ba**.

From Fig. 7.2,

$$\text{force on the vane} = \mathbf{ba} = 2mv \sin(\phi/2) \qquad (7.4)$$

where ϕ is the angle through which the jet is deflected and m is the mass flow per unit time.

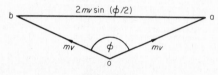

Figure 7.2

This force may, of course, be resolved into components at right-angles—for example, in the directions X–X and Y–Y of Fig. 7.1. Alternatively, the initial and final momenta of the jet may be resolved into components in these directions. With reference to Fig. 7.1,

$$\text{initial momentum in direction X–X} = +mv \cos \theta_i$$
$$\text{final momentum in direction X–X} = -mv \cos \theta_0$$
$$\text{change in momentum in direction X–X} = \text{final momentum–initial}$$
$$\text{momentum}$$
$$= (-mv \cos \theta_0) - (+mv \cos \theta_i)$$
$$= -(mv \cos \theta_0 + mv \cos \theta_i)$$

Again, if m is the mass flow per unit time, this becomes the rate of change of momentum in the direction X–X, and is thus the force *on the jet* in this direction. The force *on the vane* is equal and opposite,

$$\text{force on the vane in direction X–X} = +(mv \cos \theta_0 + mv \cos \theta_i) \qquad (7.5)$$

The force in the direction Y–Y may be obtained in a similar manner,

$$\text{change in momentum of jet in direction Y–Y} = mv \sin \theta_0 - mv \sin \theta_i$$

which is the force exerted by the vane on the jet in the direction Y–Y, if m is the mass flow per unit time. The force exerted by the jet on the vane is equal and opposite,

$$\text{force on the vane in direction Y–Y} = -(mv \sin \theta_0 - mv \sin \theta_i) \qquad (7.6)$$

Note that the forces given by eq. 7.5 and 7.6 are components of a single force, and their resultant will be the same as that given by eq. 7.4.

It is not intended that eq. 7.4, 7.5, and 7.6 should be memorized. What is important is the principles employed in obtaining them.

Suppose that the cross-sectional area of a jet is A. In unit time, a prism of fluid of volume Av will pass a given point in space. Thus,

$$\text{volumetric flow/unit time} = Av \qquad (7.7)$$

$$\text{mass flow/unit time} = \rho Av \qquad (7.8)$$

where ρ is the density of the fluid and v is the velocity of the jet.

Consider the particular case when $\theta_i = \theta_0 = \theta$ (Fig. 7.1).

From eq. 7.6, force on vane in direction Y–Y $= 0$.

From eq. 7.5, force on vane in direction X–X $= 2mv\cos\theta$,

$$\text{resultant force on the vane} = 2(\rho Av)v\cos\theta = 2\rho Av^2\cos\theta \qquad (7.9)$$

Since, in this case, the angle of deflection $\phi = 180° - 2\theta$, the same result is obtainable from eq. 7.4.

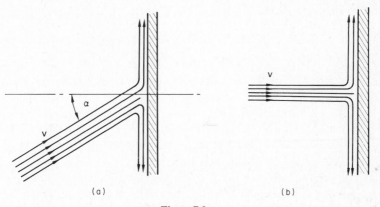

(a)   (b)

Figure 7.3

Consider, also, the particular case of a jet which impinges on a fixed flat plate as shown in Fig. 7.3a. After striking the plate, the fluid flows tangentially to the plate, so that, *normal to the plate*, the final momentum is zero.

$$\text{Initial momentum, normal to the plate} = mv\cos\alpha$$
$$= (\rho Av)v\cos\alpha$$
$$= \rho Av^2\cos\alpha$$

9

Rate of change of momentum, normal to the plate $= 0 - \rho A v^2 \cos \alpha$. This, by Newton's second law, is the force exerted by the plate on the jet. From Newton's third law,

$$\text{normal force on plate due to the jet} = +\rho A v^2 \cos \alpha \qquad (7.10)$$

If the jet is normal to the plate, as in Fig. 7.3b, then $\alpha = 0$, and

$$\text{normal force on plate due to the jet} = \rho A v^2 \qquad (7.11)$$

In the previous chapter, section 6.3, it was shown that force has the dimensions MLT^{-2}, where M, L, and T represent mass, length, and time, respectively. The expression for the force of impact of a jet on a fixed plate, as given by eq. 7.11, should therefore have the same dimensions. The density ρ is the mass per unit volume and thus has the dimensions M/L^3; the area A has the dimension L^2; and the velocity v has the dimensions L/T. Thus,

$$\text{the dimensions of } \rho A v^2 = \frac{M}{L^3} L^2 \left(\frac{L}{T}\right)^2 = ML/T^2 = MLT^{-2}$$

7.4 Conservation of momentum

Suppose a mass A overtakes a mass B as shown in Fig. 7.4a. On impact (Fig. 7.4b), the mass B will be accelerated by an impulsive force delivered by A, while the mass A will be decelerated by an impulsive force delivered by B. In accordance with Newton's third law, these impulsive forces, F,

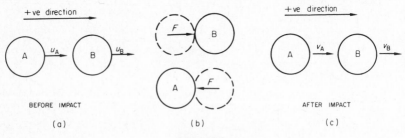

BEFORE IMPACT

(a)

(b)

AFTER IMPACT

(c)

Figure 7.4

will be equal and opposite and must, of course, act for the same small period of time, δt. After impact, A will in general have some velocity, v_A, and B some velocity, v_B, as shown in Fig. 7.4c,

$$\text{impulse received by } B = +F\delta t$$
$$= \text{change in momentum of } B = m_B v_B - m_B u_B$$
$$\text{impulse received by } A = -F\delta t$$
$$= \text{change in momentum of } A = m_A v_A - m_A u_A$$

By addition of these equations

$$0 = \text{total change in momentum of } A \text{ and } B$$
$$= (m_A v_A + m_B v_B) - (m_A u_A + m_B u_B)$$

This may be written in either of two ways:

(a) $m_A u_A + m_B u_B \quad = m_A v_A + m_B v_B$

total momentum = total momentum   (7.12)

before impact   after impact

(b) total change in the momentum

of the system, comprising A and $B = 0$ (7.13)

This is known as the principle of *conservation of momentum*. This principle may be extended to systems comprising any number of masses, and is true provided no external forces act on the system, and that mass is neither added to nor removed from the system.

For a closed system, the total linear momentum in any given direction remains constant.

The principle will be found to hold for angular motion as well, although this will not be considered here.

The principle of conservation of *momentum* must not be confused with the principle of conservation of *energy*, which is discussed in section 10.8. There are two major differences which must always be borne in mind. Momentum is a vector quantity, whereas energy is a scalar quantity; and energy can exist in many different forms, whereas momentum can not. For example, when two bodies collide, as in Fig. 7.4, the momentum of the system remains constant, but a loss of mechanical energy will occur due to the conversion, and subsequent dissipation, of some of the energy into sound and heat.

This loss of energy is due to the inelastic deformation of the bodies which occurs during impact. Experiments, conducted by Newton, showed that the relative velocity of the bodies was reduced and reversed by the impact so that, with reference to Fig. 7.4,

$$(v_A - v_B) = -e(u_A - u_B)$$ (7.14)

where e is a constant, less than unity, known as the *coefficient of restitution*, and depends only on the material of the bodies. If $e = 1.0$, the material would be perfectly elastic and no energy loss would occur. If $e = 0$, the material is perfectly plastic and the energy loss is a maximum, both bodies having a common velocity after impact. In practice, the former situation would never be achieved, and the latter only rarely.

Worked examples

1. Calculate the momentum of a body of mass 1 tonne, which is falling with a velocity of 7 m/s.

1 tonne = 1000 kg. Momentum of the body = mv = 1000 × 7 = 7000 kg m/s (vertically downwards).

2. A hammer head with a mass of 0·75 kg strikes a nail with a velocity of 1·2 m/s and after impact rebounds with a velocity of 0·20 m/s. Assuming the duration of the impact to be 0·5 ms, determine the impulsive force applied by the hammer.

Consider the direction of motion of the hammer head before impact to be positive,

$$\text{momentum of hammer head before impact} = +0\cdot75(1\cdot2)$$
$$= +0\cdot90 \text{ kg m/s}$$
$$\text{momentum of hammer head after impact} = -0\cdot75(0\cdot20)$$
$$= -0\cdot15 \text{ kg m/s}$$

$$\text{impulse on hammer head} = \text{change in momentum}$$
$$= \text{final momentum–initial momentum}$$
$$= (-0\cdot15) - (+0\cdot90) = -1\cdot05 \text{ kg m/s}$$

$$\text{impulse on nail} = +1\cdot05 \text{ kg m/s}$$
$$F \times (0.5 \times 10^{-3}) = +1\cdot05 \text{ kg m/s}$$

$$\text{impulsive force exerted by hammer} = F = 1\cdot05/(0\cdot5 \times 10^{-3}) \text{ kg m/s}^2$$
$$= 2\cdot10 \times 10^3 \text{ N} = 2\cdot10 \text{ kN}$$

3. A jet of water is 8 mm diameter and has a velocity of 15 m/s. The jet is directed towards a fixed flat plate. Calculate the force of impact normal to the plate, if (a) the jet is normal to the plate (b) the jet is inclined at 45° to the normal.

The density of water = 1000 kg/m³; c.s.a. of jet = $\pi 8^2/4$ = 50 mm².
(a) From eq. 7.11,

$$\text{force on plate} = \rho A v^2$$
$$= 1000(50 \times 10^{-6})15^2 \text{ N}$$
$$= 11\cdot25 \text{ N}$$

(b) From eq. 7.10,
$$\text{force on plate} = \rho A v^2 \cos \alpha$$
$$= 11\cdot25 \cos 45° = 7\cdot95 \text{ N}$$

4. A jet of water with a diameter of 50 mm and a velocity of 32 m/s is deflected through an angle of 60° by a fixed curved vane. Determine the magnitude and direction of the resultant force on the vane. The density of water is 1000 kg/m³.

$$\text{c.s.a. of jet} = \pi 50^2/4 = 1963 \text{ mm}^2 = 1\cdot963 \times 10^{-3} \text{ m}^2$$

$$\text{mass flow per unit time} = \rho Av = 1000(1\cdot963 \times 10^{-3}) \, 32 = 62\cdot8 \text{ kg/s}$$

$$\begin{aligned}
\text{initial momentum of } 62\cdot8 \text{ kg of water} &= mv_i \\
&= 62\cdot8 \times 32 \\
&= 2010 \text{ kg m/s} \\
&= \textbf{oa} \text{ (Fig. 7.5)}
\end{aligned}$$

$$\text{final momentum} = mv_0 = 2010 \text{ kg m/s} = \textbf{ob} \text{ (Fig. 7.5)}$$
$$\text{change in momentum per unit time} = \textbf{ob} - \textbf{oa} = \textbf{ab}$$

This is the force exerted by the vane on the jet. The force on the vane is equal and opposite,

$$\text{force on the vane} = \textbf{ba} = 2010 \text{ kg m/s}^2 = 2010 \text{ N} = 2\cdot010 \text{ kN}$$

in the direction indicated in Fig. 7.5.

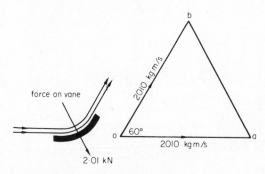

Figure 7.5

5. A gun fires a shell of mass 10 kg with a muzzle velocity of 700 m/s at 25° to the horizontal. The gun is mounted on wheels on level ground, and has a mass of 2·5 tonne. Calculate the velocity of recoil of the gun.

The principle of conservation of linear momentum may be applied to the closed system comprising the shell and gun. Consider the horizontal momentum of the system,

$$\text{total momentum after firing} = \text{total momentum before firing}$$
$$m_G v_G + m_S v_S = 0 \quad \text{(where suffixes G and S represent gun and shell, respectively)}$$

$$2500v_G + 10(700\cos 25°) = 0$$
$$v_G = -6344/2500 = -2·54 \text{ m/s}$$

The negative sign indicates that the gun moves in the opposite direction to the shell.

6. A mass A of 50 kg has a velocity of 4 m/s. A mass B of 20 kg has a velocity of 12 m/s in the opposite direction to A. Both masses are travelling in the same straight line, towards each other. Determine the total momentum of the system before and after impact, the total energy of the system before and after impact, and the velocities of the masses after impact, assuming (a) the bodies are perfectly inelastic (b) the bodies are perfectly elastic (c) the coefficient of restitution is 0·75.

Since the system is free from interference from any external source, the principle of conservation of linear momentum will apply, regardless of the value of e,

> total momentum of the system, before
> and after impact, under all conditions

$$= 50(+4) + 20(-12)$$
$$= 200 - 240 \text{ kg m/s}$$
$$= -40 \text{ kg m/s}$$

> total energy of the system before impact

$$= \text{k.e. of } A + \text{k.e. of } B$$
$$= \tfrac{1}{2}m_A u_A^2 + \tfrac{1}{2}m_B u_B^2 \text{ (see section 10.7)}$$
$$= \tfrac{1}{2}50(4)^2 + \tfrac{1}{2}20(-12)^2 \text{ J}$$
$$= 400 + 1440 = 1840 \text{ J} = 1·84 \text{ kJ}$$

(a) If the bodies are perfectly inelastic, $e = 0$, and the relative velocity of the bodies after impact is zero. The bodies thus have a common velocity v after impact. By conservation of momentum:

$$m_A v + m_B v = -40 \text{ kg m/s}$$
$$v = -40/(m_A + m_B) = -40/70 = -0·571 \text{ m/s}$$

> total energy after impact $= \tfrac{1}{2}(m_A + m_B)v^2 = \tfrac{1}{2}70(-0·571)^2 \text{ J}$
> $$= 11·43 \text{ J}$$

Owing to the impact, the energy of the system has been reduced from 1840 J to 11·43 J. Loss of energy $= 1828·6 \text{ J} = 99·38\%$.

(b) If the bodies are perfectly elastic, $e = 1 \cdot 0$, and from eq. 7.14:

$$v_A - v_B = -(u_A - u_B) = u_B - u_A$$
$$v_A - v_B = (-12) - (+4) = -16 \text{ m/s}; \ v_A = v_B - 16;$$

By conservation of momentum,

$$m_A v_A + m_B v_B = -40 \text{ kg m/s}$$

Eliminating v_A, this becomes,

$$50(v_B - 16) + 20v_B = -40 \text{ kg m/s}$$

from which,

$$v_B = +10 \cdot 86 \text{ m/s}; \ v_A = 10 \cdot 86 - 16 = -5 \cdot 14 \text{ m/s}$$

total energy after impact
$$= \tfrac{1}{2}m_A v_A^2 + \tfrac{1}{2}m_B v_B^2 = \tfrac{1}{2}50(-5 \cdot 14)^2 + \tfrac{1}{2}20(+10 \cdot 86)^2 \text{ J}$$
$$= 661 + 1179 = 1840 \text{ J} = 1 \cdot 84 \text{ kJ}$$

This demonstrates that there is no loss of energy when the bodies are perfectly elastic.

(c) If $e = 0 \cdot 75$, then from eq. 7.14,

$$v_A - v_B = -0 \cdot 75(4 - (-12))$$
$$v_A = v_B - 12$$

By conservation of momentum,

$$50v_A + 20v_B = -40 \text{ kg m/s}$$

Eliminating v_A, this becomes:

$$50(v_B - 12) + 20v_B = -40 \text{ kg m/s}$$

from which,

$$v_B = +8 \cdot 0 \text{ m/s}; \ v_A = 8 - 12 = -4 \cdot 0 \text{ m/s}$$

total energy after impact
$$= \tfrac{1}{2}m_A v_A^2 + \tfrac{1}{2}m_B v_B^2 = \tfrac{1}{2}50(-4)^2 + \tfrac{1}{2}20(8)^2 \text{ J}$$
$$= 400 + 640 = 1040 \text{ J} = 1 \cdot 04 \text{ kJ}$$

In this case, the loss of energy
$$= 1 \cdot 84 - 1 \cdot 04 = 0 \cdot 80 \text{ kJ} = 43 \cdot 5 \%.$$

Problems

1. A mass of 40 kg, moving with a velocity of 15 m/s, collides with a rigid surface and rebounds with a velocity of 4·5 m/s. The duration of the impact is estimated to be 1·2 ms.

Calculate (a) the impulse received by the mass (b) the impulsive force exerted on the mass.

(*Answer.* (a) 780 kg m/s (b) 650 kN.)

2. A bullet with a mass of 0·02 kg is travelling with a velocity of 1500 m/s when it strikes a block of wood of mass 20 kg.

Assuming the bullet remains embedded in the block and that the block is free to move, determine the common velocity after impact.

(*Answer.* 1·50 m/s.)

3. A truck *A* has a mass of 1 tonne, and a truck *B* has a mass of 600 kg. Initially *B* is at rest, but *A* is shunted towards *B* and, on collision, automatically couples with it, causing both trucks to move on with a velocity of 3 m/s.

Calculate the momentum and velocity of truck *A* just before impact.

(*Answer.* 4800 kg m/s, 4·8 m/s.)

4. A pile driver of mass 400 kg falls on to a pile of mass 80 kg, striking it with a velocity of 7·5 m/s. Determine the common velocity immediately after the impact and calculate the resulting loss of kinetic energy.

(*Answer.* 6·25 m/s, 1·876 kJ.)

5. A jet of water with a diameter of 20 mm and a velocity of 25 m/s is deflected through an angle of 180° by a fixed curved vane. Determine the magnitude and direction of the force of impact of the jet on the vane. The density of water is 1000 kg/m^3.

(*Answer.* 392·6 N, in the original direction of the jet.)

6. A 30 mm diameter jet of water impinges normally on a flat plate and leaves it tangentially without splash back. The plate is fitted with a strain gauge transducer, which records a force of 640 N. If the density of water is 1000 kg/m^3, determine the velocity of the jet.

(*Answer.* 30·1 m/s.)

7. A rectangular flat plate hangs vertically from a hinge along its upper horizontal edge. The plate has a mass of 7 kg and its centre of gravity is 150 mm below the hinge.

A horizontal jet of water with a velocity of 15 m/s and a diameter of 20 mm is directed normally on to the plate at a point 80 mm below the hinge, thus causing it to swing backwards to a new equilibrium position.

If $g = 9.81$ m/s^2 and the density of water is 1000 kg/m^3, find the inclination of the plate to the vertical.

(*Answer.* 33° 18′.)

8. A horizontal jet of water with a diameter of 40 mm and a velocity of 20 m/s is deflected by a fixed curved vane through an angle of 120°. The water enters the guide vane without shock, but friction at the surface of the vane reduces the velocity of the jet to 16 m/s at exit.

Determine the horizontal and vertical components of the force of impact on the vane. The density of water is 1000 kg/m^3.

(*Answer.* 704 N, 348 N.)

9. A mass of 15 kg moving with a velocity of 10 m/s collides with a mass of 50 kg which is at rest. The impact causes the 15 kg mass to be brought to rest.

Determine (a) the velocity of the 50 kg mass after impact (b) the coefficient of restitution (c) the loss of energy due to the impact.

(*Answer.* (a) 3 m/s (b) 0.3 (c) 525 J.)

10. A mass A of 20 kg has a velocity of 22 m/s and overtakes a mass B of 12 kg which is travelling in the same direction, in the same straight line, with a velocity of 15 m/s. Determine the velocities of A and B after impact and the resulting loss of energy, (a) if the masses are perfectly elastic (b) if $e = 0.5$.

(*Answer.* (a) +16.75 m/s, +23.75 m/s, zero (b) +18.06 m/s, +21.56 m/s, 138 J.)

8. Motion in a circular path

8.1 Centripetal acceleration

Consider the motion of a point P, which is moving along a circular path of radius r and centre O with a constant *speed* v. Let the uniform angular velocity of the radius OP be ω rad/unit time, so that $v = r\omega$ (section 5.8). Although P is moving with constant speed along the circular path, its *velocity* is constantly changing in direction. Velocity is a vector quantity and as such may be changed either by altering its magnitude or by altering its direction. Since the velocity of P is changing with time, it must possess an acceleration, which is the measure of the rate at which the velocity is changing.

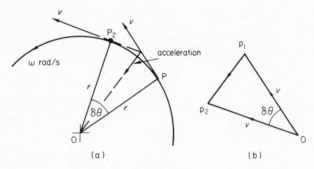

Figure 8.1

Suppose, with reference to Fig. 8.1a, that P moves from P_1 to P_2 in a very small time δt, so that the arc $P_1 P_2$ will subtend a correspondingly small angle $\delta\theta$ at the centre O. During this time, the velocity of P changes from that represented by vector $\mathbf{op_1}$ to that represented by vector $\mathbf{op_2}$.

Thus, the change in velocity in time δt = final velocity − initial velocity = $\mathbf{op_2} - \mathbf{op_1}$.

This vector difference may be obtained from Fig. 8.1b,

$$\text{change in velocity of P in time } \delta t = \mathbf{op_2} + (-\mathbf{op_1})$$
$$= \mathbf{p_1 o} + \mathbf{op_2} = \mathbf{p_1 p_2}$$

124

Since $\delta\theta$ is very small, the magnitude of $\mathbf{p}_1\mathbf{p}_2$ may be computed by assuming it to be an arc of a circle of radius v,

$$\text{change in velocity of P in time } \delta t = \mathbf{p}_1\,\mathbf{p}_2 = v\delta\theta$$
$$\text{acceleration} = \text{rate of change of velocity}$$
$$= \text{velocity change/time taken}$$
$$= v\delta\theta/\delta t$$

In the limit as δt tends to zero, this becomes:

$$\text{acceleration} = v(\mathrm{d}\theta/\mathrm{d}t) = v\omega = v^2/r \text{ or } r\omega^2 \qquad (8.1)$$

since $\mathrm{d}\theta/\mathrm{d}t = \omega$ and $v = r\omega$.

This is called the *centripetal* acceleration of P and, as the vector $\mathbf{p}_1\mathbf{p}_2$ shows, it is directed towards the centre O.

8.2 Centripetal and centrifugal force

In the previous section, it has been shown that a point moving along a curved path at constant speed has a centripetal acceleration directed towards the centre of curvature of the path. If the point is regarded as a body having mass, and therefore inertia, then it is clear, from Newton's second law, that a force must exist to produce this acceleration. Naturally, this force is called the *centripetal force* and, like the acceleration it produces, is directed towards the centre of rotation of the body.

The concept of centripetal force may be thought of in purely physical terms, and practical examples may be easily visualized. A mass on the end of a string may be swung round in a horizontal circle but this motion is only maintained by pulling *inwards* on the string, and keeping it taut. Similarly, a train travelling round a bend is only able to do so by virtue of the rails on which it runs, and in particular on the outer rail, which exerts an *inward* force on the flanges of the wheels, thereby causing the necessary change in the direction of motion. In short, to make a body move along a curved path a force must be provided to cause the continuous change of direction which this type of motion requires. If this centripetal force is removed, then the body will move with uniform motion in a straight line, in accordance with Newton's first law.

From Newton's second law,

$$\text{centripetal force} = \text{mass} \times \text{centripetal acceleration}$$
$$= m(r\omega^2) = m(v^2/r)$$
$$\text{centripetal force} = mr\omega^2 = mv^2/r \text{ (inwards)} \qquad (8.2)$$

where m is the mass of the body, r the radius of curvature of the path, v the linear velocity of the body, and ω the angular velocity of the body about its centre of rotation.

Newton's third law states that, to every action, there is an equal and opposite reaction. If this law is applied in the present instance, it must be concluded that whatever agency provides the centripetal force must itself be subjected to an equal and opposite force. This is the force exerted *by* the body *on* whatever is constraining it to move along its curved path. This inertia force, exerted by the body, is given the name *centrifugal force*. Since centrifugal force is equal and opposite to centripetal force, its direction is *away from the centre of rotation* and is given by:

$$\text{centrifugal force} = mr\omega^2 = mv^2/r \text{ (outwards)} \qquad (8.3)$$

where the symbols have the same meaning as before.

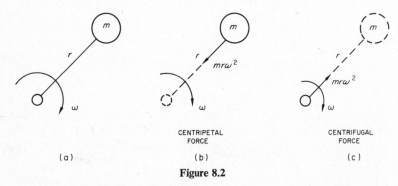

CENTRIPETAL
FORCE

CENTRIFUGAL
FORCE

(a)   (b)   (c)

Figure 8.2

In the two examples cited earlier, the centrifugal force exerted by the mass on the string is the outward pull it applies to the string and which is experienced by the holder of the other end of the string, while in the case of the train on a bend the centrifugal force is the outward force exerted by the wheels on the outer rail.

Both centripetal and centrifugal forces exist, and are *real*, but they do not act on the same body. Figure 8.2a depicts a mass m mounted eccentrically on a shaft at a radius r. The system is rotating with an angular velocity ω rad/s. Figure 8.2b shows the *centripetal* force exerted by the shaft *on the mass*. Figure 8.2c shows the *centrifugal* force exerted by the mass *on the shaft*.

8.3   Balancing of rotating masses

Perhaps the most common of all the systems encountered in mechanical engineering practice is the rotating shaft system. If the centroid of any mass, mounted on a rotating shaft, is offset from the axis of rotation, then the mass will exert a centrifugal force on the shaft, in the manner of Fig. 8.2c. Equation 8.3 shows that this force is directly proportional to the square of the speed of rotation of the shaft, so that, even if the eccentricity is small, the force may be considerable at high speeds. Such a force will tend to make the shaft bend, producing large stresses in the shaft and causing damage to the bearings as it does so. A further undesirable effect would be the inducement of sustained vibrations in the system, its supports, and the surroundings. This situation would be intolerable, so that some attempt must be made to eliminate the effect of this unwanted centrifugal force.

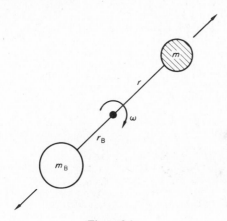

Figure 8.3

The eccentricity of the rotating mass cannot be removed, since this is either necessary to the function of the system (as in a crank), or is simply due to unavoidable imperfections in manufacture. The answer to the problem is to introduce a balancing mass, deliberately offset from the axis of rotation, such that its centrifugal force will be equal and opposite to the original out-of-balance force. In Fig. 8.3, a mass m with an eccentricity r is shown balanced in this way by a mass m_B placed diametrically opposite at radius r_B.

For balance,

$$m_B r_B \omega^2 = mr\omega^2$$
$$m_B r_B = mr \qquad (8.4)$$

Since both masses rotate at the same speed, the factor ω^2 cancels out, and the magnitude of ω is seen to be irrelevant. Equation 8.4 demonstrates that the important factor in any balancing problem is the product of m

and r. In practice, mass is distributed in space, and it becomes difficult to define a system as a discrete mass at a certain radius. Consequently, it is usual to regard the system as having an 'mr product'. At any given speed, the out-of-balance force is directly proportional to this mr product.

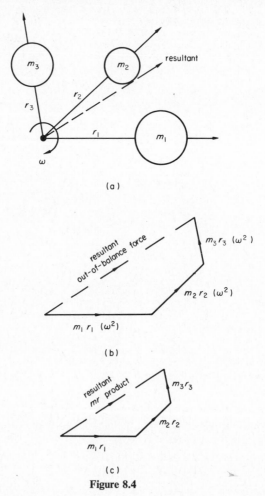

(a)

(b)

(c)

Figure 8.4

In many instances, the rotating system consists of not just one, but several eccentrically mounted masses, or mr products, as in Fig. 8.4a. Each of these will produce a centrifugal force proportional to its mr product, i.e., equal to $mr \times \omega^2$, and the vector sum of these forces may be obtained, as in Fig. 8.4b, to give the resultant out-of-balance force.

It will be noticed that the factor ω^2 is the same for each force and is merely a scale factor. This is, therefore, omitted as in Fig. 8.4c, which gives the vector sum of the mr products,

$$\text{vector sum of the } mr \text{ products} = m_1 r_1 + m_2 r_2 + m_3 r_3 = \sum mr \quad (8.5)$$

$$\text{resultant out-of-balance force} = \sum mr\omega^2 = \omega^2 \times \sum mr \quad (8.6)$$

The balancing mass m_B at radius r_B may now be placed diametrically opposite to the resultant out-of-balance force, or mr product, as shown in Fig. 8.4a.

For balance,

$$m_B r_B \omega^2 = \omega^2 \times \sum mr$$
$$m_B r_B = \sum mr \quad (8.7)$$

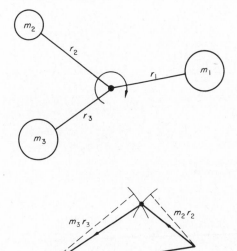

Figure 8.5

Alternatively, if it is possible to adjust the relative angular positions of the eccentric masses, then a balance may be achieved by arranging for the centrifugal force polygon to close. This is the situation illustrated by Fig. 8.5.

For balance,

$$\omega^2 \times \sum mr = 0$$
$$\sum mr = 0 \quad (8.8)$$

In this case, of course, no additional balancing mass is required.

Note that, in every case so far discussed, it has been assumed that all the masses, including the balancing mass, lie in one plane. The problem of balancing masses which rotate in different planes is outside the scope of this book.

Worked examples

1. A link AB in a mechanism moves such that, at a particular instant, the velocity of A relative to B is 18 m/s. The link is 120 mm long. Determine the magnitude and direction of the centripetal acceleration of A relative to B, and also of B relative to A.

This problem emphasizes that all motion is relative (see chapter 5). If the motion of A is considered relative to B, then B must be regarded as 'fixed'. *Instantaneously*, A must then be moving in a circle of centre B and radius BA with a speed of 18 m/s. From eq. 8.1,

> centripetal acceleration of A relative to B
> $= v^2/r$ towards the centre of rotation
> $= 18^2/0 \cdot 120$ towards B
> $= 2700$ m/s^2 or $2 \cdot 7$ km/s^2 towards B

If the motion of B is considered relative to A, then A is the 'fixed' point, and B must, instantaneously, be moving in a circle of centre A and radius AB with a speed of 18 m/s,

> centripetal acceleration of B relative to A
> $= v^2/r$ towards the centre of rotation
> $= 18^2/0 \cdot 120$ towards A
> $= 2700$ m/s^2 or $2 \cdot 7$ km/s^2 towards A

2. A mass of 5 kg is attached to a fixed pivot by means of a light radial arm of length 150 mm. The arm is rotated in a vertical plane at a constant speed of 210 rev/min.
Determine the tension in the radial arm when the mass is at its highest point and when it is at its lowest point.

A body will only move in a circle if a force is provided to bring about the necessary change in the direction of motion. This centripetal force is, in this case, provided by the tension in the radial arm, but the mass is also acted upon by the force due to gravity. Let F_T be the tension in the radial arm. At the highest point,

resultant force on the mass $= F_T + mg$ downwards, i.e., towards the pivot

From Newton's second law,

$$F_T + mg = \text{mass} \times \text{acceleration}$$
$$= mr\omega^2$$
$$F_T = mr\omega^2 - mg$$

This shows that, at the highest point, the centripetal force is provided, in part, by the force due to gravity. The tension required to make the mass conform to its circular path is thus correspondingly less,

angular velocity $= 210$ rev/min $= 22$ rad/s, and $g = 9\cdot81$ m/s^2

$$F_T = 5(0\cdot150)22^2 - 5(9\cdot81) = 5(72\cdot6 - 9\cdot81) = 314 \text{ N}$$

At the lowest point,

resultant force on the mass $= F_T - mg$, upwards, i.e., towards the pivot

From Newton's second law,

$$F_T - mg = mr\omega^2$$
$$F_T = mr\omega^2 + mg$$

The tension must now overcome the force due to gravity as well as providing the required centripetal force.

$$F_T = 5(0\cdot150)22^2 + 5(9\cdot81) = 5(72\cdot6 + 9\cdot81) = 412 \text{ N}$$

3. A mass A of $1\cdot5$ kg and a mass B of $2\cdot0$ kg are mounted eccentrically on a shaft O in the same plane at radii 60 mm and 40 mm, respectively, as shown in Fig. 8.6a. Determine the resultant out-of-balance force acting on the shaft when the system rotates at 1000 rev/min.

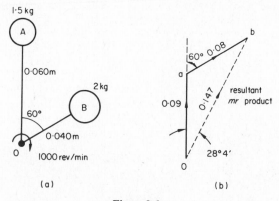

Figure 8.6

angular velocity $= 1000$ rev/min $= 1000(2\pi/60) = 104\cdot7$ rad/s
the mr product due to mass $A = 1\cdot5(0\cdot060) = 0\cdot090$ kg m
the mr product due to mass $B = 2\cdot0(0\cdot040) = 0\cdot080$ kg m

From Fig. 8.6b,
resultant mr product $= \sum mr = 0\cdot147$ kg m
From eq. 8.6,

$$\begin{aligned} \text{resultant out-of-balance force} &= \omega^2 \sum mr \text{ (outwards)} \\ &= (104\cdot7^2)0\cdot147 = 1614 \text{ N (outwards)} \\ &= 1\cdot614 \text{ kN at } 28°\ 4' \text{ to OA (outwards)} \end{aligned}$$

4. Determine the magnitude and angular position relative to OA of a suitable balancing mass, to be placed at a radius of 50 mm, such that the system of Fig. 8.6a will be in balance.

The balancing mass must be placed diametrically opposite to the resultant out-of-balance mr product, so that:

$$m_B r_B = \sum mr = 0\cdot147 \text{ kg m}$$
$$m_B = 0\cdot147/r_B = 0\cdot147/0\cdot050 = 2\cdot94 \text{ kg}$$

With reference to Fig. 8.6, this must be placed at 50 mm radius at $208°\ 4'$, measured clockwise, to OA.

5. Three masses, A, B, and C, are firmly attached to a circular plate at radii $0\cdot75$ m, $0\cdot25$ m, and $0\cdot40$ m, respectively. A is a mass of 12 kg, B 20 kg, and C 20 kg. Determine suitable angular positions for the masses, so that the system will be in dynamic balance when the plate rotates about its polar axis.

the mr product due to $A = 12(0\cdot75) = 9\cdot0$ kg m
the mr product due to $B = 20(0\cdot25) = 5\cdot0$ kg m
the mr product due to $C = 20(0\cdot40) = 8\cdot0$ kg m

For balance, the vector sum of these mr products must be zero (eq. 8.8). This may be arranged by constructing a triangle of vectors with sides of length proportional to these mr products. This vector diagram is shown in Fig. 8.7a, from which,

the angular position of B relative to $A = 117°\ 49'$
the angular position of C relative to $A = 213°\ 34'$

both these angles being measured clockwise as in Fig. 8.7b.

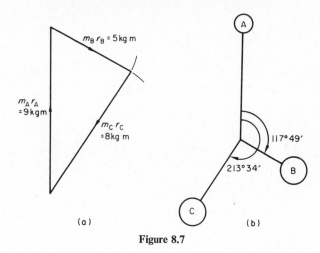

Figure 8.7

Problems

1. What is the acceleration of a point on the rim of a flywheel of 0·5 m diameter which is rotating at a constant speed of 500 rev/min?

(*Answer.* 685 m/s² towards the axis of rotation.)

2. A horizontal circular flat plate is fitted with frictionless guides along a diameter. Two masses, each of 0·25 kg, are placed in these guides equidistant from, and on either side of, the centre of the plate. Each mass is tied to the central axis of the plate by a spring of stiffness 5 kN/m. Initially, each mass is 100 mm from the central axis with the slack in the springs just taken up.

When the plate is rotated at constant speed about its vertical axis, the masses are observed to move outwards to a radius of 150 mm. Calculate the speed of rotation of the plate in rev/min.

(*Answer.* 780 rev/min.)

3. The driver of a motor car has a mass of 80 kg. Assuming $g = 9 \cdot 81$ m/s², determine the minimum force exerted by the driver on his seat as the car passes over a humped-back bridge at 36 km/h. The radius of curvature of the bridge is 20 m.

(*Answer.* 385 N.)

4. A flywheel is keyed to a rigid shaft, which is 2 m long, at a point 0·6 m from one end. The total mass of the assembly is 27 kg and its centre of gravity lies in the plane of the flywheel but, owing to imperfections in

manufacture, is offset 1 mm from the axis of rotation. The shaft is supported horizontally by bearings at each end. Assuming $g = 10$ m/s², estimate the maximum and minimum load on each bearing when the shaft rotates at 1000 rev/min.

(*Answer*. 396·2 N and 169·8 N, downwards; 18·2 N and 7·8 N, upwards.)

5. The brake wheel of a rope-brake dynamometer is to be cooled by supplying water to the inside of the rim, which has a diameter of 1·0 m. What is the minimum speed of rotation, in rev/min, of the brake wheel, if the water is to be carried round the full perimeter of the wheel without falling out at its highest point? Take $g = 9·81$ m/s².

(*Answer*. 42·3 rev/min.)

6. Equal masses, *A*, *B*, and *C*, of 2·5 kg each, are mounted in the same plane on a shaft at radii 200 mm, 300 mm, and 400 mm, respectively. The angular positions of the masses, measured clockwise, are *A* 0°, *B* 90°, and *C* 140°.

Find the resultant out-of-balance force acting on the shaft when it rotates at 400 rev/min, and also the magnitude and position of a mass, to be placed at 250 mm radius, which will nullify its effect.

(*Answer*. 2·49 kN, acting outwards at 100° 49′ to mass A; 5·672 kg, at 280° 49′ to mass A.)

7. Four masses, *A*, *B*, *C*, and *D*, lie in the same plane and are rigidly connected to a shaft *O*. The angle *AOB* is 90°; *A* is 1·2 kg at 50 mm radius; *B* is 1·0 kg at 120 mm radius; *C* is 2·0 kg at 70 mm radius; and *D* is 0·9 kg at 200 mm radius. If the system is dynamically balanced, determine the angular positions of the masses *C* and *D*.

(*Answer*. Measured from *OA*, in the same direction as *B*, *C* 161° 26′ and *D* 293° 48′, or *D* 193° 4′ and *C* 325° 26′.)

9. Friction

9.1 The nature of friction

Very few engineering situations occur in which friction does not play some part. In some cases, it is gainfully employed, as in clamping devices and friction drives. More frequently, it exists as an integral part of the situation merely because it cannot be eradicated, and results in the dissipation of energy and the gradual erosion of material from the component involved.

This erosion of material, or wear, due to friction represents a substantial economic loss to the community in general. Because of this, a considerable amount of research has been undertaken in recent years aimed at a greater understanding of the processes involved and the development of methods by which it may be reduced.

Friction, and hence wear, may be reduced by the method of lubrication, in which surfaces having relative motion are separated by a fluid film. The cheapest fluid which could be used for this purpose is water. Unfortunately, this has a corrosive effect on ferrous materials and so the second most plentiful fluid—oil—is normally used.

Friction, wear, and lubrication, are thus inevitably bound together, and the study of these related topics is called 'tribology'. This subject is very large and, of necessity, this chapter must confine itself to the basic laws of dry friction or, as it is sometimes called, Coulomb friction.

Surfaces, normally described as 'flat' or 'smooth', are in fact covered with undulations and bumps. Microscopic examination of a so-called 'flat' surface would reveal a terrain which one notable tribologist has likened to the Lake District! This comparison is a good one because it emphasizes not only the irregular surface geometry but also the surface contamination which is always present. A 'dry' surface is, by definition, one with *all* surface contamination removed—and this includes dust particles and surface film as well as any moisture. It will be appreciated from this definition that a *dry* surface is difficult, if not impossible, to achieve in practice. It is for this reason that elementary laboratory experiments designed to verify the laws of dry friction frequently prove to be unsatisfactory.

Consider two dry surfaces in contact as in Fig. 9.1. The surface irregularities are shown magnified to illustrate that the real area of contact, A_r, is considerably smaller than the apparent area of contact, A_a. Because the real area is so small, the stresses at points of contact will be very large. If the normal force, F_N, pressing the surfaces together, is increased two things will happen: the existing points of contact will tend to flatten under the large stresses and, in consequence, further points of contact will be established, both occurrences causing the real area of contact to increase. A reasonable hypothesis is that A_r is directly proportional to F_N, so that:

$$F_N = k_1 A_r \qquad (9.1)$$

where k_1 is a constant depending on the surface geometry and the properties of deformation of the materials.

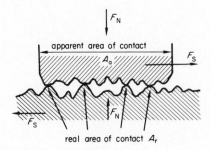

Figure 9.1

Suppose now a force F_S is applied tending to cause relative sliding of the surfaces (Fig. 9.1). If sliding is to occur, the force F_S must shear the points of contact, which will have welded together under the action of the very large stresses there. The force F_S required will thus be directly proportional to the area of material to be sheared, A_r, so that:

$$F_S = k_2 A_r \qquad (9.2)$$

where k_2 is a constant, and will in fact be the ultimate shear stress of the material.

Dividing eq. 9.1 and 9.2 gives:

$$\frac{F_S}{F_N} = \frac{k_2 A_r}{k_1 A_r} = \frac{k_2}{k_1} = \mu \qquad (9.3)$$

The ratio of the force necessary to produce sliding to the normal force of reaction between the surfaces is thus seen to be a constant, independent of the real area of contact since this cancels out. This constant is called the *coefficient of limiting friction* and is denoted by μ.

For extremely dry surfaces, obtainable by special high-vacuum techniques, μ can be quite large, but surface contamination which is always present under normal conditions reduces its value to less than 1·0. A typical value for two relatively smooth metal surfaces in contact is about 0·3.

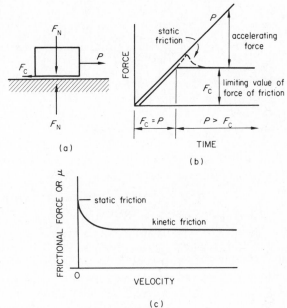

Figure 9.2

By its very nature, the force due to friction is a *reaction*, in that it opposes any force tending to slide one surface relative to the other. As a reaction, it is equal and opposite to the applied force tending to produce motion, but there is a *limit* to the value it may reach. It is to this limiting value that eq. 9.2 refers. In Fig. 9.2a, a block resting on a fixed surface is acted on by a force P which gradually increases from zero as indicated by the graph of Fig. 9.2b. This produces a reactionary coulomb friction force F_C which, at first, is equal and opposite to P so that no motion occurs. Eventually, however, P reaches a value beyond which F_C cannot rise, and as P continues to increase F_C remains at this limiting value. The limiting value of the force of friction is given by eq. 9.3, which may be written in the form:

$$F_C = F_S = \mu F_N \qquad (9.4)$$

When P exceeds this value, slipping occurs. On the point of slipping, however, a slightly larger force is required to overcome friction. Figure 9.2c shows how the limiting value of the friction force, or μ, varies with the velocity. Static friction, or 'stiction' as it is sometimes colloquially called, is seen to be greater than the kinetic value which, for dry friction remains constant as the velocity of sliding increases.

9.2   The laws of dry friction

A number of conclusions may be drawn from the foregoing discussion, and may be presented as a series of laws. These laws were first pro-pounded by Coulomb (hence the term 'Coulomb friction') and are based mainly on experimental observations. These laws are by no means exact, partly because 'dry' surfaces do not in practice occur and partly because the laws themselves tend to over-simplify the problem. Neverthe-less, these laws form a useful basis for engineering calculations, and suffice for the majority of general applications.

(1) When external forces tend to cause one surface to slide over another surface, a reactionary force of friction, acting tangentially to the surfaces, is set up so as to oppose the motion.

(2) There is a limiting value of the force of friction beyond which it cannot rise. If the forces tending to produce the relative motion exceed this value, slipping begins.

(3) The force necessary to initiate relative motion is greater than that needed to maintain it. Static friction is greater than kinetic friction.

(4) The limiting value of the force of friction is quite independent of the area of contact.

(5) The limiting value of the force of kinetic friction is independent of the velocity of sliding.

(6) The limiting value of the force of friction bears a constant ratio to the normal reaction between the surfaces. This constant ratio is called the coefficient of limiting friction, and is denoted by μ.

(7) The coefficient of limiting friction is dependent on the nature of the surfaces in contact. This refers to the surface geometry, the surface contamination, and the physical properties of the materials involved.

The sixth law gives rise to eq. 9.4, which is now restated:

$$F_C = \mu F_N \qquad (9.4)$$

where F_C is the limiting value of the force of Coulomb friction,

μ is the coefficient of limiting friction,

F_N is the normal reaction between the surfaces.

Note carefully that this equation may be applied only when there is relative sliding between the surfaces, in which case the value of μ will be that corresponding to kinetic friction. If the equation is applied when the surfaces are *on the point of slipping*, then the value of μ used should be that corresponding to static friction, and will be greater (see Fig. 9.2c).

9.3   The angle of friction

Figure 9.3 shows a block of mass m which is moving with constant velocity along a horizontal plane. The block is subjected to two externally applied forces, the horizontal force P, and the force due to gravity mg. The force of gravity is reacted by the normal reaction F_N, and the force P is reacted

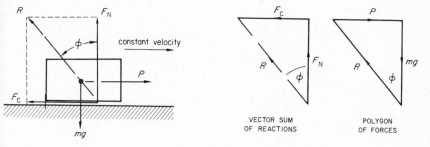

Figure 9.3

by the frictional force F_C which, because the block is moving, will be at its limiting value. Equation 9.4 thus applies, μ having its kinetic value. F_C and F_N are both reactions and may be regarded as components of a single resultant reaction R, which is the vector sum of F_C and F_N. Because of friction, this resultant reaction R is inclined backwards from the normal to the plane by an angle ϕ. This is called the *angle of friction*. With reference to the vector sum of the reactions (Fig. 9.3),

$$\tan \phi = \frac{F_C}{F_N} = \mu \qquad (9.5)$$

Since the block has constant velocity, it is in equilibrium under the action of the three forces P, mg, and the resultant reaction R. This fact is expressed by the polygon of forces, also shown in Fig. 9.3.

9.4　Friction on an inclined plane

The angle of friction, referred to in the previous section, is the *limiting* value of the angle which the resultant reaction R may make with the normal. When the frictional force is less than the limiting value, R will assume whatever angle is necessary to maintain static equilibrium. However, the angle which R makes with the normal may never exceed the angle of friction ϕ. At this point, a distinction must be made between

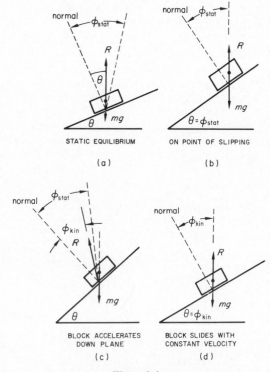

Figure 9.4

the angle of *static* friction and the angle of *kinetic* friction. Reference to eq. 9.5 and Fig. 9.2c shows that the angle of static friction will be larger than the kinetic angle of friction.

Consider a block of mass m which is *at rest* on an inclined plane. Suppose that the inclination, θ, of the plane to the horizontal may be varied. In Fig. 9.4a, θ is less than the angle of static friction, and it is quite possible for the resultant reaction R to balance the force due to gravity and maintain the block in static equilibrium. If now the inclination θ is increased, so that θ equals the angle of static friction, R is inclined at its maximum possible angle to the normal in its efforts to maintain the state of rest (Fig. 9.4b). This particular angle of inclination of the plane, when the block is on the point of slipping, is often called the *angle of repose*. Any further increase in θ makes it impossible for R to adopt the vertical direction necessary to balance the force of gravity, and the block slides down the plane. This state of affairs is shown in Fig. 9.4c, which also indicates that, because of the motion, ϕ now reduces to its kinetic value and the block is thereby caused to accelerate. If the block is required to slide down the plane with constant velocity, that is, in a state of kinetic equilibrium, it will be necessary to reduce the inclination θ until it equals the angle of kinetic friction as in Fig. 9.4d.

The condition of Fig. 9.4d is dealt with in a slightly different manner in Fig. 9.5. In this diagram, the resultant reaction is shown resolved into

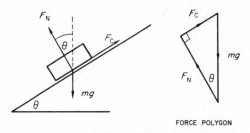

FORCE POLYGON

Figure 9.5

its components F_C and F_N. If the block is in equilibrium under the action of these two forces and the force of gravity, as indicated by the force polygon, then:

$$\tan \theta = F_C/F_N = \mu = \tan \phi$$

so that

$$\theta = \phi$$

Three important cases of the motion of a body on an inclined plane must now be considered. These cases relate to a body which moves at constant velocity up or down the incline under the influence of a horizontal force P, and have an important practical application in the operation of a screw thread, which is basically only an inclined plane.

The first case is shown in Fig. 9.6, in which a body of mass m is being drawn up the plane at constant velocity by means of a horizontal force P. From the force polygon representing the equilibrium of the body:

$$\text{force required} = P = mg \tan (\theta + \phi) \tag{9.6}$$

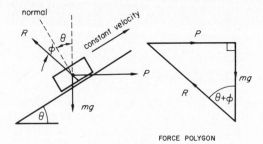

FORCE POLYGON

Figure 9.6

In the second case (Fig. 9.7), the horizontal force P is resisting the motion of the body down the plane, and it is evident that the inclination θ of the plane is greater than the angle of repose. If P is the force required to maintain a constant velocity down the plane, then from the force polygon:

$$P = mg \tan(\theta - \phi) \tag{9.7}$$

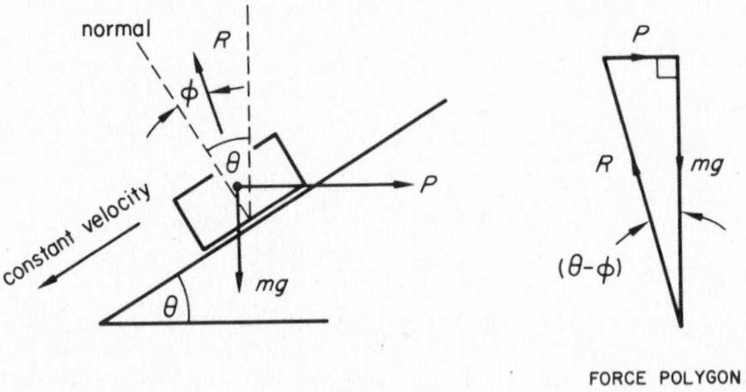

FORCE POLYGON

Figure 9.7

Finally, Fig. 9.8 shows a body of mass m being drawn down the inclined plane by a horizontal force P. Evidently, in this case, θ is less than the angle of repose, because otherwise P would be unnecessary and the situation would revert to that of Fig. 9.7. Again, for constant velocity, the body is in equilibrium and from the force polygon:

$$\text{force required} = P = mg \tan(\phi - \theta) \tag{9.8}$$

In a more general case, the force P may act in any direction. Provided this direction is known and the body is in equilibrium, precisely the same methods may be used as in the above cases. If the body is not in equilibrium and the magnitude of P is known, as well as its direction, the resultant force acting on the body can normally be found. Newton's second law will then give the subsequent acceleration of the body.

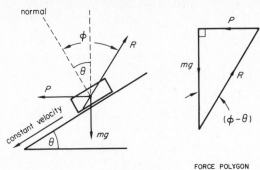

Figure 9.8

Worked examples

1. A body of mass 10 kg rests on a horizontal plane. The coefficient of static friction between the contact surfaces is 0.4, and the coefficient of kinetic friction is 0·25. A gradually increasing horizontal force is applied to the body, and this eventually causes the body to slide along the plane.

Determine the force of friction acting on the body (a) when the body is at rest (b) when the body is on the point of slipping (c) when the body is actually sliding.

The situation described is similar to those of Fig. 9.2a and Fig. 9.3. The normal reaction will equal the force due to gravity.

$$F_N = mg = 10 \times 9{\cdot}81 = 98{\cdot}1 \text{ N (since } g = 9{\cdot}81 \text{ m/s}^2)$$

(a) When the body is at rest, the force of friction will be equal and opposite to the applied horizontal force, at any particular instant. This will apply until the body is on the point of slipping.

(b) When the body is on the point of slipping:

$$F_C = \mu F_N \quad \text{where } \mu = 0{\cdot}4$$
$$F_C = 0{\cdot}4 \times 98{\cdot}1 = 39{\cdot}24 \text{ N}$$

(c) When sliding is taking place:

$$F_C = \mu F_N \quad \text{where } \mu = 0{\cdot}25$$
$$F_C = 0{\cdot}25 \times 98{\cdot}1 = 24{\cdot}53 \text{ N}$$

2. A block of mass 10 kg is pushed along horizontal fixed guides by a force acting downwards at 30° to the horizontal, as shown in Fig. 9.9a. Assuming $g = 10$ m/s² and that the coefficient of limiting friction is 0·3,

determine the minimum value of the force necessary to maintain constant velocity, the normal reaction between block and guides, and the magnitude of the friction force.

$$\text{force due to gravity} = mg = 10 \times 10 = 100 \text{ N}$$

The block is in equilibrium under the action of the applied force P, the force of gravity mg, and the resultant reaction R. Since sliding is occurring, R will be inclined to the normal at the angle of friction ϕ, where $\tan \phi = 0.3$; $\phi = 16° 42'$. The polygon of forces may now be drawn to some suitable scale, as in Fig. 9.9b, from which: $R = 126.3$ N; $P = 41.9$ N. The resultant reaction R may now be resolved into its normal and tangential components, F_N and F_C, as indicated by Fig. 9.9c,

$$\text{normal reaction } F_N = R \cos \phi = 126.3 \cos 16° 42' = 121.0 \text{ N}$$
$$\text{frictional force } F_C = R \sin \phi = 126.3 \sin 16° 42' = 36.3 \text{ N}$$

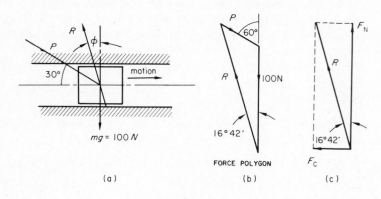

Figure 9.9

3. With reference to the previous problem, calculate the work done against friction when the block moves a distance of 500 mm along the fixed guides. In what form will this energy expended reappear?

The work done by a force is dealt with in the next chapter, section 10.1,

$$\text{work done against friction} = \text{frictional force} \times \text{displacement}$$
$$= 36.3 \times 0.500 \text{ J}$$
$$= 18.15 \text{ J}$$

Energy expended in overcoming friction always reappears in the form of *heat*.

4. A screw-jack supports a body of mass 200 kg. The mean diameter of the screw is 60 mm and the helix angle is 7°. If the coefficient of friction for the screw and nut is 0·2, calculate the torque required (a) to raise the load (b) to lower the load. Assume $g = 10$ m/s².

Since the development of a screw thread is an inclined plane, the situations described here are identical with Figs. 9.6 and 9.8. The angle of friction $\phi = \tan^{-1}(0·2) = 11° 19'$.

(a) From eq. 9.6,

$$\text{force to raise load} = mg \tan (\theta + \phi)$$
$$= (200)(10) \tan (7° + 11° 19') = 662 \text{ N}$$
$$\text{torque to raise load} = \text{force} \times \text{mean radius}$$
$$= 662 \times 0·030 = 19·86 \text{ N m}$$

(b) From eq. 9.8,

$$\text{force to lower load} = mg \tan (\phi - \theta)$$
$$= (200)(10) \tan (11° 19' - 7°) = 151 \text{ N}$$
$$\text{torque to lower load} = \text{force} \times \text{mean radius}$$
$$= 151 \times 0·030 = 4·53 \text{ N m}$$

5. A mass of 50 kg is dragged up an incline, making 30° with the horizontal, by a force of 400 N inclined at 40° to the vertical, as shown in Fig. 9.10a. Assuming that the mass moves at constant speed and that

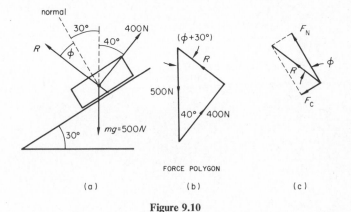

FORCE POLYGON

(a) (b) (c)

Figure 9.10

$g = 10$ m/s², determine the coefficient of friction between the mass and the plane. Find also the normal reaction and the force of friction acting on the mass.

$$\text{force due to gravity} = mg = 50 \times 10 = 500 \text{ N}$$

The force polygon, representing the equilibrium of the mass, may be drawn to some suitable scale, and is shown in Fig. 9.10b, from which:

$$\text{resultant reaction } R = 321 \cdot 8 \text{ N}$$

and

$$\phi + 30^\circ = 53^\circ \, 3'$$
$$\text{the angle of friction } \phi = 23^\circ \, 3'$$
$$\text{the coefficient of friction } \mu = \tan\phi = \tan 23^\circ \, 3' = 0 \cdot 4255$$

R may be resolved into its normal and tangential components, as in Fig. 9.10c, from which:

$$\text{normal reaction } F_N = R\cos\phi = 321 \cdot 8 \cos 23^\circ \, 3' = 296 \text{ N}$$
$$\text{frictional force } F_C = R\sin\phi = 321 \cdot 8 \sin 23^\circ \, 3' = 126 \text{ N}$$

6. If, in the previous problem, the 400 N force is changed in direction so that it is parallel to the plane, what would be the acceleration of the mass up the plane?

The situation would now appear as in Fig. 9.11. The angle of friction would remain unchanged, so that:

$$\text{resultant force up the plane} = 400 - 500\sin 30^\circ - R\sin 23^\circ \, 3'$$
$$\text{resolving forces normal to the plane: } R\cos 23^\circ \, 3' = 500\cos 30^\circ$$

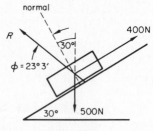

Figure 9.11

from which:

$$R = 470 \cdot 7 \text{ N}$$
$$\text{resultant force up the plane} = 400 - 250 - 470 \cdot 7 \sin 23^\circ \, 3' = -34 \cdot 3 \text{ N}$$

From Newton's second law,

$$\text{acceleration} = \text{force/mass} = -34 \cdot 3/50 = -0 \cdot 686 \text{ m/s}^2$$

Thus, assuming the mass was already moving up the plane at constant velocity, the effect of changing the direction of the force to coincide with the direction of motion is to give the mass a *deceleration* of 0·686 m/s². This is because, by altering the direction of the applied force, the normal reaction between the contact surfaces, and hence the frictional force, has been increased.

7. A simple journal bearing carries a load of 10 kN. The diameter of the bearing is 50 mm, and the shaft rotates at 3000 rev/min. If the coefficient of friction is 0·01, estimate the power absorbed by friction.

The normal reaction at the point of contact of shaft and bearing will be approximately equal to the bearing load,

$$\text{tangential force of friction} = \mu F_N = (0\cdot01)(10\ 000) = 100\ \text{N}$$
$$\text{frictional torque} = \text{force} \times \text{radius} = 100(0\cdot025) = 2\cdot5\ \text{N m}$$
$$\text{angular velocity of shaft} = 3000(2\pi/60) = 314\cdot2\ \text{rad/s}$$

From section 10.6,

$$\text{power absorbed} = T\omega = 2\cdot5 \times 314\cdot2\ \text{W}$$
$$= 785\cdot4\ \text{W} = 0\cdot785\ \text{kW}$$

This is also the rate at which heat must be removed from the bearing to prevent over-heating—that is, 785·4 J of heat must be removed each second.

Problems

1. Define the term 'coefficient of limiting friction'.
A mass of 100 kg is dragged along a horizontal surface at constant velocity by means of a horizontal force of 0·2 kN. Assuming $g = 10$ m/s², calculate the coefficient of limiting friction between the mass and the floor.
If the mass is dragged 5 m in this manner, what is the work done against friction?

(*Answer*. 0·2, 1·0 kJ.)

2. A block is placed on a plane inclined at 25° to the horizontal. The coefficient of friction between the block and the plane is 0·3. Determine the acceleration of the block down the plane. Assume $g = 9\cdot81$ m/s².

(*Answer*. 1·48 m/s².)

11

3. A horizontal force of 60 N is required to move a mass of 24 kg over a horizontal surface at constant velocity. Determine the force required to pull the mass over the same surface at constant velocity, when both surface and force are inclined at 20° to the horizontal. Assume $g = 10 \text{ m/s}^2$.

(*Answer*. 138·5 N.)

4. The coefficient of friction between the table of a planing machine and its slideways is 0·1. The cutting stroke is 1·5 m long, and the number of cutting strokes per minute is 25. If the combined mass of the table and work-piece is 1200 kg, estimate the average power absorbed by friction. Assume $g = 10 \text{ m/s}^2$.

(*Answer*. 1·5 kW.)

5. Distinguish between static friction and kinetic friction. A mass of 50 kg is at rest on a horizontal floor. The coefficient of kinetic friction between the mass and the floor is 0·3. A force, acting upwards at 45° to the horizontal, is applied to the mass, and is gradually increased from zero. When this force reaches 200 N, the mass just begins to slide. What is the coefficient of static friction between the mass and the floor? If the force is subsequently maintained at 200 N, what will be the acceleration of the mass?

(*Answer*. 0·394, 0·676 m/s².)

6. A cable is attached to a casting of mass 1·5 tonne, which is then drawn a distance of 12 m at constant velocity across the foundry floor. If the coefficient of friction is 0·4 and $g = 9·81 \text{ m/s}^2$, determine the tension in the cable and the total work done if (a) the cable is horizontal (b) the cable is inclined at 25° to the horizontal. (1 tonne = 1000 kg.)

(*Answer*. (a) 5·89 kN, 70·6 kJ (b) 5·47 kN, 59·5 kJ.)

7. What is meant by 'the angle of friction'?

A mass of 40 kg is pushed up an inclined plane at constant velocity by a force, parallel to the plane, of 0·25 kN. If the angle of inclination of the plane to the horizontal is 30° and $g = 10 \text{ m/s}^2$, determine the angle of friction, and hence the coefficient of friction, between the mass and the plane. What force, parallel to the plane, is required to make the mass slide down the plane at constant velocity?

(*Answer*. 8° 13', 0·1444, 150 N *up* the plane.)

8. A screw-jack requires a torque of 64 N m applied to the axis of the screw to raise a mass of 1 tonne against the pull of gravity. The mean diameter of the screw is 80 mm, and the helix angle is 4°. If $g = 9·81$ m/s², estimate the coefficient of friction for the screw-thread. (1 tonne = 1000 kg.)

(*Answer.* 0·092.)

9. A 100 mm diameter shaft runs in a journal bearing at 1000 rev/min. The load on the bearing is 25 kN and the coefficient of friction is 0·008. If the bearing is cooled by circulating water, at the rate of 1·5 l/min, through passages in the bearing housing, estimate the rise in temperature of the cooling water, assuming steady-state conditions. The specific heat of water is 4·2 kJ/kg °C, and the mass of 1 litre of water is 1 kg.

(*Answer.* 9·97 °C.)

10. Work, power, and energy

10.1 Work done by a force

Work is said to be done by a force when its point of application moves in the direction of its line of action. For a constant force F whose point of application moves a distance s in the direction of its line of action, as in Fig. 10.1, the amount of work done is measured by the product of force and displacement, that is,

$$\text{work done} = Fs \tag{10.1}$$

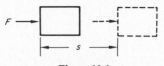

Figure 10.1

In the SI system, the unit of work is the joule (symbol J), and this is defined as the work done when unit force (1 newton) has unit displacement (1 metre). As will be seen later in this chapter, work is a form of *energy* and the joule, although defined as above, is the unit not only of work but of all other forms of energy, including electrical energy and heat.

It should be noted that the displacement s must be measured in the direction in which the force F acts. If the displacement is perpendicular to the direction of the force, no work is done. A railway truck being pulled along a level track, for example, is acted on by two kinds of force: (a) an upward force which supports its weight and (b) the horizontal force necessary to overcome friction. Only force (b) does work on the truck. If, as in Fig. 10.2, the motion of a body is at an angle to the direction of the force acting on it, the work done may be calculated in either of two ways. The displacement of the body in the direction of the force may be found, as in Fig. 10.2a, when

$$\text{work done} = F(s \cos \theta)$$

150

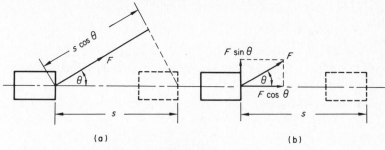

Figure 10.2

Alternatively, the force may be resolved into two components at right-angles as in Fig. 10.2b. The component of force perpendicular to the motion, $F\sin\theta$, will do no work; hence

$$\text{work done} = (F\cos\theta)\,s$$

10.2 Work done by a variable force

In practice, calculations are often concerned with forces which vary during the motion of their points of application. A force which stretches a spring, for example, increases uniformly as the spring extends; and the force on a press tool varies in an irregular manner during its stroke. The way in which a force varies may be shown by a force-displacement diagram such as Fig. 10.3. In order to find the work done, the motion may be imagined to be divided into a number of parts, for example A–B in Fig. 10.3. If A and B are very close together, the force acting during this part of the motion may be considered constant and if this force is F, and the corresponding displacement δs,

$$\text{work done between A and B} = F\delta s$$

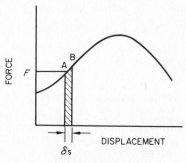

Figure 10.3

But $F\delta s$ is the area of the small vertical strip of the diagram between points A and B. The whole of the motion may be thought of as a series of very small displacements such as the one considered, and for each of these the work done will be represented by the corresponding vertical strip of the diagram. Thus the total area under the force-displacement diagram represents the total work done.

In many cases the force-displacement diagram is a simple geometrical shape (such as a triangle or trapezium) so that its area may be calculated. If the relationship between force and displacement is an irregular one, it will be necessary to construct the diagram accurately, to measure its area, and to multiply this area by the scales of force and displacement in order to obtain the work done. Areas may be found by using a planimeter, by counting squares, or by the 'mid-ordinate method' in which the diagram is divided into a number of vertical strips of equal width, and a 'mid-ordinate' is drawn at the centre of each strip. The area of each strip is, approximately, the product of its width and the length of its mid-ordinate, hence, since all strips are of equal width,

$$\text{total area} = \text{width of one strip} \times \text{sum of mid-ordinates}$$

10.3　Power

Power is defined as the *rate of doing work*. If work is being done at a steady rate,

$$\text{power} = \text{work done/time taken}$$

The unit of power is the watt (symbol **W**), which is defined as a rate of working of 1 joule per second.

Like the joule, the watt can also refer to other forms of energy. Since the joule is the unit not only of work but of energy in general, an alternative definition of the watt is a rate of transfer of energy of 1 joule per second. Thus the watt is also the unit of electrical power and of rate of heat transfer.

If a moving body has applied to it a constant force F acting in the direction of its motion, then, for a small displacement δs, from eq. 10.1,

$$\text{work done} = F\delta s$$

If this takes place in time δt,

$$\begin{aligned}\text{power} &= \text{work done/time taken}\\ &= F\delta s/\delta t\end{aligned}$$

But, from eq. 5.2, $\delta s/\delta t$ is the average velocity of the body. If δs and δt are made infinitely small, eq. 5.3 applies and

$$\text{power} = F\,ds/dt = Fv \qquad (10.2)$$

where v is the instantaneous velocity of the body.

Equation 10.2 gives the constant power input to a body moving with uniform velocity or the instantaneous power in the case of a body whose velocity varies.

Worked examples

1. The force required to move a planer table against the combined resistance of cutting force and friction is 2 kN, and this force remains constant during the cutting stroke of 3 m. Find (a) the work done (b) the power required if the table moves at a steady speed and the stroke is completed in 5 s.

(a) From eq. 10.1,

$$\text{work done} = Fs$$
$$= 2000 \times 3$$
$$= 6000 \text{ J or 6 kJ}$$

(b)

$$\text{Power} = \text{work done/time taken}$$
$$= 6000/5$$
$$= 1200 \text{ W or } 1 \cdot 2 \text{ kW}$$

2. A barge is towed along a canal by a rope which is inclined at $27°$ to the direction of motion of the barge. If a steady pull of 400 N is applied to the rope, how much work is done in towing the barge a distance of 1 km?

Resolving the force applied to the barge (Fig. 10.4), we have

$$\text{component of force in direction of motion}$$
$$= 400 \cos 27°$$
$$= 400 \times 0 \cdot 8910$$
$$= 356 \cdot 4 \text{ N}$$

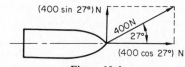

Figure 10.4

Therefore,

$$\text{work done} = 356 \cdot 4 \times 1000$$
$$= 356\ 400 \text{ J or } 356 \cdot 4 \text{ kJ}$$

3. A spring has a free length of 200 mm and its stiffness is 12 N/mm. What is the work done in stretching the spring (a) from 200 mm to 230 mm (b) from 250 mm to 280 mm?

(a) The force varies uniformly from zero to $(230 - 200) \times 12 = 360$ N. Figure 10.5a shows the force-displacement diagram, and

$$\text{work done} = \text{area of force-displacement diagram}$$
$$= \tfrac{1}{2} \times 0 \cdot 03 \times 360 = 5 \cdot 4 \text{ J}$$

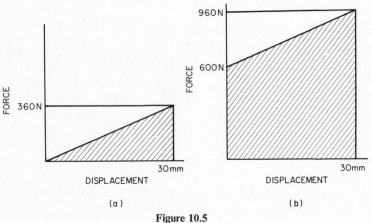

Figure 10.5

(b) Initial force on spring $= (250\text{–}200) \times 12 = 600$ N

Final force on spring $= (280\text{–}200) \times 12 = 960$ N

Figure 10.5b shows the force-displacement diagram, and

$$\text{work done} = \text{area of force-displacement diagram}$$
$$= 0 \cdot 03 \times (600 + 960)/2 = 23 \cdot 4 \text{ J}$$

4. A train has a mass of 200 tonnes and travels along a level track. If the frictional resistance to motion is 18 kN, find (a) the power developed by the locomotive when it is travelling at a steady speed of 75 km/h (b) the instantaneous power developed when it is accelerating at $0 \cdot 5$ m/s^2 and its instantaneous speed is 15 km/h.

(a) From eq. 10.2,

$$\text{power} = Fv$$

$$75 \text{ km/h} = 75 \times 10^3/(60 \times 60) \text{ m/s}$$

Therefore,

$$\text{power} = 18 \times 10^3 \times 75 \times 10^3/(60 \times 60)$$
$$= 375 \times 10^3 \text{ W or } 375 \text{ kW}$$

(b) From eq. 6.2, the force required to accelerate the train,

$$F = ma$$
$$= 200 \times 10^3 \times 0.5$$
$$= 100 \times 10^3 \text{ N or } 100 \text{ kN}$$

Therefore, total force to be exerted on train is

$$(18 + 100) = 118 \text{ kN}$$

Hence, from eq. 10.2,

$$\text{power} = 118 \times 10^3 \times 15 \times 10^3/(60 \times 60)$$
$$= 492 \times 10^3 \text{ W or } 492 \text{ kW}$$

10.4 Work done by a torque

Figure 10.6 shows a crank which rotates about a fixed centre O, and is acted on by a force F at a point P, distant r from O. The line of action of F is always perpendicular to OP so that its moment about O is constant; in other words, a constant torque $T = F \times r$ is applied to the shaft to which the crank is connected. Let the crank move through an angle θ (measured in radians) so that P moves to P'.

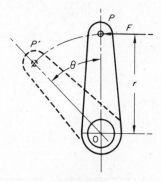

Figure 10.6

From eq. 10.1,

$$\text{work done on crank} = F \times \text{arc PP}'$$
$$= F(r\theta)$$
$$= (Fr)\theta$$

But (Fr) is the applied torque T. Therefore,

$$\text{work done} = T\theta \qquad (10.3)$$

10.5 Work done by a fluctuating torque

The torque applied to a shaft may be constant, as in the case of the output shaft of an electric motor or a steam turbine, or it may fluctuate, as in the case of the crankshaft of a reciprocating engine. It has been shown in section 10.2 that the work done by a variable force may be found by drawing a force-displacement diagram and measuring its area; the work done by a variable torque may be found in a similar way.

If a torque with an instantaneous value T acts over a very small angular displacement $\delta\theta$, it follows from eq. 10.3 that

$$\text{work done} = T\delta\theta$$

This is the area of a small vertical strip of a diagram in which instantaneous values of torque are plotted vertically and angular displacements horizontally. Since the motion as a whole may be considered as a series of small angular displacements it follows that the work done by a variable torque is represented by the area of the corresponding torque-angular displacement diagram.

10.6 Power transmitted by a torque

If the torque applied to a rotating shaft is T, then for a small angular displacement $\delta\theta$, from eq. 10.3,

$$\text{work done} = T\delta\theta$$

If this takes place in time δt,

$$\text{power} = \text{work done/time taken}$$
$$= T\delta\theta/\delta t$$

If $\delta\theta$ and δt are made infinitely small, eq. 5.6 applies and

$$\text{power} = T\,d\theta/dt = T\omega \qquad (10.4)$$

where ω is the angular velocity of the shaft. If both T and ω are constant, the power will also be constant; when torque or speed are varying, eq. 10.4 gives the instantaneous power.

Worked examples

5. A nut is being turned by a spanner to which a force of 150 N is applied. The perpendicular distance between the line of action of this force and the centre of the nut is 0·4 m. Find (a) the torque applied to the nut (b) the work done in turning it through an angle of 30°, assuming the torque to remain constant.

- (a) Torque = $150 \times 0·4 = 60$ N m
- (b) Angular displacement = $30° = 30 \times 2\pi/360$ rad
  From eq. 10.3,

$$\text{work done} = T\theta = 60 \times 30 \times 2\pi/360$$
$$= 31·42 \text{ J}$$

6. A 'rope brake' is used to absorb the power output of an engine under test. The arrangement is as shown in Fig. 10.7. A rope of 20 mm diameter is wrapped once round a drum of diameter 1·5 m, its upper

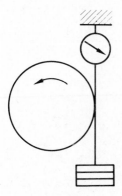

Figure 10.7

end attached to a spring balance, and a suitable mass attached to its lower end. Find the power output of the engine when its speed is 300 rev/min, the mass attached to the rope being 40 kg, and the spring balance reading 25 N. Take $g = 9·81$ m/s² and assume that the tension in the rope acts along its centre line.

Force on 40 kg mass due to gravity $= mg = 40 \times 9.81$
$$= 392.4 \text{ N}$$

This force is balanced by the tension in the rope, which is assumed to act at its centre. Hence the clockwise torque on the drum due to this tension is

$$392.4 \times (0.75 + 0.01) \text{ N m}$$

Similarly, anticlockwise torque due to spring balance is

$$25 \times (0.75 + 0.01) \text{ N m}$$

Therefore,

net torque acting on drum $= (392.4 - 25)(0.75 + 0.01)$
$$= 367.4 \times 0.76 = 279.3 \text{ N m}$$

From eq. 10.4,

power $= T\omega$
$$= 279.3 \times 300 \times 2\pi/60$$
$$= 8.77 \times 10^3 \text{ W or } 8.77 \text{ kW}$$

7. The end of a 120 mm diameter bar is being faced in a lathe. The bar is rotated at 100 rev/min and the tool is fed radially inwards at a steady rate. If the cutting force is 1 kN and remains constant, find (a) the instantaneous power absorbed at the start of the operation (b) the total work done if it is completed in 120 revolutions.

(a) At the start of the operation,

$$T = 1000 \times 0.06 = 60 \text{ N m}$$

From eq. 10.4,

instantaneous power $= T\omega = 60 \times 100 \times 2\pi/60$
$$= 628 \text{ W}$$

(b) The cutting force is constant, but the radius at which it acts decreases steadily. Hence, the torque-angular displacement diagram is a triangle (Fig. 10.8) and

work done $=$ area of torque-angular displacement diagram
$$= \tfrac{1}{2} \times 120 \times 2\pi \times 60$$
$$= 22\ 620 \text{ J or } 22.62 \text{ kJ}$$

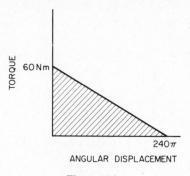

Figure 10.8

10.7 Potential and kinetic energy

Energy is defined as *the capacity to do work* and, in all its forms, the unit of energy is the joule.

Potential energy is the energy possessed by a body because of its position in a gravitational field—that is, because of its height above the ground (or any convenient datum level). Consider (Fig. 10.9) a body of mass m

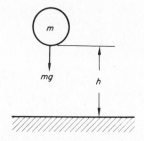

Figure 10.9

at a height h above the ground. The force exerted on the body by gravity is mg, and if it is lowered to the ground gravity will do work on it; from eq. 10.1, the amount of work done will be mgh. In other words, the position of the body relative to the ground gives it the capacity to do mgh joules of work, or

$$\text{potential energy} = mgh \qquad (10.5)$$

Kinetic energy is the energy a body possesses due to motion. From Newton's first law, it follows that a moving body can only be brought to rest by an opposing force, and while being brought to rest it will do work in overcoming this force. The amount of work the body is capable of doing before coming to rest is its kinetic energy.

Consider a body of mass m moving with velocity v, and let it be uniformly decelerated to rest in time t,

$$\text{deceleration} = v/t$$

From eq. 6.2, force required

$$F = ma = mv/t$$

From eq. 5.14,

$$\text{distance travelled } s = \tfrac{1}{2}vt$$

Hence, from eq. 10.1,

$$\begin{aligned}\text{work done} &= F \times s \\ &= (mv/t) \times (\tfrac{1}{2}vt) \\ &= \tfrac{1}{2}mv^2\end{aligned}$$

Therefore,

$$\text{kinetic energy} = \tfrac{1}{2}mv^2 \tag{10.6}$$

10.8 Conservation of energy

The 'principle of conservation of energy' is that *energy can neither be created nor destroyed*. Energy exists in many forms, and can be converted from one form to another, but it is found that in all such conversions the total amount of energy remains constant. It is, of course, necessary to account for *all* forms of energy when applying this principle. Energy is often said to be 'lost'—for example, by friction in a machine, or when two bodies collide—but this does not mean that it has been destroyed; only that it has been converted into an unwanted form (usually heat).

Many situations arise in which the potential energy of a body is converted into kinetic energy—for example, when a body is allowed to fall freely—and vice versa. Provided that there is no conversion of energy to heat by friction, and that the body does not receive energy by, say, having work done on it by an external force, the principle of conservation of energy means that potential energy + kinetic energy = constant. If friction is present, the energy of the body will be reduced by the work done in overcoming frictional resistances and initial total energy = final total energy + work done against friction.

Worked examples

8. A body of mass 5 kg is projected vertically upwards with initial velocity 20 m/s. What is its initial kinetic energy, and to what height will it rise?

From eq. 10.6,

$$\text{kinetic energy} = \tfrac{1}{2}mv^2$$
$$= \tfrac{1}{2} \times 5 \times 20^2$$
$$= 1000 \text{ J or 1 kJ}$$

At maximum height, the body will have zero velocity and hence zero kinetic energy. All its initial kinetic energy will have been converted to potential energy. From eq. 10.5,

$$\text{potential energy} = mgh$$

Hence, at maximum height,

$$1000 = 5 \times 9\cdot81 \times h$$

Therefore,

$$h = 1000/(5 \times 9\cdot81) = 20\cdot4 \text{ m}$$

9. In a drop-forging operation, the top die and its holder, with a combined mass of 20 kg, fall freely for 3 m before contacting the metal resting on the bottom die. Calculate (a) the velocity of the top die at the moment of contact and (b) the force exerted on the metal (assuming it to be constant) if the top die travels a further distance of 15 mm before coming to rest.

(a) Potential energy lost = kinetic energy gained
$$mgh = \tfrac{1}{2}mv^2$$
Therefore, $$v = \sqrt{2gh}$$
$$= \sqrt{(2 \times 9\cdot81 \times 3)}$$
$$= 7\cdot67 \text{ m/s}$$

(b) Potential energy lost = work done on metal
$$mgh = Fs$$
Therefore, $$F = mgh/s$$
$$= 20 \times 9\cdot81 \times 3\cdot015/0\cdot015$$
$$= 39\,400 \text{ N or } 39\cdot4 \text{ kN}$$

10. A railway truck has a mass of 6 tonnes and is at rest on an incline of 1 in 30. The brakes are released and the truck runs down the incline. If the frictional resistance to motion is 300 N, what will be its speed after travelling 20 m?

$$\text{potential energy lost} = \text{kinetic energy gained} + \text{work}$$
$$\text{done against friction}$$
$$mgh = \tfrac{1}{2}mv^2 + Fs$$
$$6000 \times 9 \cdot 81 \times (20/30) = \tfrac{1}{2} \times 6000\,v^2 + 300 \times 20$$
$$39\ 240 = 3000\,v^2 + 6000$$

Therefore,
$$v^2 = 33\ 240/3000 = 11 \cdot 08$$
and so,
$$v = 3 \cdot 33 \text{ m/s}$$

11. A train of mass 250 tonnes starts from rest and accelerates up an incline of 1 in 100, attaining a speed of 45 km/h after travelling 250 m. The frictional resistance to motion is 30 kN. Find the work done by the locomotive and its tractive effort, assuming this to be constant.

$$45 \text{ km/h} = 45\ 000/3600 = 12 \cdot 5 \text{ m/s}$$

work done on train

= increase in potential and kinetic energies + work done
against friction
$$= mgh + \tfrac{1}{2}mv^2 + Fs$$
$$= 250\ 000 \times 9 \cdot 81 \times 250/100 + \tfrac{1}{2} \times 250\ 000 \times 12 \cdot 5^2$$
$$+ 30\ 000 \times 250$$
$$= 6 \cdot 13 \times 10^6 + 19 \cdot 53 \times 10^6 + 7 \cdot 5 \times 10^6$$
$$= 33 \cdot 16 \times 10^6 \text{ J or } 33 \cdot 16 \text{ MJ}$$

work done = tractive effort × distance travelled

$$33 \cdot 16 \times 10^6 = F \times 250$$

Therefore,
$$F = 33 \cdot 16 \times 10^6/250$$
$$= 132 \cdot 6 \times 10^3 \text{ N or } 132 \cdot 6 \text{ kN}$$

Problems

Take the acceleration due to gravity, $g = 9 \cdot 81$ m/s^2.

1. A casting of mass 30 kg is dragged 5 m along a rough horizontal floor ($\mu = 0 \cdot 4$). Find (a) the work done (b) the average power absorbed if the time taken is 9 s.

(*Answer*. (a) 588·6 J (b) 65·4 W.)

2. A vehicle is towed along a level road by a rope which is inclined at 30° to the horizontal and in which the tension is 150 N. Find the work done in moving the vehicle 100 m.

(*Answer*. 12·99 kJ.)

3. The combined mass of a lift and its contents is 600 kg. Its supporting cable passes over a driving pulley and is attached to a counterweight of mass 500 kg.

Commencing from a point at which the lengths of cable on either side of the driving pulley are equal, the lift is raised 12 m. Calculate the work done if the mass of 1 m of cable is 3 kg.

(*Answer*. 7·54 kJ.)

4. A truck, initially at rest, is pulled along a track by a force F which varies with its displacement s as shown in the following Table:

F(N)	500	490	470	440	400	350	290
s(m)	0	5	10	15	20	25	30

Draw, to scale, a force-displacement diagram and find the work done on the truck in moving it 30 m from rest.

(*Answer*. 12·75 kJ.)

5. An electric motor runs at 1450 rev/min. Assuming its efficiency to be 80%, calculate its output torque when its power consumption is 2 kW.

(*Answer*. 10·5 N m.)

6. A 100 mm diameter bar is being turned in a lathe. The speed of the lathe is 110 rev/min and the force on the cutting tool is 1·5 kN. Calculate the power absorbed.

(*Answer*. 864 W.)

7. The torque required to drive a machine varies over one complete revolution as follows. For the first 100 degrees the torque is 50 N m and remains constant. The torque then increases uniformly over 100 degrees to a maximum of 350 N m, then decreases uniformly over 160 degrees to 50 N m. Draw a torque-angular displacement diagram and find the work done for one revolution.

(*Answer*. 995 J.)

12

8. A motor vehicle of mass 600 kg is travelling at 100 km/h when its brakes are applied, reducing its speed to 20 km/h. By how much is its kinetic energy reduced? What becomes of this energy?

(*Answer*. 222 kJ.)

9. A hydro-electric power station is 140 m below the level of its reservoir. If the overall efficiency of its plant is 60%, what will be the electrical power output when water flows to it from the reservoir at a rate of 30 m³/s? The density of water is 1000 kg/m³.

(*Answer*. 24·7 MW.)

10. A vehicle of mass 800 kg is at rest on a road inclined at 20° to the horizontal. Its brakes are released and it runs downhill a distance of 10 m (measured along the road). If the frictional resistance to motion is 150 N, find (a) its velocity at this point. It continues to coast along the road, which now slopes upwards at an angle of 10° to the horizontal. If the frictional resistance is, as before, 150 N, find (b) how far it will now travel before coming to rest.

(*Answer*. (a) 7·96 m/s (b) 16.8 m.)

11. A truck of mass 10 tonnes is moving at 1 m/s when it strikes spring-loaded buffers. The initial resisting force of the buffers is 10 kN and the resisting force increases by 100 N per mm of compression. Calculate the maximum compression of the buffers.

(*Answer*. 232 mm.)

12. A projectile of mass 4 kg is fired vertically upwards with initial velocity 250 m/s. Neglecting air resistance, calculate (a) its initial kinetic energy, (b) its velocity when at a height of 1000 m, (c) its maximum height.

(*Answer*. (a) 125 kJ (b) 207 m/s (c) 3185 m)

13. A train of total mass 200 tonnes starts from rest and accelerates up an incline of 1 in 80. If the locomotive exerts a steady tractive effort of 100 kN and the frictional resistance to motion is 25 kN, what will be the speed of the train after it has travelled 300 m?

(*Answer*. 12·3 m/s.)

11. Simple machines

11.1 The purpose of a machine

A machine is a device which enables work to be done more conveniently. In general, it has an input member to which is applied an input force or torque, known as the *effort*, and an output member which carries an output force or torque, known as the *load*. Usually, the purpose of the machine is fulfilled if, by virtue of its design, the effort required is very much smaller than the load. A properly designed lifting device, for example, enables large gravitational loads to be overcome by the application of quite small forces. A machine can, thus, allow a man to lift a load which otherwise he would not have the physical strength to raise.

When the output member of a machine moves the load applied to it, work is done *by* the machine on, or against, the load. This may be called the *work output*. This work output occurs only in consequence of the work done *on* the machine when the effort moves the input member. The work done on the machine by the effort may be called the *work input*. By the principle of conservation of energy (section 10.8), it is impossible for the work output to exceed the work input. Indeed, in practice, the work output is always less than the input because some energy must be expended within the machine itself in overcoming friction which resists the relative motion of the moving parts.

An *ideal machine* is one in which there is no friction (and no inertia), so that for such a machine (Fig. 11.1):

$$\text{work input} = \text{work output} \qquad (11.1)$$
$$F_i x_i = F_o x_o$$

where F_i = input force or effort, F_o = output force or load, x_i = input displacement, x_o = output displacement.

It is clear, from eq. 11.1, that if F_i is to be small while F_o is large, the reverse must be true of the corresponding displacements. Thus, to gain the advantage offered by the concept of a machine, it must be designed so that the input displacement of the effort is greater than the output displacement of the load.

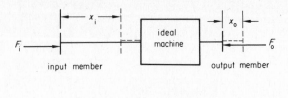

Figure 11.1

11.2 Mechanical advantage and velocity ratio

The advantage offered by a machine is that the effort can be very much smaller than the load. The measure of this advantage is the ratio of load to effort, and this is called the *mechanical advantage* (M.A.),

$$\text{mechanical advantage} = \frac{\text{load}}{\text{effort}} = \frac{F_o}{F_i} \qquad (11.2)$$

To obtain this mechanical advantage, the machine must be designed so that the input displacement of the effort is much greater than the output displacement of the load. The measure of this is the ratio of input to output displacements, and is called the *velocity ratio* (V.R.),

$$\text{velocity ratio} = \frac{\text{input displacement of effort}}{\text{output displacement of load}} = \frac{x_i}{x_o} \qquad (11.3)$$

Since both displacements occur in the same time, this is also the ratio of the input and output velocities.

The V.R. of a machine is a constant, since it is entirely dependent on the physical geometry given to it by its design and manufacture. On the other hand, the M.A. of a machine varies with the load it carries. This is because, except in an ideal machine, the effort required to overcome the frictional forces within the machine compares differently with the various loads applied. With a very small load, for example, more effort may be needed to overcome the friction than the load itself, whereas, for a large load, the part of the effort used to overcome friction may be only a small percentage of the whole. The situation is further complicated by the increase in the frictional forces as the loading is increased, owing to the tendency of the load to increase the normal reactions between the contact surfaces of the moving parts.

For these reasons, the M.A. to be expected from an ideal machine is never achieved in practice. In general, however, the M.A. increases with the load and tends towards a limiting value, as shown in section 11.4.

11.3 Efficiency

In practice, the useful work output of a machine is less than the work input (Fig. 11.2). The difference represents energy wasted, and this must be reduced to the smallest possible proportions by suitable design and use of the machine. The aim should be to make the useful work output as high a proportion of the work input as possible, and the measure of success achieved in this respect is called the *efficiency* of the machine,

$$\text{efficiency} = \eta = \frac{\text{work output}}{\text{work input}} = \frac{F_o x_o}{F_i x_i} \tag{11.4}$$

This is usually expressed as a percentage, in which case the ratio is multiplied by 100.

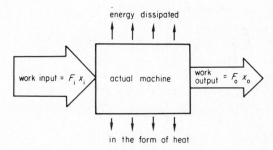

Figure 11.2

In the ideal machine, no energy is wasted and the efficiency is 1·0, or 100%, so that eq. 11.4 reverts to eq. 11.1. Since x_o and x_i are fixed by the geometry of the machine, the only quantity which may vary for a given load, F_o, is the input force or effort, F_i. In a real machine, the *actual effort* is always greater than the *ideal effort* because of friction in the machine. The difference between these two is called the *friction effort*.

It is possible to express the efficiency of a machine in terms of its M.A. and V.R. Equation 11.4 may be re-written:

$$\text{efficiency} = \eta = \frac{F_o}{F_i} \times \frac{x_o}{x_i} = \frac{F_o/F_i}{x_i/x_o} = \frac{\text{M.A.}}{\text{V.R.}} \tag{11.5}$$

Since, for any given machine, the V.R. is a constant, the efficiency must vary in the same manner as the M.A. does, so that the efficiency will increase with the load. However, the efficiency tends towards a limiting value as the load is increased, as will be shown in section 11.4. In general, machines with high velocity ratios, such as the screw-jack, tend to have lower efficiencies than those having only moderate velocity ratios.

A 'mechanism' is a device for converting one form of motion to another. When its members are strong enough to carry the forces involved, it becomes capable of transmitting power and is called a 'machine'. The efficiency of such a mechanism is referred to as its 'mechanical efficiency'. Many heat engines, for example, employ the slider-crank mechanism, which converts reciprocating motion to rotary motion, to transmit power from the engine cylinder to the crankshaft. The input to this mechanism is the indicated power in the engine cylinder (see chapter 12, sections 12.11, 12.12, and 12.13), while its output is the power available at the crankshaft. Thus, for an engine mechanism:

$$\text{mechanical efficiency} = \frac{\text{brake power}}{\text{indicated power}} \qquad (11.6)$$

where the brake power is the power available at the crankshaft, as measured in a brake test.

Note that the definition of efficiency as work output/work input is applicable over a wide field. The purpose of some machines, for example, is to convert energy from one form to another, as in a heat engine or electrical generator. Since all forms of energy have the same units, this presents no problem.

Consider a simple machine, say a lifting device, which does work on a load, and suppose the load retains the useful work output in the form of potential energy. If this potential energy was 51 J and the work input had been 100 J, then the efficiency would be 51 % and 49 J of energy would have been expended in overcoming friction. If the effort is now removed, the machine will run backwards because the 51 J of energy contained by the load is sufficient to overcome friction, since this will require only a further 49 J, leaving 2 J to spare. On the other hand, if 51 J had been required to overcome friction during the run-up, the 49 J retained by the load would be insufficient for the further expenditure of energy needed to make the machine run backwards, when the effort is removed. This reversal of a machine, which may occur on removal of the effort, is called *overhauling*. A machine having an efficiency less than 50 % cannot overhaul. Machines with efficiencies greater than 50 % should, therefore, be fitted with a non-reversal device—a safety ratchet, for example—to prevent them running-back.

11.4 The characteristics of a machine

For any given machine, the V.R. is fixed and may be calculated from its geometry. The actual effort, the M.A., and the efficiency of the machine, however, all vary with the load and cannot be calculated. These must therefore be determined experimentally. The graphs showing their variation with load are called the characteristics of the machine.

The fundamental characteristic is the variation of actual effort with load. Once this is known, the M.A. and efficiency may be deduced from it. Figure 11.3 shows a typical graph of actual effort against load for a simple machine. Since this is a straight line, its equation is of the form:

$$F_i = aF_o + b \qquad (11.7)$$

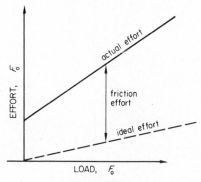

Figure 11.3

where a and b are constants. This equation is known as 'the law of the machine'. The constant b is evidently the effort required when there is zero load on the machine. For an ideal machine, this is zero, so that the ideal effort is represented by a straight line passing through the origin (shown dotted in Fig. 11.3). The difference between the actual and ideal efforts is the effort required to overcome friction. This also is indicated in Fig. 11.3.

The M.A. may be deduced from the law of the machine.

$$\text{M.A.} = \frac{F_o}{F_i} = \frac{F_o}{aF_o + b} = \frac{1}{a + (b/F_o)} \qquad (11.8)$$

The variation of the M.A. with load, as represented by this equation, is shown in Fig. 11.4. When F_o is very large, b/F_o becomes negligible compared with a, so that the M.A. approaches a limiting value and eq. 11.8 reduces to:

$$\text{M.A.}_{\text{(limiting)}} = \frac{1}{a} \qquad (11.9)$$

Having obtained the M.A., the efficiency is best found from eq. 11.5.

$$\text{efficiency} = \eta = \frac{\text{M.A}}{\text{V.R}} = \frac{1}{\text{V.R.}[a + (b/F_o)]} \tag{11.10}$$

Since the V.R. is a constant, the variation of efficiency with load is similar to that of the M.A. (see Fig. 11.4), and it also will approach a limiting value.

$$\eta_{\text{(limiting)}} = \frac{1}{(\text{V.R.})a} \tag{11.11}$$

since b/F_o tends to zero as F_o becomes large.

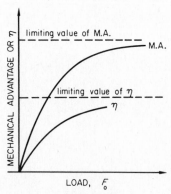

Figure 11.4

11.5 Examples of simple machines

The foregoing theory is common to all simple machines, whatever their form. The one thing which is individual to a particular machine is its velocity ratio. To demonstrate the method by which the V.R. of a machine is found, therefore, a particular machine must be specified. Figure 11.5 shows a number of simple machines, and some of these will be taken as examples.

The method is basically the same for all machines. The input member is given some convenient displacement and the corresponding displacement of the output member is either measured directly or evaluated from the geometry of the machine.

Wheel and axle

This is shown in Fig. 11.5a and is an extension of the simple lever principle.

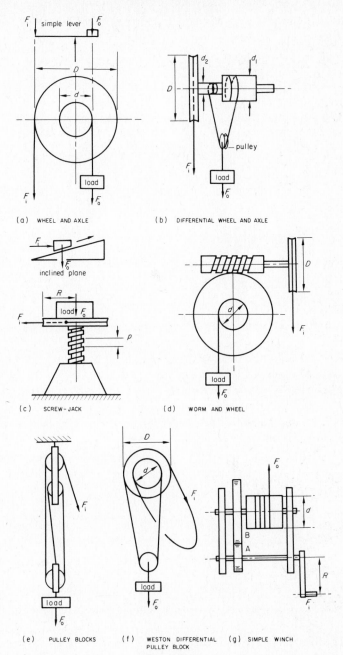

Figure 11.5

Let the effort F_i be given a downward displacement equivalent to one revolution of the wheel,

$$\text{input displacement of effort} = x_i = \pi D$$

since a length of cord equal in length to the circumference of the wheel will be unwound from the wheel.

This will cause the load to be displaced upwards, as a length of cord equal to the circumference of the axle is wound on to the axle,

$$\text{output displacement of load} = x_o = \pi d$$

$$\text{velocity ratio} = \frac{x_i}{x_o} = \frac{\pi D}{\pi d} = \frac{D}{d} \tag{11.12}$$

Differential wheel and axle

In this case, the axle is stepped (Fig. 11.5b), and each end of a cord is attached to, and wrapped around, different sections of the axle with diameters d_1 and d_2. At the bottom of the loop thus formed, a pulley carries the load F_o.

For one revolution of the wheel, the input displacement is the same as before: $x_i = \pi D$.

As the axle rotates, however, one end of the looped cord *unwinds* from the smaller diameter d_2, while the other end *winds onto* the larger axle diameter d_1. The net result is that the loop shortens by an amount $\pi d_1 - \pi d_2 = \pi(d_1 - d_2)$. This effective contraction is shared between the two halves of the cord (on either side of the pulley), so that the load is caused to rise by half this amount,

$$\text{output displacement of load} = x_o = \tfrac{1}{2}\pi(d_1 - d_2)$$

$$\text{velocity ratio} = \frac{x_i}{x_o} = \frac{\pi D}{\tfrac{1}{2}\pi(d_1 - d_2)} = \frac{2D}{(d_1 - d_2)} \tag{11.13}$$

This can be made very large by making d_1 and d_2 very nearly equal.

The screw-jack

The early Egyptians discovered that very large masses could be raised by pushing them up inclined planes having a shallow gradient. The modern equivalent is the screw thread, in which the inclined plane is 'wrapped' round a cylindrical core, and the same effect achieved by rotation of the *screw* thus formed.

The screw-jack is shown in Fig. 11.5c and consists of a vertical screw, which runs in a fixed 'nut' at the base and carries a circular table at the top. The load is placed on this table and is caused to rise (or fall) when the table is rotated.

If p is the *pitch* of the screw—that is, the distance between corresponding points of adjacent threads—then this is the axial displacement of the screw, and therefore of the load, when the screw makes one complete revolution. This, however, is only true if the screw has a *single-start* thread. A *two-start* thread consists essentially of two separate threads arranged alternately on the cylindrical core of the screw, so that one complete revolution causes it to move an axial distance equal to two pitch lengths. The axial displacement of the screw for one complete revolution is called the *lead* of the screw, and, in general:

$$\text{lead of a screw} = np \tag{11.14}$$

where p = pitch of the screw thread and n = the number of starts.

Let the screw make one complete revolution,

$$\text{input displacement of effort} = x_i = 2\pi R$$

where R is the radius of the table, or torque arm.

$$\text{output displacement of load} = x_o = \text{lead of screw} = np$$

$$\text{velocity ratio} = \frac{x_i}{x_o} = \frac{2\pi R}{np} \tag{11.15}$$

It is frequently not possible for the load to rotate with the screw, and under such circumstances the top of the screw must be allowed to rotate in a fixed collar. This introduces additional friction and must inevitably reduce the efficiency of the machine.

Worm and wheel

This is shown in Fig. 11.5d. The worm is similar in appearance to a screw but the thread engages with gear teeth on the wheel. For the system to function, the circular pitch of the teeth on the wheel must be the same as the pitch of the thread on the worm,

$$\text{lead of the worm} = np$$

where p = the common pitch of teeth and thread and n = the number of starts of the worm.

One revolution of the worm will cause each tooth on the wheel to be displaced along the circumference of the wheel a distance equal to the lead of the worm. The corresponding rotation of the wheel will depend on the relationship between this distance and the circumference of the wheel,

$$\text{corresponding revolutions of wheel} = \frac{np}{\text{circumference}} = \frac{np}{Tp} = \frac{n}{T}$$

where T is the total number of teeth on the wheel.

Thus, for one complete revolution of the worm,

$$\text{input displacement of effort} = x_i = \pi D$$

$$\text{output displacement of load} = x_o = \pi d(n/T)$$

$$\text{velocity ratio} = \frac{x_i}{x_o} = \frac{\pi D}{\pi d(n/T)} = \frac{DT}{dn} \tag{11.16}$$

Also shown in Fig. 11.5 is a set of simple pulley blocks, the Weston differential pulley block, and a simple winch. In the simple pulley-block arrangement, pulleys of equal diameter are used in two blocks, as shown, with a single rope passing over each pulley in turn. One end of the rope is fixed, either to the upper or to the lower block (whichever is convenient), while the free end is used for applying the effort. For the case illustrated, the lower block is suspended from the upper block by three sections of the rope. The rope between the blocks is shortened by whatever displacement is given to the effort, and this contraction must be shared between the three sections. The load is therefore raised by only one-third of the input displacement, and the V.R. is evidently 3. In general, the V.R. of a set of pulley blocks is equal to the number of sections of rope by which the lower block is supported, or, alternatively, is equal to the total number of pulleys used. The Weston differential pulley block is similar, but incorporates the principle of the differential wheel and axle.

The winch, Fig. 11.5g, basically employs a gear train to develop the required V.R., with a handle or pulley wheel at the input end and a load drum at the output end. The load is attached to the free end of a cord which is attached to, and coiled around, the load drum. A larger V.R. may be obtained by using a compound gear train instead of the simple train shown.

Worked examples

1. A pulley-block arrangement with three pulleys in both upper and lower blocks is used to lift a mass of 150 kg against the pull of gravity. If the effort required is 0·5 kN, calculate the efficiency of the device at this particular load. Assume $g = 9·81$ m/s^2.

Since a total of six pulleys is used, the V.R. = 6,

$$\text{load } F_o = mg = 150 \times 9\cdot81 = 1472 \text{ N} = 1\cdot47 \text{ kN}$$

$$\text{effort } F_i = 0\cdot5 \text{ kN}$$

$$\text{M.A.} = \frac{F_o}{F_i} = \frac{1\cdot47}{0\cdot5} = 2\cdot94$$

$$\text{efficiency} = \frac{\text{M.A.}}{\text{V.R.}} = \frac{2\cdot94}{6} = 0\cdot49 = 49\%$$

2. A screw-jack has a single-start thread with a pitch of 5·5 mm. The jack is operated by means of a torque arm of length 0·7 m. Calculate its velocity ratio.

A load of mass 0·5 tonne was found to require an effort of 50 N applied to the end of the torque arm, while a load of mass 1·5 tonne required an effort of 100 N similarly applied. Assuming a linear relationship between effort and load, and that $g = 10$ m/s², determine the law of the machine.

Hence find (a) the effort required to lift a load of mass 4 tonne and the efficiency at this load (b) the limiting values of the mechanical advantage and of the efficiency.

From eq. 11.15,

$$\text{V.R.} = \frac{2\pi(0\cdot7)}{(5\cdot5 \times 10^{-3})} = 800$$

The law of the machine will be of the form:

$$F_i = aF_o + b$$

where F_i is the effort and $F_o(=mg)$ is the gravitational force on the load mass.

Since 1 tonne = 1000 kg and $g = 10$ m/s²,

gravitational force on 0·5 tonne mass = $500 \times 10 = 5000$ N
gravitational force on 1·5 tonne mass = $1500 \times 10 = 15\,000$ N

Substituting corresponding values of F_i and F_o,

$$50 = a\,5000 + b$$
$$100 = a\,15\,000 + b$$

By subtraction

$$50 = 10\,000a$$
$$a = 5 \times 10^{-3} = 0\cdot005$$

Re-substituting,

$$b = 50 - 5000(5 \times 10^{-3}) = 25$$

The law of the machine is:

$$F_i = 0 \cdot 005 \, F_o + 25$$

where F_i and F_o are measured in newtons.

(a) Gravitational force on 4 tonne mass,

$$F_o = 4000 \times 10 = 40\,000 \text{ N}$$

$$\text{effort required} = F_i = 0 \cdot 005(40\,000) + 25 = 225 \text{ N}$$

$$\text{M.A.} = \frac{F_o}{F_i} = \frac{40\,000}{225} = 178$$

$$\text{efficiency} = \frac{\text{M.A.}}{\text{V.R.}} = \frac{178}{800} = 0 \cdot 2225 = 22 \cdot 25\%$$

(b) From eq. 11.9,

$$\text{M.A.}_{\text{(limiting)}} = \frac{1}{a} = \frac{1}{0 \cdot 005} = 200$$

From eq. 11.11,

$$\eta_{\text{(limiting)}} = \frac{(1/a)}{\text{V.R.}} = \frac{200}{800} = 0 \cdot 25 = 25\%$$

3. A simple winch, similar to that of Fig. 11.5g, has the following particulars: length of effort handle, $R = 250$ mm; diameter of load drum, $d = 100$ mm; number of teeth on wheel $A = 50$; number of teeth on wheel $B = 250$. What is the ideal effort required to operate the winch against a load of 2 kN? What is the actual effort required to overcome this load, and the corresponding friction effort, if the efficiency is 20%?

With reference to Fig. 11.5(g), let the effort handle be turned through one complete revolution. Since the wheel A has 50 teeth, the same number of teeth will be engaged on wheel B,

$$\text{revolutions of wheel B and load drum} = \frac{T_A}{T_B} = \frac{50}{250} = \frac{1}{5}$$

where T_A and T_B are the numbers of teeth on A and B, respectively.

$$\text{input displacement of effort} = x_i = 2\pi R = 500 \text{ mm}$$
$$\text{output displacement of load} = x_o = \tfrac{1}{5}(\pi d) = 20 \text{ mm}$$

$$\text{V.R.} = \frac{x_i}{x_o} = \frac{500\pi}{20\pi} = 25$$

For an ideal machine,

$$\text{efficiency} = \text{M.A.}/\text{V.R.} = 1\cdot0$$
$$\text{ideal M.A.} = \text{V.R.} = 25$$

$$\frac{\text{load}}{\text{ideal effort}} = 25$$

$$\text{ideal effort} = \frac{\text{load}}{25} = \frac{2000}{25} = 80 \text{ N}$$

From eq. 11.5,

$$\text{actual M.A.} = \eta(\text{V.R.}) = 0\cdot20(25) = .5$$

$$\text{actual effort} = \frac{\text{load}}{5} = \frac{2000}{5} = 400 \text{ N}$$

$$\begin{aligned}\text{friction effort} &= \text{actual effort} - \text{ideal effort}\\ &= 400 - 80\\ &= 320 \text{ N}\end{aligned}$$

4. A double-start lead screw of 6 mm pitch operates the saddle of a lathe, moving it horizontally along the lathe bed at a constant speed of 15 mm/s. The coefficient of sliding friction is 0·1, the mass of the saddle is 160 kg, and g is 9·81 m/s². Determine the speed of rotation of the lead screw, and, assuming an efficiency of 40%, the torque and power which must be supplied to the screw.

Lead of the screw = $np = 2 \times 6$ mm = 12 mm. This is the axial displacement for one revolution of the screw.

$$\text{speed of rotation of the screw} = \frac{\text{speed of advance}}{\text{lead of screw}}$$

$$= \frac{15 \text{ mm/s}}{12 \text{ mm}} = 1\cdot25 \text{ rev/s} = 75 \text{ rev/min}$$

gravitational force on saddle = $mg = 160(9\cdot81) = 1570$ N
frictional resistance of saddle = $\mu F_N = \mu(mg) = 0\cdot1(1570) = 157$ N
power output = load × speed = $157 \times 0\cdot015 = 2\cdot355$ W

$$\text{efficiency} = \frac{\text{power output}}{\text{power input}}$$

$$\text{power input} = \frac{\text{power output}}{\text{efficiency}} = \frac{2\cdot355}{0\cdot40} = 5\cdot89 \text{ W}$$

But, power input $= T\omega$, where T is the torque applied to the lead screw and ω is its angular velocity in rad/s.

$$T(75 \times 2\pi/60) = 5\cdot89 \text{ W}$$
$$T = 5\cdot89/7\cdot854 = 0\cdot75 \text{ N m}$$

Problems

1. The effective wheel and axle diameters of a wheel and axle are, respectively, 240 mm and 50 mm. Using this machine, a load of mass 60 kg was raised by an effort of 180 N and a 200 kg mass required an effort of 500 N.

Determine the law of this machine, and also the maximum efficiency theoretically possible. Take $g = 9\cdot81$ m/s^2.

(*Answer.* $F_i = (0\cdot233F_o + 43)$N, 89·4%.)

2. Determine the velocity ratio of the Weston differential pulley block shown in Fig. 11.5f, assuming D is 200 mm, and d is 180 mm.

If the efficiency of this device is 30% when lifting a load of mass 0·6 tonne against the pull of gravity, calculate the effort required. Assume $g = 9\cdot81$ m/s^2.

(*Answer.* 20; 981 N.)

3. A set of pulley blocks has four pulleys in the upper block and three in the lower. Using this lifting tackle, an effort of 120 N is required to raise a mass of 60 kg against the force of gravity. Calculate the efficiency of the device at this load, and also the effort required to overcome friction. Assume $g = 9\cdot81$ m/s^2.

(*Answer.* 70·1%, 35·9 N.)

4. A differential wheel and axle, similar to that of Fig. 11.5b, has an effective wheel diameter of 200 mm, and the stepped axle has diameters of 60 mm and 50 mm. Determine the velocity ratio of the machine and calculate the ideal effort required to lift a load of mass 300 kg. Take $g = 9\cdot81$ m/s^2.

If the actual effort required for this load is 115 N, determine the efficiency of the machine and the total work done by the effort when the load is raised a vertical height of 2 m.

(*Answer.* 40, 73·6 N, 64%, 9·2 kJ.)

5. A screw-jack has a single-start thread of 11 mm pitch. The axis of the screw is vertical, and the load is carried on a circular table of diameter 490 mm. The jack is operated by rotating the table, by means of a cord wrapped around its rim, as shown in Fig. 11.5c. With a mass of 175 kg on the table, an effort of 50 N is required to make it rise.

Assuming $g = 10$ m/s^2, calculate the efficiency at this load and the work done against friction when the table rises 100 mm.

(*Answer.* 25%, 525 J.)

6. In a test on a machine to determine its characteristics, the following results were obtained:

Load (kN)	1·0	3·0	5·0	7·0	9·0
Effort (kN)	0·165	0·290	0·425	0·555	0·685

The velocity ratio of the machine is 32.

From these results, deduce the law of the machine. Hence deduce the limiting values of the mechanical advantage and the efficiency, and state whether under any conditions it is possible for the machine to overhaul.

Draw graphs showing the variation of efficiency and friction effort with load. What is the friction effort when the load is 8 kN?

(*Answer.* $F_i = (0·065F_o + 100)$ N, 15·38, 48%, 0·37 kN.)

7. A worm and wheel lifting device has a two-start worm and a wheel with 60 teeth. The load drum keyed to the wheel shaft has a diameter of 0·25 m. Assuming an efficiency of 40%, determine the torque required at the worm shaft to raise a load of mass 200 kg against the pull of gravity. Assume $g = 9·81$ m/s^2.

(*Answer.* 20·4 N m.)

8. A winch is used to drag a mass of 2 tonnes up a plane inclined at 20° to the horizontal. The winch is arranged at the top of the incline so that the cable is parallel to the plane. The coefficient of friction between the mass and the plane is 0·3 and g may be taken to be 10 m/s^2.

The input member of the winch is driven by an electric motor at a constant speed of 500 rev/min, and compound gearing between the motor and the 200 mm diameter load drum gives a reduction of 50 to 1. Assuming the efficiency of the machine is 15%, find (a) the speed of the 2 tonne mass up the incline (b) the torque applied by the motor to the input member of the winch (c) the power supplied by the motor.

(*Answer.* (a) 0·1047 m/s (b) 166·4 N m (c) 8·71 kW.)

13

12. Pressure and its measurement

12.1 The meaning of pressure

In everyday language, the word 'pressure' is used to describe any kind of steady positive force exerted by one body on another; but in engineering usage the term is applied only to fluids, and its meaning is not total force but *force per unit area*. A fluid (that is, a liquid, vapour, or gas) exerts a force on the walls of its container. Since a fluid is defined as a substance which offers no permanent resistance to shear forces, it follows that in a fluid at rest there can be no shear stresses. Hence, the force exerted by the fluid is always at right-angles to the containing surface, or to any surface in contact with the fluid. The force exerted on unit area of any such surface is defined as the *pressure* of the fluid.

From the above definition, the basic unit of pressure is unit force/unit area, so that, in the SI system, pressure is measured in N/m^2 or, since this is a rather small unit, in kN/m^2 or MN/m^2. An alternative unit of pressure is the *bar*, defined by

$$1 \text{ bar} = 10^5 \text{ N/m}^2 = 100 \text{ kN/m}^2$$

Although basic units are to be preferred, the bar is a convenient practical unit (being roughly equivalent to atmospheric pressure) and is widely used. In any calculation, pressures must be expressed in N/m^2, but throughout this book, wherever appropriate, equivalents in bars will be given.

12.2 Pressure at a depth in a liquid

Figure 12.1a shows a vertical tube with a uniform cross-sectional area a containing a liquid of density ρ whose free surface is a height h above the horizontal base of the tube. If it is assumed that no pressure acts on the free surface, the only vertical forces acting on the liquid are the downward force due to gravity and the upward reaction F of the base of the tube.

180

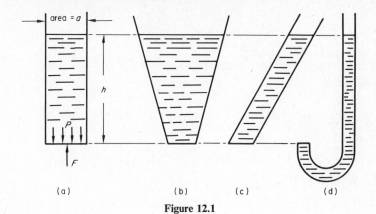

Figure 12.1

Hence, for equilibrium, the force F must be equal to the gravitational force on the liquid,

$$\text{volume of liquid} = ah$$

Therefore,

$$\text{mass of liquid} = \rho ah$$

Therefore,

$$\text{gravitational force on liquid} = \text{mass} \times g = \rho ahg$$

Therefore,

$$F = \rho gah$$

If the pressure exerted by the fluid on the base of the tube is p, then, by definition, $p = F/a$ or $F = pa$.

Hence,

$$pa = \rho gah$$

and so,

$$p = \rho gh \qquad (12.1)$$

If a pressure p' acts on the free surface of the liquid, there will be an additional downward force $p'a$ and the condition for equilibrium will be

$$F = \rho gah + p'a$$

from which

$$p = \rho gh + p' \qquad (12.2)$$

From this it follows that the surface of the liquid need not in fact be 'free'—the pressure p' could be due to, say, a piston—and that the pressure is the same at all points at the same depth in a liquid. It may also be shown, either theoretically or by experiment, that the shape of the containing vessel has no effect on the pressure of the liquid. Although eq. 12.1 has been developed for a container with vertical sides, it will apply equally well to other containers including tapered vessels (Fig. 12.1b), inclined vessels (Fig. 12.1c) and U-shaped vessels (Fig. 12.1d). It should, however, be emphasized that eq. 12.1 and 12.2 apply only to liquids at rest, and for this reason the pressure p is called the 'hydrostatic' pressure.

12.3   The barometer

An instrument for measuring atmospheric pressure is called a *barometer*. A simple and accurate barometer may be made from a glass tube about 1 m long and closed at one end. The tube is filled with mercury and inverted so that its lower end dips into a bath of mercury, as shown by Fig. 12.2, no air being allowed to enter the tube during this process. The

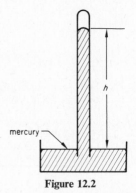

Figure 12.2

mercury column falls, leaving a space at the top of the tube which is empty (that is, a 'perfect vacuum') apart from a very small amount of mercury vapour. The surface of the mercury bath is exposed to atmospheric pressure, and, for practical purposes, the pressure on the upper surface of the mercury column is zero. Hence, from eq. 12.1, the pressure of the atmosphere is $\rho g h$, where h is the vertical distance from the level of the mercury bath to the top of the mercury column. At standard atmospheric pressure (defined as 101 325 N/m², which is equivalent to 1·01325 bars or 1013·25 millibars), this distance is 760 mm.

Mercury barometers are widely used. All consist basically of the arrangement shown in Fig. 12.3, differences being chiefly in the way in which the height *h* is measured: but since a glass tube at least 800 mm long is involved, all are both bulky and fragile. An alternative instrument is the *aneroid barometer,* in which the measuring element is a sealed metal capsule or bellows from which the air has been exhausted, so that the internal pressure is zero. Atmospheric pressure acts on the outside of the bellows and, as this varies, the bellows will expand or contract. A pointer is attached to the bellows by a suitable linkage.

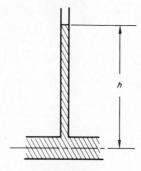

Figure 12.3

12.4 Absolute pressure, gauge pressure, and vacuum

A barometer measures the true or *absolute* pressure of the atmosphere. The pressure indicated by almost all other instruments, however, is the difference between the pressure being measured and atmospheric pressure. For example, if the pressure gauge on a compressed air tank reads 'zero', this does not mean that there is a perfect vacuum in the tank but that the pressure inside it is equal to atmospheric pressure. If air is pumped into the tank, the gauge will show the amount by which the tank pressure exceeds atmospheric pressure. A pressure measured in this way is called a *gauge pressure,* and from the above example it may be seen that:

absolute pressure = gauge pressure + atmospheric pressure

If, in Fig. 12.1, the tube is open to the atmosphere, the pressure p' acting on the free surface of the liquid is atmospheric pressure. Hence, in this case, eq. 12.2 becomes

$$p_{\text{absolute}} = \rho g h + p_{\text{atmospheric}}$$

Hence

$$\rho g h = p_{\text{absolute}} - p_{\text{atmospheric}} = p_{\text{gauge}} \qquad (12.3)$$

Gauge pressures are normally distinguished from absolute pressures by adding the word 'gauge' when stating them (for example, 10 kN/m² gauge). In this book, pressures are absolute unless otherwise stated.

If a pressure lower than atmospheric is being measured, the difference between it and atmospheric pressure is usually called the 'degree of vacuum' or simply the 'vacuum'. Often this is stated in 'mm of mercury', that is, in terms of the height of a mercury column, so that it may be compared directly with the reading of a mercury barometer. In this case,

absolute pressure = atmospheric pressure − vacuum

12.5   Piezometers and manometers

The simplest way of measuring the pressure of a liquid is to connect an open-ended vertical glass tube to its container. This is called a pressure tube or piezometer, and Fig. 12.3 shows such a tube connected to a pipe-line containing a liquid under pressure. The liquid will rise in the tube until the pressure due to the column of liquid equals the pressure in the pipe line. Since the free surface of the liquid in the tube is acted on by atmospheric pressure, eq. 12.3 applies and the gauge pressure at the centre of the pipe line will be given by $\rho g h$, where h is the vertical distance from this point to the free surface of the liquid.

The use of the piezometer is limited in two ways: it can only be used for liquids and, if the density of the liquid is low, the height h may be inconveniently large. If, for example, the liquid is water at a gauge pressure of 100 kN/m² (1 bar), the height of the piezometer column will be about 10·2 m. Both difficulties may be avoided if the fluid pressure is balanced, not by a column of the same fluid, but by one of a different fluid (for example, mercury). A device which works in this way is called a *manometer*. A U-tube manometer (Fig. 12.4a) consists of a glass tube bent into the shape of a letter U and containing a quantity of liquid. One end of the U-tube is open to the atmosphere and the other is connected to the fluid under pressure, so that the liquid in the U-tube is forced down in this limb and up in the open ended limb.

If Fig. 12.4a is compared with Fig. 12.1d, it will be seen that eq. 12.3 may be applied to the liquid in the U-tube and that the gauge pressure of this liquid at the point X is given by $\rho g h$, where ρ is its density and h is the difference in its levels. This must also be the pressure of the fluid at the point X and, if this fluid is a gas, will for practical purposes be the pressure of the gas in the container to which the manometer is connected, since differences in level will have little effect. If the fluid concerned is a liquid, however, it will be necessary to allow for the difference in level between the point X and the point where the connection to the liquid container is made (see worked example 4).

An alternative form of the U-tube manometer in which one limb of the tube is replaced by a metal container is shown in Fig. 12.4b. Any liquid

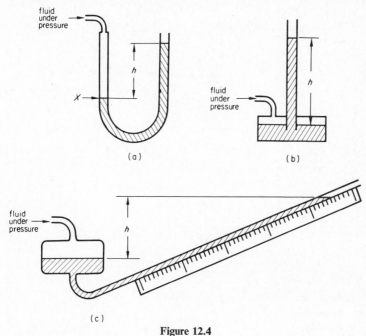

Figure 12.4

may be used in the U-tube provided that its density is greater than that of the fluid under investigation, and that it does not mix or react with this fluid; but the usual choice is mercury (for high pressures) and water or paraffin (for low pressures). For the measurement of low pressures the *inclined tube manometer* (Fig. 12.4c) gives increased sensitivity since a small change in the difference in levels h produces a relatively large movement of the surface of the liquid in the inclined tube.

Worked examples

1. If the density of sea water is 1025 kg/m³, what is (a) the gauge pressure (b) the absolute pressure at a point 50 m below the surface of the sea when the height of a mercury barometer is 755 mm? The density of mercury is 13 600 kg/m³.

(a) From eq. 12.3,

$$p_{gauge} = \rho g h$$
$$= 1025 \times 9 \cdot 81 \times 50$$
$$= 502\ 800\ N/m^2 \text{ or } 502 \cdot 8\ kN/m^2\ (5 \cdot 028\ bar)$$

(b) Applying eq. 12.1 to the mercury barometer, we get

$$p_{atmospheric} = \rho g h$$
$$= 13\ 600 \times 9 \cdot 81 \times 0 \cdot 755$$
$$= 1007\ N/m^2$$
$$p_{absolute} = p_{gauge} + p_{atmospheric}$$
$$= 502\ 800 + 1007$$
$$= 603\ 500\ N/m^2 \text{ or } 603 \cdot 5\ kN/m^2\ (6 \cdot 035\ bar)$$

2. A piezometer is connected to a water pipe and the free surface rises to a height of 2 m above the centre line of the pipe. Taking the density of water as 1000 kg/m³, find the gauge pressure at the centre of the pipe.

From eq. 12.3,

$$p_{gauge} = \rho g h$$
$$= 1000 \times 9 \cdot 81 \times 2$$
$$= 19\ 620\ N/m^2 \text{ or } 19 \cdot 62\ kN/m^2\ (0 \cdot 1962\ bar)$$

3. The pressure of a domestic gas supply is measured by means of a U-tube manometer. The liquid in the U-tube is paraffin (density 800 kg/m²) and the difference in levels is found to be 60 mm. What is the gauge pressure of the gas supply?

From eq. 12.3,

$$p_{gauge} = \rho g h$$
$$= 800 \times 9 \cdot 81 \times 0 \cdot 06$$
$$= 471\ N/m^2\ (4 \cdot 71\ millibars)$$

4. A U-tube containing mercury is connected to a water pipe as shown in Fig. 12.5. The difference in levels of the mercury is found to be 0·5 m and the lower mercury level is 0·7 m below the centre of the water pipe. Taking the densities of mercury and of water as 13 600 kg/m³ and 1000 kg/m³ respectively, find the gauge pressure at the centre of the pipe.

Applying eq. 12.3 to the mercury column,

$$p_{gauge} \text{ at point X} = \rho g h$$
$$= 13\ 600 \times 9 \cdot 81 \times 0 \cdot 5$$
$$= 66\ 710\ N/m^2 \text{ or } 66 \cdot 71\ kN/m^2$$

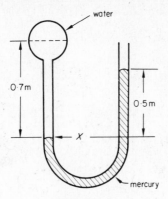

Figure 12.5

The pressure in the pipe may be found by considering the column of water between the surface of the mercury and an imaginary surface at the centre of the pipe (shown dotted in Fig. 12.5).

From eq. 12.2,

$$p = \rho g h + p'$$

or, adding atmospheric pressure to both sides,

$$p_{\text{gauge}} = \rho g h + p'_{\text{gauge}}$$

Hence, in this case,

$$p_{\text{gauge}} \text{ at point X} = \rho g h + p'_{\text{gauge}}$$

where p'_{gauge} is the gauge pressure at the centre of the pipe.
   Substituting values,

$$66\ 710 = (1000 \times 9 \cdot 81 \times 0 \cdot 7) + p'_{\text{gauge}}$$

Therefore,

$$p'_{\text{gauge}} = 66\ 710 - (1000 \times 9 \cdot 81 \times 0 \cdot 7)$$
$$= 66\ 710 - 6870$$
$$= 59\ 840 \text{ N/m}^2 \text{ or } 59 \cdot 84 \text{ kN/m}^2 \ (0 \cdot 5984 \text{ bar})$$

12.6 Simple pressure gauges

The term 'gauge' is applied to mechanical pressure-indicating devices, and of these the most widely used is the *Bourdon gauge*, shown diagrammatically in Fig. 12.6. The pressure-sensitive element in this gauge is a thin-walled tube of elliptical section (the 'Bourdon tube'), curved into about three-quarters of a circle. One end of this tube is fixed and the fluid under pressure is connected to this end. The other end is sealed and, since the outside of the tube is exposed to atmospheric pressure, the pressure difference between the inside and the outside of the tube is the gauge pressure of the fluid. This pressure difference tends to change the section of the tube from elliptical to circular, and this in turn tends to straighten the tube so that its free end moves outwards. Provided the material of the tube is not stressed beyond its limit of proportionality,

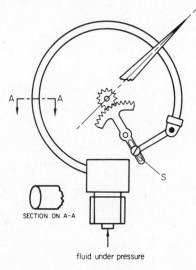

SECTION ON A-A

fluid under pressure

Figure 12.6

this movement is, for practical purposes, proportional to the gauge pressure applied to the tube and it is converted into rotation of a pointer by a quadrant and pinion. Often a small spiral spring (not shown in Fig. 12.6) is attached to the shaft carrying the pointer to ensure that backlash in the mechanism is always taken up in the same direction.

The pressure range for which a Bourdon gauge is suitable is determined by the thickness of the Bourdon tube and its material (usually phosphor-bronze or, for high pressures, alloy steel). Different thicknesses of tube may be used to give pressure ranges from 0–100 kN/m² to 0–50 MN/m². For lower pressure ranges, the Bourdon tube is not sufficiently sensitive and an alternative is to use a corrugated metal diaphragm (Fig. 12.7a) or a metal bellows (Fig. 12.7b). One side of the diaphragm (or bellows) is exposed to the atmosphere and the other side to the fluid under pressure. The force acting on the diaphragm (or bellows) thus depends on the gauge pressure of the fluid, and the resulting deflection is magnified by a suitable mechanism (shown in Fig. 12.7a and b as a simple lever) which rotates a pointer.

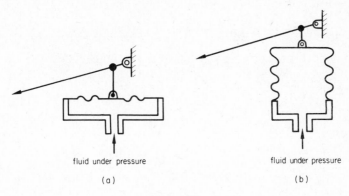

fluid under pressure

(a)

fluid under pressure

(b)

Figure 12.7

12.7 Calibration of a pressure gauge

The calibration of a pressure gauge involves the application to it of accurately known pressures. These may be applied by compressed air or by oil, and measured either by (a) a 'standard pressure gauge' (b) a manometer, or (c) the force exerted on a piston of known area. Method (a) is simple and convenient, particularly if the gauge is to be tested in its working position, but it relies on the accuracy of the 'standard gauge' and this gauge will itself have been calibrated by method (b) or method (c). Method (b) is suitable for low pressures only; practical manometers seldom allow for a difference in levels of more than 2 m, which, if the liquid used is mercury, corresponds to a pressure of about 270 kN/m^2 (2·7 bar).

Method (c) is the basic principle of the *dead weight tester*, shown diagrammatically in Fig. 12.8.

In this tester, oil under pressure acts both on the gauge under test and on a small vertical cylinder containing a close-fitting piston. Calibrated masses ('weights') are placed on a tray attached to the piston, and, by rotating the screw at the right-hand end of the apparatus, the ram is forced inwards until the piston starts to rise—that is, until the piston is supported only by the oil pressure acting on its lower end. The upward force on the piston is, from the definition of pressure, *pa*, where *p* is the

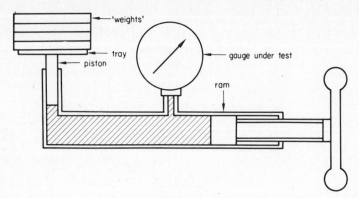

Figure 12.8

oil pressure and a the cross-sectional area of the piston. Hence, for equilibrium of vertical forces,

$$pa = mg$$

or

$$p = mg/a \qquad (12.4)$$

where m is the total mass of the piston, tray, and 'weights'. It may be noted that atmospheric pressure also acts on the piston, but has not been included in the above equation so that p is the gauge pressure of the oil, and that friction between piston and cylinder is assumed negligible. In order to eliminate frictional effects, the piston assembly is set spinning slowly while a reading of the gauge under test is taken.

12.8   Sources of error in a pressure gauge

Errors in the reading of a pressure gauge may be due to incorrect calibration of the gauge, or they may be associated with the connection between the gauge and the point at which pressure is to be measured. The pressure at the gauge may not be the same as the pressure in the vessel to which it is connected, either because of mechanical faults (such as blockages or leaks in the connecting pipe), or because of a difference in level. If the gauge is a distance h below the level of the vessel under pressure, it follows from eq. 12.2 that its reading will be increased by ρgh, where ρ is the density of the fluid in the connecting pipe. If this is a gas, ρ is relatively small and the effect will probably be negligible, but if a liquid, the additional pressure may be considerable. A typical example is that of a steam pressure gauge, since in this case the tapping point is often some distance above the gauge and the connecting pipe contains not steam but condensed water. Usually, in such cases, the pressure-gauge pointer is reset so that the gauge reads correct steam pressure.

Errors in the calibration of a Bourdon gauge may be divided into (a) zero errors (b) errors in magnification and (c) departures from proportionality. Of these, (c) depends on the construction of the gauge and should be negligible, while (a) and (b) may be corrected by resetting the pointer and adjusting the position of the screw S in Fig. 12.6. Errors may be identified from a graph of gauge reading against true pressure, as shown by worked example 7.

Worked examples

5. The piston of a dead-weight tester has a diameter of 11·28 mm and, together with the attached tray, has a mass of 0·5 kg. What will be the pressure applied to the gauge under test when the piston supports an additional mass of 10 kg?

$$\text{cross-sectional area of piston } a = \tfrac{1}{4}\pi d^2$$
$$= \tfrac{1}{4}\pi (0\cdot01128)^2$$
$$= 0\cdot0001 \text{ m}^2$$

From eq. 12.4,

$$p = mg/a$$
$$= (10 + 0\cdot5) \times 9\cdot81/0\cdot0001$$
$$= 1\ 030\ 000 \text{ N/m}^2 \text{ or } 1\cdot03 \text{ MN/m}^2 \text{ gauge}$$

6. A pipe-line contains oil of density 900 kg/m³ at a gauge pressure of 200 kN/m². Assuming the connecting pipe to be full of oil, what will be the reading on a pressure gauge situated (a) 5 m below the pipeline (b) 5 m above it?

(a) From eq. 12.2,

$$p = \rho g h + p'$$

or, adding atmospheric pressure to both sides,

$$p_{\text{gauge}} = \rho g h + p'_{\text{gauge}}$$

Applying this equation to the connecting pipe, the pressure at the gauge will be

$$p_{\text{gauge}} = (900 \times 9\cdot81 \times 5) + 200\ 000$$
$$= 44\ 100 + 200\ 000$$
$$= 244\ 100 \text{ N/m}^2 \text{ or } 244\cdot1 \text{ kN/m}^2 \text{ gauge.}$$

(b) In this case, since the gauge is at the upper end of the pipe,

$$200\,000 = (900 \times 9\cdot81 \times 5) + p'_{\text{gauge}}$$

Therefore pressure at gauge,

$$p'_{\text{gauge}} = 200\,000 - 44\,100$$
$$= 155\,900 \text{ N/m}^2 \text{ or } 155\cdot9 \text{ kN/m}^2 \text{ gauge}$$

7. In Fig. 12.9 the results of a test on a 0–5 MN/m² Bourdon gauge are expressed in the form of a graph of gauge reading against true pressure. What errors does the graph indicate, and how could they be rectified?

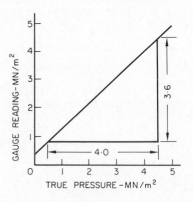

Figure 12.9

The graph is a straight line, indicating that movements of the gauge pointer are directly proportional to pressure changes, but the graph does not pass through the origin, indicating a zero error, and its slope is not unity, indicating an error in magnification. Measurements taken from the graph show that its slope is $3\cdot6/4\cdot0 = 0\cdot9$, hence the magnification of the gauge mechanism should be increased in the proportion 0·9:1. For the arrangement shown in Fig. 12.6, this would be done by moving the screw S (to which is attached the link from the Bourdon tube) nearer to the quadrant shaft, and, in practice, this adjustment would be made by 'trial and error'. The final operation would be to reset the pointer.

12.9 Work done by a constant pressure

Consider a cylinder with a close-fitting piston (Fig. 12.10) into which fluid under a constant pressure p can be admitted. If the area of the piston

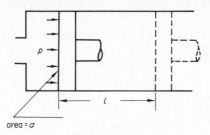

Figure 12.10

is a, the force exerted on it by the fluid is pa, and if the piston is moved a distance l,

$$\text{work done on piston} = \text{force} \times \text{distance}$$
$$= (pa) \times l$$
$$= pal \qquad (12.5)$$

But $a \times l$ is the volume of a cylinder of cross-sectional area a and length l, and this is the volume of the space left by the piston when it moves from its initial to its final position (usually called the 'volume swept by the piston'). Hence an alternative form of eq. 12.5 is

$$\text{work done on piston} = p \times (al)$$
$$= pV \qquad (12.6)$$

where V is the volume swept by the piston.

12.10 Work done by a variable pressure

It has already been shown in section 10.2 that the work done by a variable force is given by the area of the force-displacement diagram. In a similar way, it may be shown that the work done on a piston by a variable pressure is given by the area of the corresponding pressure-volume diagram. The force-displacement diagram for the piston is, in fact, similar to the pressure-volume diagram since, if the area of the piston is a, force = pressure $\times a$ and displacement = swept volume/a. Hence the pressure-volume diagram becomes a force-displacement diagram if its vertical scale is multiplied by a and its horizontal scale divided by a, and it will be seen that this leaves the area of the diagram unchanged.

12.11 The engine indicator

In internal combustion engines and steam engines, work is done on a piston by a fluid under pressure, and this pressure does not remain constant. It follows from the previous section that, in order to find the work done on the piston of such an engine, it is necessary to draw a pressure-volume diagram, and an 'engine indicator' is a device which does this automatically.

The principle of the engine indicator is shown in Fig. 12.11. By means of a valve, a small cylinder can be connected to the engine cylinder so that the pressure in the engine cylinder acts on a small piston, tending to move it upwards. This movement is controlled by a spring; hence the upward motion will be directly proportional to the force on the piston (which in turn is proportional to the pressure) and this motion is magnified by a

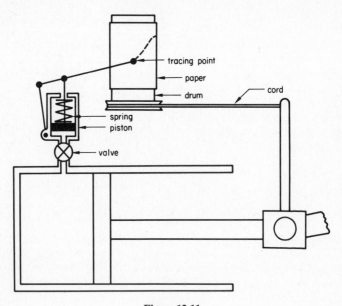

Figure 12.11

linkage to give an upward movement of the tracing point. The diagram is drawn on a sheet of paper whose surface has a coating which is marked by the tracing point. The paper is attached to a drum, which is rotated by a cord so that its motion is directly proportional to the motion of the engine piston. This may be done by attaching the cord directly to an extension of the engine crosshead, as in Fig. 12.11 or, if this cannot be done (for example, if the stroke of the engine is too long), by attaching the cord to a linkage connected to the engine piston. Thus the tracing point has a vertical motion which is directly proportional to the pressure in the engine cylinder, and the paper has a horizontal motion which is directly proportional to the movement of the piston, and hence to the volume swept by it. If the tracing point is brought into contact with the paper for one complete engine cycle, a pressure-volume diagram will be drawn. Diagrams obtained in this way are called *indicator diagrams*.

12.12 Mean effective pressure

A typical indicator diagram for a slow speed oil engine is shown in Fig. 12.12a. This corresponds to two strokes of the piston, the compression stroke ABC and the expansion stroke CDA. During the compression stroke, work is done on the air in the cylinder by the piston, and this work is represented by the area below the line ABC, that is, the area ABCEF.

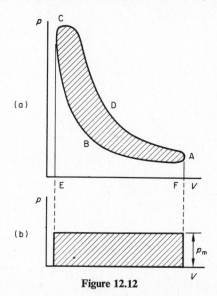

Figure 12.12

During the expansion stroke, work is done on the piston by the products of combustion, and this is represented by the area CDAFE. The net work output for the two strokes will be the difference between the work done on the piston and the work done by it, so that it will be represented by the difference in the two corresponding areas. From Fig. 12.12a, it will be seen that this difference is the area ABCD. Hence the area enclosed by an indicator diagram represents the work done during the corresponding cycle.

The work done in an engine cycle could thus be found by measuring the area of the indicator diagram and multiplying this area by the scales of pressure and volume, but this is seldom done since it involves the

14

calculation of the volume scale of the diagram. A more convenient method is to find, from the diagram, the *mean effective pressure* p_m. This is defined as the constant pressure which, acting on the piston for one complete stroke, would do the same work as is actually done during one engine cycle. The corresponding pressure-volume diagram would be a rectangle of height p_m, as shown in Fig. 12.12b, and from the definition of p_m the area of this rectangle must be equal to the area enclosed by the indicator diagram in Fig. 12.12a.

12.13 Estimation of work done from an indicator diagram

For the calculation of the mean effective pressure of an engine from an indicator diagram, it is necessary to find (1) the height of the corresponding rectangle, usually referred to as the mean height of the diagram, and (2) the pressure represented by this height.

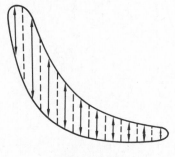

Figure 12.13

Since the rectangle in Fig. 12.12b has the same area as the indicator diagram in Fig. 12.12a, it follows that its height may be found by dividing this area by the distance EF, that is, the length of the diagram. Hence,

mean height of diagram = area of diagram/length of diagram

The area of the diagram may be found by using a planimeter. Alternatively, the 'mid-ordinate method' may be used. The diagram is divided into a number of vertical strips of equal width, as shown in Fig. 12.13, and at the centre of each strip a 'mid-ordinate' is drawn. The mid-ordinates are measured, and the sum of their length is divided by the number of strips to give an average. Since it may be shown that the area of the diagram is, approximately, the product of its length and the average of the mid-ordinates, this average is the mean height of the diagram.

The relationship between the pressure applied to an engine indicator and the resulting vertical movement of its tracing point depends on the area of the indicator piston, the stiffness of the spring, and the magnification of the linkage. The pressure required to cause unit vertical movement of the tracing point is called the *spring scale* of the indicator; hence

$$p_m = \text{mean height of diagram} \times \text{spring scale}$$

If the area of the engine piston is a and the length of stroke l, it follows from eq. 12.5 that

$$\text{work done on piston per cycle} = p_m la$$

The rate at which this work is done is called the *indicated power* of the engine, hence

$$\text{indicated power} = p_m lan \qquad (12.7)$$

where n is the number of complete cycles (or the number of 'working strokes') per second. For a two-stroke internal combustion engine or a single-acting steam engine, one cycle is performed for every revolution of the engine so that n is equal to the number of revolutions per second. For a four-stroke engine, one cycle is performed for every two revolutions; hence $n = (\text{rev/s}) \times \frac{1}{2}$. For a double-acting steam engine, two cycles are performed every revolution; hence $n = (\text{rev/s}) \times 2$.

Worked examples

8. An indicator diagram obtained during a test on a steam engine has a length of 70 mm and its area is found to be 19·6 cm². If the indicator spring scale is 20 kN/m² (0·2 bar) per mm, what is the mean effective pressure?

$$\text{mean height of diagram} = \text{area/length}$$
$$= 19\cdot6 \times 10^2/70 = 28 \text{ mm}$$

Therefore,

$$p_m = \text{mean height} \times \text{spring scale}$$
$$= 28 \times 20 = 560 \text{ kN/m}^2 \text{ (5.6 bar)}$$

9. An indicator diagram similar to Fig. 12.13 was obtained from a four-stroke oil engine. As in Fig. 12.13, the diagram was divided into 10 strips and the lengths of the mid-ordinates in mm were as follows: 14, 23, 16, 12, 10, 8, 7, 6, 5, 4. The indicator spring scale was 50 kN/m²

per mm. The bore of the engine was 200 mm, its stroke 250 mm, and its running speed 300 rev/min. Calculate the indicated power of the engine.

$$\text{sum of mid-ordinates} = 105 \text{ mm}$$

Therefore,

$$\text{mean height of diagram} = 105/10 = 10 \cdot 5 \text{ mm}$$

$$p_m = \text{mean height} \times \text{spring scale}$$
$$= 10 \cdot 5 \times 50 = 525 \text{ kN/m}^2$$

From eq. 12.7,

$$\text{indicated power} = p_m \, lan$$

Here,

$$\text{length of stroke } l = 250 \text{ mm} = 0 \cdot 25 \text{ m}$$
$$\text{piston area } a = \pi r^2$$
$$= \pi (0 \cdot 1)^2 = 0 \cdot 01\pi \text{ m}^2$$

For a four-stroke engine,

$$n = (\text{rev/s}) \times \tfrac{1}{2} = (300/60) \times \tfrac{1}{2} = 2 \cdot 5$$

Therefore,

$$\text{indicated power} = 525 \times 10^3 \times 0 \cdot 25 \times 0 \cdot 01\pi \times 2 \cdot 5$$
$$= 10 \cdot 3 \times 10^3 \text{ W or } 10 \cdot 3 \text{ kW}$$

Problems

Take the acceleration due to gravity, $g = 9 \cdot 81$ m/s^2.

1. A reservoir contains water (density 1000 kg/m^3) to a depth of 20 m. If the height of a mercury barometer is 750 mm, what is (a) the gauge pressure (b) the absolute pressure at the bottom of the reservoir? The density of mercury is 13 600 kg/m^3.

(*Answer.* (a) 196·2 kN/m^2 (1·962 bar) (b) 296·3 kN/m^2 (2·963 bar).)

2. The following readings were taken from gauges on a steam turbine: steam inlet pressure, 30 bar; condenser vacuum, 740 mm mercury. An aneroid barometer gave a reading of 1010 millibars. Express the gauge readings as absolute pressures. The density of mercury is 13 600 kg/m^3.

(*Answer.* 3·101 MN/m^2 (31·01 bar), 2·3 kN/m^2 (23 millibars).)

3. A pipe-line carries oil of density 860 kg/m³. If the level of the free surface in a piezometer connected to the pipe is 3·5 m above the centre-line of the pipe, what is the gauge pressure of the oil in the pipe-line?

(*Answer.* 29·5 kN/m² (0·295 bar).)

4. A U-tube manometer is used to measure the pressure of a gas. If the gauge pressure of the gas is 9 kN/m² (90 millibars) what will be the difference in levels of the liquid in the U-tube if this liquid is (a) water (density 1000 kg/m³) (b) mercury (density 13 600 kg/m³)?

(*Answer.* (a) 917 mm (b) 67·5 mm.)

5. A pipe-line containing oil of density 900 kg/m³ has connected to it a U-tube containing mercury, the arrangement being similar to Fig. 12.5. The level of the mercury in the limb connected to the pipe-line is 0·6 m below the level of the mercury in the open limb and 0·9 m below the centre of the pipe-line. Calculate the gauge pressure at the centre of the pipe-line. The density of mercury is 13 600 kg/m³.

(*Answer.* 72·1 kN/m² (0·721 bar).)

6. A steam pressure gauge gives a reading of 500 kN/m² (5 bar) gauge. It is connected to a steam pipe at a point 6 m higher than the level of the gauge. Assuming the connecting pipe to be full of water (density 1000 kg/m³), what is the true steam pressure?

(*Answer.* 441·1 kN/m² (4·441 bar) gauge.)

7. Describe, with the aid of a diagram, the operation of a dead-weight tester. A dead-weight tester has a piston of diameter 5·64 mm. The combined mass of the piston and its attached tray is 0·8 kg. Calculate (a) the pressure applied to the gauge under test when the mass supported by the tray is 5 kg (b) the mass to be placed on the tray in order to obtain a test pressure of 1 MN/m² (10 bar) gauge.

(*Answer.* (a) 2·276 MN/m² (22·76 bar) gauge (b) 1·748 kg.)

8. A 0–1 MN/m² pressure gauge was connected to a dead-weight tester and found to read correctly at 800 kN/m², but to read 140 kN/m² for a true pressure of 200 kN/m.² Assuming the relationship between true pressure and gauge reading to be linear, what errors are indicated by the test?

(*Answer.* The magnification of the gauge mechanism is 10% high, and the zero setting of the pointer is 80 kN/m² low.)

9. A hydraulic ram has a 40 mm diameter piston. Oil at a steady pressure of 12 MN/m² (120 bar) gauge acts on one side of the piston during the whole of its working stroke of 250 mm, the other side of the piston being open to the atmosphere. Find (a) the work done on the piston during one working stroke (b) the average power developed if the stroke is completed in 5 s.

(*Answer*. (a) 3·77 kJ (b) 754 W.)

10. An indicator diagram obtained during a test on a four-stroke single-cylinder diesel engine has a length of 75 mm and its area is found to be 6·24 cm². The indicator spring scale is 100 kN/m² (1 bar) per mm. The engine has a bore of 250 mm and a stroke of 400 mm, and runs at 360 rev/min. Find (a) the mean effective pressure (b) the indicated power of the engine.

(*Answer*. (a) 832 kN/m² (8·32 bar) (b) 49·0 kW.)

11. An indicator diagram taken during a test on a single-cylinder double-acting steam engine was divided into 10 strips. The lengths of the mid-ordinates in mm were as follows: 41, 46, 47, 34, 25, 20, 17, 14, 11, 7. The indicator spring scale was 20 kN/m² (0·2 bar) per mm. The bore of the engine was 120 mm, its stroke 150 mm, and its running speed 270 rev/min. Find (a) the mean effective pressure (b) the indicated power of the engine.

(*Answer*. (a) 524 kN/m² (5·24 bar) (b) 8·0 kW.)

12. A four-stroke four-cylinder petrol engine of 80 mm bore and 75 mm stroke has a mean effective pressure of 700 kN/m² (7 bar) when running at 2000 rev/min. Find (a) the total swept volume in cm³, (b) the indicated power of the engine.

(*Answer*. (a) 1508 cm³ (b) 17·6 kW.)

13. A four-stroke four-cylinder internal combustion engine gives an output torque of 90 Nm when running at 3000 rev/min. Each cylinder has a bore of 90 mm and a stroke of 100 mm. If the mechanical efficiency of the engine is 78 %, find (a) the indicated power, (b) the mean effective pressure.

(*Answer*. (a) 36·2 kW (b) 569 kN/m² (5·69 bar).)

13. Temperature and its measurement

13.1 The meaning of temperature

A simple description of temperature is 'a measure of hotness'. We are able to sense that an object is 'hot' or 'cold' by touching it and, within a limited range, to establish a primitive scale of temperature by describing it as 'warm', 'hot', 'very hot', and so on. The sense of touch is, of course, of little use outside this range—very high and very low temperatures both result in a sensation of pain—and it is rather unreliable, so that two questions arise. What is it that makes objects feel hot, and how can we measure this property without using the sense of touch?

The answer to the first question is given by the molecular theory (see section 15.1). The molecules of an object are in motion, and the greater their kinetic energy, the higher the temperature. A direct measurement of temperature might thus be possible if the molecules could be observed and their kinetic energies calculated—but this cannot be done. However, molecular motion produces many effects which can be observed so that although we cannot measure temperature directly, we can measure its effects. A familiar one is that of *expansion*: when the molecular motion increases, the molecules of a body move further apart and its dimensions increase. There are many other effects, any of which may be used to indicate changes in temperature—that is, to form the basis of a *thermometer*.

13.2 Temperature scales

The earliest successful thermometers were made (as are many present-day ones) by blowing a bulb at the end of a small-bore glass tube and filling this with a liquid, usually mercury. Since, in general, liquids expand more than solids when their temperature is raised, an increase in temperature causes some liquid to be forced out of the bulb and up the glass tube.

201

Thus the height of the liquid column is an indication of temperature. Only one operation remains—the marking of some kind of scale on the glass tube—and here the early constructors had a free hand, since this is quite an arbitrary matter. It involves the choice of two 'fixed points' (that is, two readily reproducible temperatures), and the division of the interval between them into a number of 'degrees'. In the thermometer made by Anders Celsius, a Swedish astronomer, in 1742, the fixed points were the temperatures of melting ice and of boiling water (both at normal atmospheric pressure), and the number of degrees 100. For practical purposes, the Celsius scale is still defined in this way, but an improvement has been made in the way in which the scale is divided and a more reliable 'fixed point' has been introduced.

13.3   The Kelvin thermodynamic temperature scale

The obvious way of calibrating a mercury-in-glass thermometer is to mark the glass tube at freezing point and at boiling point, then to divide the distance between the two marks into 100 equal parts. The objection to this method is that the scale thus produced depends on the properties of mercury and glass. If, for example, another thermometer is made using alcohol instead of mercury, it will be found that '50°C' on this thermometer is not precisely the same temperature as '50°C' on the first (although for practical purposes the difference is negligible). A way out of this difficulty was found by Lord Kelvin, who showed that a temperature scale might be divided in a way which did not depend on the properties of any particular substance. He also proposed that 'zero' should not be located at an arbitrary temperature such as the freezing point of water, but should be the lowest possible temperature. Both theoretical considerations (see section 15.5) and practical experience indicate that it is impossible to reach a temperature lower than $-273 \cdot 15°C$, and this is known as *the absolute zero of temperature*. The resulting scale is known as the Kelvin Thermodynamic Temperature Scale, and its unit of temperature is the kelvin (K). It is based on the concept of an ideal heat engine and starts at the absolute zero of temperature (hence it is often referred to as the absolute temperature scale). It is the fundamental temperature scale of the SI system and the Celsius scale is defined from it by the relationship

Celsius temperature (°C)

$$= \text{Kelvin temperature (K)} -273 \cdot 15 \qquad (13.1)$$

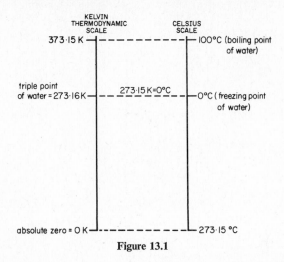

Figure 13.1

Figure 13.1 shows this relationship and it may be seen that a temperature interval is the same on both scales—that is, 1°C = 1 kelvin. It may also be seen that

Absolute temperature (K)

$$= \text{Celsius temperature (°C)} + 273 \cdot 15 \qquad (13.2)$$

In any calculations involving the gas laws, absolute temperatures must be used and, for practical purposes, the above relationship may be approximated to

$$K = °C + 273 \qquad (13.3)$$

13.4 The triple point of water

At atmospheric pressure, water freezes at 0°C and boils at 100°C. If the pressure is reduced, the boiling point is lowered and the freezing point raised so that eventually, at a pressure of 611 N/m², both points coincide at 0·01°C. Under these conditions ice, water, and water vapour are all in equilibrium, and this is known as the *triple point*. The triple point temperature can be reproduced readily and with great accuracy, and it has been adopted as the 'fixed point' by which the Kelvin thermodynamic scale is defined: the definition being that there are 273·16 kelvins between the triple point temperature and absolute zero. The triple point temperature may be used when calibrating or checking thermometers (although for many practical purposes the temperature of melting ice may be used

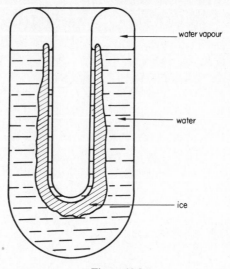

water vapour

water

ice

Figure 13.2

with sufficient accuracy) and it is obtained using a 'triple point cell' (Fig. 13.2). This is a sealed glass vessel containing only pure water and its vapour. The central tube is chilled until some ice forms, then warmed slightly so that a thin layer of water separates the ice from the glass. When equilibrium has been reached the temperature of the cell is, by definition, 273·16 K or 0·01°C and, if used correctly, the cell can provide this reference temperature with an accuracy of ±0·0001 K.

13.5   Expansion thermometers

One of the effects of a temperature increase is that, with a few exceptions, substances expand. They do so at different rates, so that a thermometer may be based on the difference in the expansion rates of two substances. Two solids may be used, as in the bimetallic strip. This is made by welding together strips of two metals having different expansion coefficients. When the temperature is raised, one metal expands more than the other causing the strip to bend. In a *bimetallic thermometer*, the strip is formed into either a spiral or a helix so that the bending effect is converted into a rotation of one end relative to the other. One end is fixed, and the other attached to a pointer.

The most widely used form of expansion thermometer, however, relies on the difference between the expansions of a solid and a liquid—as in the familiar liquid-in-glass thermometer (the construction and operation of which has already been described in section 13.2). Usually the liquid is mercury, and in this form the thermometer may be used to measure temperatures up to about 600°C. For temperatures higher than 300°C, the space above the liquid column is filled with nitrogen or carbon dioxide under pressure to prevent evaporation of the mercury. The freezing point of mercury is −38·9°C, so that for the measurement of low temperatures alcohol-in-glass thermometers are often used. These will measure temperatures down to −80°C, and if pentane is used instead of alcohol the lower limit is about −200°C.

The liquid-in-glass thermometer is simple and inexpensive, but fragile.

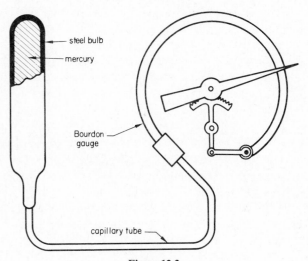

Figure 13.3

A more robust version of this instrument is the mercury-in-steel thermometer (Fig. 13.3). In this, the glass bulb is replaced by a steel bulb, and the mercury expands not into a graduated tube but into a Bourdon gauge, the pointer of which indicates the amount of expansion and hence the temperature. The two parts are connected by a tube of very small bore (the 'capillary tube') so that the gauge may be placed some distance from the bulb. Thus this instrument has the added advantage that it may be used in situations where a liquid-in-glass thermometer would be inaccessible.

The liquid-in-glass thermometer is subject to four main sources of error, apart from any faults in manufacture and calibration. Two of these, *zero change* and *stem exposure error*, are peculiar to this type of thermometer and the others, *time lag* and *incorrect positioning*, apply to thermometers in general.

Zero changes occur because glass is not a perfectly stable solid. The volume of the bulb is liable to change slightly over a period of time, introducing an error which will be the same over the whole scale. Errors of this kind are called 'zero errors'.

Stem exposure errors arise from the fact that the bulb may or may not be at the same temperature as the rest of the thermometer. Thermometers are often marked 'total immersion', meaning that when calibrated the whole thermometer was immersed in a liquid so that all parts were at the same temperature. If, as often happens in normal use, only the bulb is at the temperature to be measured and most of the stem is at a lower temperature, the liquid column is, in effect, shortened because it is cooler than when the thermometer was calibrated. A low reading will result and, for accurate work, a 'correction' should be added to the scale reading. For a mercury-in-glass thermometer calibrated for total immersion, this correction is

$$0 \cdot 00016n(t_1 - t_2)^\circ\text{C} \tag{13.4}$$

where n is the number of degrees exposed, t_1 is the temperature of the bulb, and t_2 the average temperature of the exposed stem.

There is a time lag in the response of any kind of thermometer. In the case of a liquid-in-glass thermometer, this lag is considerable: if the thermometer is placed in a hot liquid it will be some time before its reading becomes steady. The reason for this is that before the liquid in the thermometer can attain the temperature of its surroundings, heat must be transferred to it through the glass of the bulb. This takes time, and, furthermore, the closer the two temperatures approach each other the slower the heat transfer becomes, so that theoretically the thermometer bulb will never quite reach the temperature of its surroundings. In practice this means that a reasonable time—say, one minute—should be allowed before taking a reading of a steady temperature, and this kind of thermometer is incapable of giving the true value of a changing temperature.

Incorrect positioning of thermometers and thermometer pockets is an often unsuspected source of error. It must be remembered that the reading given by any thermometer is the temperature of its bulb (or other sensitive element), and it does not always follow that this is the temperature of the object or fluid under investigation. A thermometer pocket in a pipe-line, for example, will give reliable results only if it projects well into the stream of fluid. If badly positioned, it may be surrounded by a stagnant layer of fluid and, owing to heat leakage, be at a temperature much lower than that of the bulk of the fluid.

13.6 Electrical resistance thermometers

For almost all metals and alloys, a rise in temperature causes an increase in electrical resistivity. Over a small range, this increase is directly proportional to the increase in temperature so that, if the resistance of a length of wire at $0°C$ is R_0, its resistance R at a temperature $t°C$ is given by

$$R = R_0(1 + \alpha t)$$

The constant α is called the *temperature coefficient of resistance*. An electrical resistance thermometer makes use of this effect and consists of a small coil of wire together with an electrical circuit which measures the change in its resistance. Three kinds of wire are in common use—copper, nickel and platinum—but usually platinum is chosen since it resists

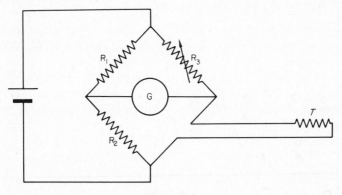

Figure 13.4

oxidation and corrosion. A typical platinum resistance thermometer has a resistance of about 100 ohms, and is made from wire of about 0·1 mm diameter, wound on a mica former which is enclosed in a protective cover.

Measurement of the change in resistance is usually made by the circuit known as the Wheatstone bridge, the thermometer coil being made one arm of the bridge as shown in Fig. 13.4. This circuit may be used in two ways. In its original form, the resistance R_3 is adjusted until the meter G shows no current, when it may be shown that $R_1/R_2 = R_3/T$. This method is accurate but time-consuming, so that for industrial use the resistance R_3 is left unaltered and changes in the thermometer resistance T cause an out-of-balance current to flow through the meter G. This meter can be scaled so as to give a direct reading of temperature.

Sources of error in the resistance thermometer are (a) variations in the resistance of the connecting leads (b) departures from direct proportionality in the relationship between temperature change and resistance change (c) the heating effect of the small current flowing through the thermometer coil and (d) possible thermo-electric effects (see section 13.7). Compensation for (a) may be included in the Wheatstone bridge circuit, and (b) may be dealt with by modifying the division of the temperature scale on the meter G. If this is done, the platinum resistance thermometer is capable of measuring temperatures from −200°C to a maximum of about 1000°C with great accuracy.

An alternative to the use of a coil of wire as the temperature-sensitive element is provided by the *thermistor*. This is a semiconductor, usually in the form of a small bead, the resistance of which decreases with rise in temperature. The change in resistance is much greater than would be obtained by using a metal wire, but it is not directly proportional to the temperature change. Furthermore, thermistors tend to be unstable, so that accuracy cannot be guaranteed. Their chief advantages are that they can detect small temperature changes, and that, because of the large changes in their resistance, it is not always necessary to use a Wheatstone bridge. If a high degree of accuracy is not required, the resistance of a thermistor may be measured by simply applying a known voltage to it and measuring the resulting current. This is the method used in motor vehicles, where thermistors are extensively used for the measurement of cooling water temperature.

13.7 Thermocouples

This method of temperature measurement depends on the fact that, if an electrical circuit is made using two different metals, an e.m.f. will be generated if their junctions are at different temperatures, causing a current to flow as shown in Fig. 13.5. This is known as the *thermo-electric effect*, and the arrangement is called a *thermocouple*. If one of

low
temperature

high
temperature

Figure 13.5

the junctions is kept at a steady temperature, the e.m.f. developed will thus be an indication of the temperature of the other, so that a practical thermometer consists of a 'hot junction' at the temperature to be measured, a 'cold junction' kept at a reference temperature, and a device which measures the e.m.f. developed. The simplest measuring instrument is a millivoltmeter, and the circuit will then be as shown in Fig. 13.6. Alternatively, for greater accuracy, the e.m.f. may be measured by means of a potentiometer. In this case, no current flows in the thermocouple circuit and voltage drops due to the resistances of the junctions and connecting leads are eliminated.

Junctions are made by twisting the wires together and either welding or soldering, and various combinations of metals may be used. A typical thermocouple for temperatures up to about 400°C uses copper and an alloy of copper and nickel called constantan. For high temperatures, the usual combination is platinum and an alloy of platinum and

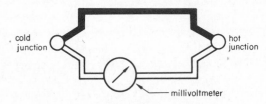

Figure 13.6

rhodium, and this may be used at temperatures up to 1400°C continuously, or up to 1650°C for short periods. Higher temperatures are usually measured by radiation pyrometers, but for special applications a thermocouple may be used if materials capable of withstanding the required temperature are available. For example, a thermocouple made from the metals tungsten and rhenium will measure temperatures up to 2200°C.

The e.m.f. developed will depend on the pair of metals used and, in general, will not be directly proportional to the difference in temperature between hot and cold junctions so that if the e.m.f. is measured in millivolts, a calibration table or chart must be used. Alternatively, the meter may be suitably scaled so as to give a direct reading of temperature, and this is usual in industrial applications.

A particular advantage of the thermocouple is that the hot junction is usually small, so that its time lag (see section 13.5) is also small, particularly if used without a protective cover. For special applications it may be made very small, making possible the measurement of rapidly varying temperatures. As an industrial instrument, the thermocouple has the added advantage that the hot junction is of simple and robust construction, and is easily replaced if damaged.

Sources of error are the voltage drop due to the resistance of the junctions and leads, stray thermo-electric effects, and variations in the temperature of the cold junction. Stray thermo-electric effects arise because, although ideally the circuit should consist of two metals only, inevitably there will be others. The millivoltmeter, for example, will probably have brass terminals, and if a platinum-platinum/rhodium thermocouple is being used it will obviously be too costly to provide leads of the same materials. Thus in practice the circuit will contain junctions other than the 'hot junction' and the 'cold junction'. It may be shown that these will have no effect provided all are at the same temperature, but usually this cannot be arranged. Effects can, however, be minimized by correct design: in particular, connections to the hot junction are made by 'compensating leads', the compositions of which are carefully chosen.

Variations in the temperature of the cold junction may be avoided by immersing it in melting ice, but this is a method suitable for laboratory work rather than industrial use. Often, in industrial applications, the cold junction is, in effect, one of the terminals of the millivoltmeter and the 'reference temperature' is simply the temperature of this instrument, which will vary along with the temperature of its surroundings. In such cases a correction must be applied to the scale reading, and often this is done automatically: the meter contains a bimetallic strip which responds to variations in its temperature and adjusts its zero setting.

13.8   Radiation pyrometers

All hot objects emit radiation (see section 14.5), and, if their temperature is high enough, some of this radiation is in the form of visible light. If the temperature of an object is raised, the total amount of radiation increases and it is emitted at shorter wavelengths. This gives two visual effects: the object appears brighter and there is a change in the colour of the light emitted. Of these, the first is the one used for purposes of measurement, while the second means that temperatures may be judged, very approximately, by colour. For example, an object between 700°C and 800°C is usually described as 'cherry red', between 800°C and 900°C as 'orange', and at about 1200°C as 'white'. Radiation pyrometers are concerned not with the colour of the radiation but with its intensity, and are of two types: *total radiation pyrometers*, which make use of all the energy radiated, including the longer wavelengths ('infra-red') to which the eye is not sensitive, and *selective radiation pyrometers,* which deal with a narrow band of wavelengths only.

Figure 13.7 shows, diagrammatically, the arrangement of a total

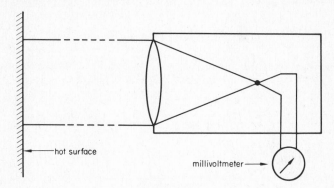

Figure 13.7

radiation pyrometer. A lens receives a sample of radiation from the hot surface and this is focused on to the junction of a thermocouple. This junction absorbs the radiant energy and its temperature rises by an amount which depends on the radiant energy received (which, in turn,

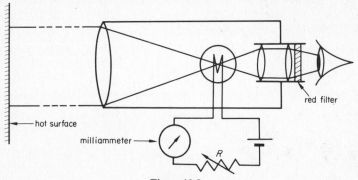

Figure 13.8

depends on the temperature of the hot surface). The e.m.f. generated is measured by a millivoltmeter, which may be calibrated so as to give a direct reading of the temperature of the hot surface.

Selective radiation pyrometers are also known as *optical pyrometers* since they deal only with visible radiation, and rely on visual matching for the measurement of brightness. A widely used type is the *disappearing filament pyrometer* and this is shown diagrammatically in Fig. 13.8.

15

An eyepiece views, simultaneously, an image of the hot surface and the filament of a small lamp. A red filter attached to the eyepiece allows only a narrow band of wavelengths to be observed. If the filament of the lamp is cold, it will appear as a dark line on the image of the hot surface as shown in Fig. 13.9a. A current is now passed through the lamp and adjusted by means of the variable resistance R. For a large current, the filament will be brighter than the image of the hot surface, as in Fig. 13.9c, and by careful adjustment the brightness of the filament may be matched exactly to that of the image so that the two become indistinguishable and the filament 'disappears' as in Fig. 13.9b. The current flowing

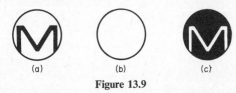

(a)   (b)   (c)

Figure 13.9

through the lamp is measured by a milliammeter which is calibrated to give a direct reading of temperature.

The chief source of error for both types of radiation pyrometer is the fact that the intensity of radiation from a hot object depends not only on its temperature but also on the condition of its surface. Two objects at the same temperature but with different kinds of surface will not appear equally bright. It is a fundamental fact that surfaces which are good absorbers of radiation are also good emitters, and the reverse is also true so that a polished metal surface is a very poor radiator and a black surface a very good one. All radiation pyrometers are calibrated on the assumption that the source of radiation is a 'black body', that is, a perfect absorber and hence that best possible radiator. If the hot surface is not 'black' the pyrometer will give a low estimate of its temperature.

Worked examples

1. A mercury-in-glass thermometer is calibrated for total immersion. It is being used with the lower part only immersed in a liquid, the surface of the liquid being level with the 10°C graduation on the stem. Assuming that above this point the stem is at room temperature (20°C), what is the true temperature of the liquid when the thermometer reads 85°C?

From eq. 13.4, the correction to be added to the scale reading is

$$0{\cdot}00016n(t_1 - t_2)°C$$

Here, number of degrees exposed $n = (85 - 10) = 75$, and temperature of exposed stem $t_2 = 20°C$.

Strictly, the temperature of the bulb t_1 is the true temperature of the liquid, but for this calculation the thermometer reading may be used and $t_1 = 85°C$. Hence, the required correction is $0.00016 \times 75 \times (85 - 20) = 0.78°C$ and the true temperature is $85 + 0.78 = 85.78°C$.

(This statement assumes that the accuracy of the thermometer is within $\pm 0.01°C$: for most thermometers a more realistic statement of the true temperature would be $85.8°C$.)

2. A platinum resistance thermometer has been calibrated by placing the resistance coil first in a triple point cell, and then in the steam above water boiling at standard atmospheric pressure. In each case its resistance was measured by a Wheatstone bridge, values of 102.515 ohms and 142.482 ohms respectively being obtained. When placed in a liquid of unknown temperature, its resistance is found to be 131.635 ohms. Assuming a linear relationship between temperature and resistance, what is the temperature of the liquid (a) on the Celsius scale (b) on the Kelvin scale?

The triple point temperature is defined as $0.01°C$ exactly, and the boiling point of water is, for practical purposes, defined as $100°C$. Hence for a change in temperature of $100 - 0.01 = 99.99°C$, the change in resistance is $142.482 - 102.515 = 39.967$ ohms. A 'linear relationship' between temperature and resistance means that the graph of resistance against temperature is a straight line, so that changes in resistance are directly proportional to changes in temperature. If the unknown temperature is $t°C$, it follows that

$$\frac{99.99}{39.967} = \frac{t - 0.01}{131.635 - 102.515}$$

This is shown graphically in Fig. 13.10.

Therefore,

$$t - 0.01 = \frac{99.99 \times 29.120}{39.967} = 72.85$$

and so

$$t = 72.86°C$$

From eq. 13.2,

$$T = t + 273.15$$
$$= 346.01 \text{ K}$$

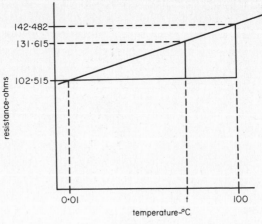

Figure 13.10

Problems

1. Three temperatures used in the calibration of thermometers are the boiling point of oxygen (−182·97°C), the freezing point of mercury (−38·87°C) and the boiling point of sulphur (444·60°C). What are the corresponding temperatures on the Kelvin scale?

(*Answer.* 90·18 K; 234·28 K; 717·75 K.)

2. What are the principal sources of error in the measurement of temperature by a liquid-in-glass thermometer? A mercury-in-glass thermometer, calibrated for total immersion, is immersed in oil with its 15°C graduation level with the surface, and gives a reading of 165°C. If the average temperature of the exposed stem is 25°C, what is the true temperature of the oil?

(*Answer.* 168·36°C.)

3. A platinum resistance thermometer has a resistance of 56·680 ohms at the temperature of the triple point of water, and 78·925 ohms at the temperature of the boiling point of water at standard atmospheric pressure. What is its temperature when its resistance is (a) 64·560 ohms (b) 93·120 ohms, assuming the relationship between temperature and resistance to be linear?

(*Answer.* (a) 35·43°C (b) 163·82°C.)

4. What is meant by 'a thermocouple'? Explain, with the aid of a circuit diagram, the arrangement of a thermocouple thermometer. In a test on a copper-constantan thermocouple, the hot junction was immersed in an oil bath together with a standard mercury-in-glass thermometer, and the cold junction was immersed in melting ice. The temperature of the bath was raised from 40°C to 200°C and the thermocouple e.m.f. in millivolts was measured at intervals of 40°C. The five readings of e.m.f. thus obtained were as follows: 1·54, 3·38, 5·37, 7·46, and 9·62. Use this information to plot a calibration curve for the thermocouple, and from it estimate the temperature indicated by an e.m.f. of 5·99 mV.

(*Answer.* 132°C.)

5. Give, from your own experience if possible, one practical application of each of the following thermometers: (a) alcohol-in-glass (b) mercury-in-glass (c) mercury-in-steel (d) electrical resistance (e) thermocouple. In each case explain briefly why you think this particular type of thermometer has been chosen.

6. Explain, with the aid of a diagram, the operation of an optical pyrometer. What are the essential differences between this instrument and a total radiation pyrometer?

7. A mercury in glass thermometer has been calibrated for total immersion. It is used to measure the temperature of a water bath in which it is immersed up to the 10°C graduation; above this point the stem may be assumed to be at the room temperature of 20°C. What will be the true temperature of the bath when the thermometer reads (a) 50°C, (b) 90°C?

(*Answer.* (a) 50·192°C (b) 90·896°C.)

8. What are the principal sources of error in the measurement of temperature by (a) an electrical resistance thermometer, (b) a thermocouple? What practical steps may be taken to minimize these errors?

14. Heat transfer

14.1 The meaning of heat

Heat is defined as *energy in transit between two bodies because of a difference in temperature.* If bodies at different temperatures are brought into contact, it is a matter of experience that their temperatures tend to become equal. As will be seen in chapter 15, the molecules of a body are in motion and hence possess kinetic energy, and the higher the temperature of the body, the greater the mean kinetic energy of its molecules. Thus, when two bodies are brought into contact, the kinetic energy of the molecules of the hotter body tends to decrease and that of the molecules of the cooler body to increase until both are at the same temperature. There is a transfer of energy from the hotter to the cooler body, and energy transferred in this way is called heat. It must be emphasized, however, that the term 'heat' is applied only to *energy in transit* and cannot be used to describe *stored energy.* The energy possessed by the molecules of a body is called *internal energy,* so that the cooler body receives 'heat', but stores the energy received as 'internal energy'.

Heat transfer tends to occur wherever there is a temperature difference, and there are three ways in which energy may be transferred: by *conduction,* by *convection,* and by *radiation.*

14.2 Conduction

Conduction is the name given to the process by which, for example, heat is transferred along a metal bar. Fast-moving molecules at the hotter end of the bar transfer energy directly to slower-moving molecules with which they are in contact, and these in turn transfer energy to adjacent molecules. This is repeated for layer after layer of molecules until the other end of the bar is reached, so that there is a continuous transmission of energy along the bar. Each layer of molecules is at a slightly lower temperature than the preceding one—that is, there is a *temperature gradient* along the bar.

It is found by experiment that the amount of heat Q transferred in time

216

t through a flat plate of material of thickness x and area A, whose faces are kept at uniform temperatures T_1 and T_2, is directly proportional to the area A; directly proportional to the temperature difference $(T_1 - T_2)$; directly proportional to the time t; and inversely proportional to the thickness x. Hence

$$Q \propto \frac{A(T_1 - T_2)t}{x}$$

or

$$Q = \frac{kA(T_1 - T_2)t}{x} \tag{14.1}$$

where k is a constant known as the *thermal conductivity* of the material.

Stated in terms of the rate of heat transfer $\dot{Q}$ (where $\dot{Q} = Q/t$), eq. 14.1 becomes

$$\dot{Q} = \frac{kA(T_1 - T_2)}{x} \tag{14.2}$$

An alternative form of eq. 14.2 is obtained by regarding the ratio $(T_1 - T_2)/x$ as the *temperature gradient* dT/dx, so that

$$\dot{Q} = -kA\,dT/dx \tag{14.3}$$

The negative sign in eq. 14.3 is necessary because heat is always transferred in the direction of decreasing temperature, so that if x is measured in the direction in which heat transfer takes place, dT/dx will always be negative.

Transposing eq. 14.2,

$$k = \frac{\dot{Q}x}{A(T_1 - T_2)}$$

In the SI system, therefore, thermal conductivity has the units

$$\frac{W \times m}{m^2 \times K} = W/m\ K$$

(or, since $1\ K = 1°C$, $W/m\ °C$)

Values of k vary considerably. Metals have high thermal conductivities, the best being silver ($k = 419\ W/m\ °C$), copper ($k = 388\ W/m\ °C$), and aluminium ($k = 203\ W/m\ °C$). Non-metals have, in general, relatively low values of k. Cork, for example, has $k = 0.04\ W/m\ °C$ and is often used as a *heat insulator*. It should, of course, be remembered that here the word 'insulator' merely means 'relatively poor conductor'; all materials conduct heat to some extent.

14.3 Conduction through a composite wall

In many practical cases heat transfer involves more than one material. For example, heat may escape from a boiler furnace by travelling first through a layer of firebrick and then through a layer of insulating brick of different thermal conductivity; and heat transferred through the base of a domestic kettle usually has to pass through a layer of scale as well as through the metal. The calculation of the rate of heat transfer in such cases depends on the fact that the total amount of energy transferred during a given period is the same for all the layers.

Figure 14.1 shows a composite wall consisting of layers of two different materials. The outer surfaces are at uniform temperatures T_1 and T_2, and,

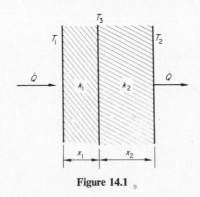

Figure 14.1

since the layers are of uniform thickness, the temperature of the junction of the two layers will also be uniform; let this temperature be T_3. Applying eq. 14.2 to each layer in turn ,we get

$$\dot{Q} = k_1 A(T_1 - T_3)/x_1$$
$$\dot{Q} = k_2 A(T_3 - T_2)/x_2$$

Hence,

$$k_1 A(T_1 - T_3)/x_1 = k_2 A(T_3 - T_2)/x_2$$

From this equation, the unknown temperature T_3 may be found and, by substituting this value in either of the previous equations, the rate of heat transfer $\dot{Q}$ may be calculated. The application of this method is illustrated by worked example 3.

14.4 Convection

Most fluids (that is, liquids, vapours, and gases) are poor conductors of heat, and heat transfer in a fluid usually depends not on conduction through the fluid but on movement of the fluid. Fluid flowing past a hot object is heated by direct contact, and thus there is a continuous transfer of energy from the object to the fluid—a process called *convection*. The flow of fluid may be caused by, say, a pump or fan (*forced convection*), or it may be due to differences in density caused by differences in temperature (*natural convection*).

Natural convection is a familiar process. If a hot object is placed in still air, the layer of air surrounding the object is heated by conduction. The expansion caused by its temperature rise makes it less dense (and therefore lighter) than the surrounding air, so that it rises and is replaced by cool air. A stream of heated air rises continuously from the object,

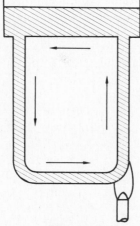

Figure 14.2

and this is called a 'convection current'. Such convection currents may be observed rising from hot-water radiators and other domestic heaters. Another example of natural convection is the breeze which often blows from sea to land on warm days. The sea maintains an almost steady temperature, but the land is warmed by the sun, and warm air rising from it is replaced by cooler air from over the sea.

A similar effect in a liquid may be demonstrated by the apparatus shown in Fig. 14.2. The column of liquid in the right-hand limb is heated and becomes lighter than the column of cold liquid in the left-hand limb, causing a circulation as shown. Such an arrangement is called a 'thermosyphon"

If natural convection can be prevented (or, at least, greatly reduced), the low thermal conductivity of air and other fluids makes them useful 'heat insulators'. In such insulating materials as wool, glass fibre and foam plastics, the function of the material is to separate the air which it contains into small pockets so that normal convection cannot take place; and it is this air which is, in fact, the insulator.

14.5 Radiation

Conduction and convection both depend on direct contact, either between two bodies or between a body and a fluid. Radiation differs fundamentally from these in that no contact of any kind is required; the energy can travel through a vacuum, and it is by radiation that the earth receives heat from the sun. The energy is transmitted in the form of *electromagnetic waves*. Other well-known kinds of electromagnetic waves are light and radio waves, and they differ from radiation only in that different wavelengths are involved. All can be transmitted through space, and all travel at the same speed of 300 000 km/s.

All bodies emit radiation, and the rate at which energy is emitted depends on the temperature of the body, its surface area, and the nature of its surface. The temperature of the body also determines the range of wavelengths of the radiation, so that at high temperatures this range extends into the region to which the eye is sensitive and the body emits visible light.

It may be shown that there is a connection between the ability of a surface to *emit* radiation and its ability to *absorb* it. Good absorbers are also good emitters. Thus a polished metal surface reflects most of the radiation falling on it and absorbs very little, so that it is also a poor radiator. A surface which appears black, on the other hand, does so because it absorbs most of the light falling on it, and it would also absorb most of the radiation. A body which absorbs *all* the radiation falling on it is called a *black body*, and it follows that such a body is an ideal radiator.

It has been found experimentally that, for a black body, the rate at which energy is radiated, $\dot{E}$, is proportional to the area of the body A, and to the fourth power of its absolute temperature T.

$$\dot{E} \propto AT^4$$

or

$$\dot{E} = \sigma AT^4 \qquad (14.4)$$

This is known as the Stefan-Boltzmann law, and σ, the Stefan-Boltzmann constant, is found to have the value

$$5{\cdot}67 \times 10^{-8} \ \text{W/m}^2 \ \text{K}^4$$

If the body is not 'black', less energy will be radiated and eq. 14.4 becomes

$$\dot{E} = \epsilon\sigma AT^4 \tag{14.5}$$

where the factor ϵ, which varies in practice from almost unity for lamp black to about 0·02 for polished silver, is called the *emissivity*.

This is the rate at which energy would be given out by a body completely isolated from all others (a close approximation to which would be a body in outer space) or surrounded by a black enclosure at zero absolute temperature. Normally the body will be surrounded by other bodies and the heat transfer by radiation is calculated on the principle that *all* bodies radiate energy in accordance with eq. 14.5, and the net heat transfer for any particular body is the difference between the energy radiated and the energy absorbed. If, for example, a furnace and its contents have reached a uniform temperature, all will be radiating energy but the net heat transfer will be zero. Thus, if a black body of area A at absolute temperature T_1 is completely surrounded by a black surface at absolute temperature T_2, then in unit time it will radiate energy σAT_1^4 and absorb energy σAT_2^4, so that the rate of heat transfer will be

$$\dot{Q} = \sigma A(T_1^4 - T_2^4) \tag{14.6}$$

Worked examples

1. A small building has concrete walls 150 mm thick. If the thermal conductivity of the concrete is 1·1 W/m °C, what is the rate of heat leakage through a wall 2·5 m high and 5 m long when the inside temperature is 20°C and the outside temperature 2°C?

$$\text{area of wall} = 2\cdot5 \times 5 = 12\cdot5 \text{ m}^2$$

From eq. 14.2,

$$\begin{aligned}
\dot{Q} &= kA(T_1 - T_2)/x \\
&= 1\cdot1 \times 12\cdot5 \times (20 - 2)/0\cdot15 \\
&= 1650 \text{ W or } 1\cdot65 \text{ kW}
\end{aligned}$$

2. A steam boiler is made from 15 mm steel plate and is designed for a heat transfer rate of 850 kW. Its heating surface has a total area of 23 m². Assuming heat transfer to be uniformly distributed over the heating surface, and neglecting any effects due to curvature, what will be the temperature difference between the inner and outer surfaces of the plate? The thermal conductivity of the steel is 45 W/m °C.

From eq. 14.2,

$$\dot{Q} = kA(T_1 - T_2)/x$$

Hence

$$850 \times 10^3 = 45 \times 23(T_1 - T_2)/0{\cdot}015$$

and so

$$(T_1 - T_2) = 850 \times 10^3 \times 0{\cdot}015/45 \times 23$$
$$= 12{\cdot}3\ °C$$

3. A brick wall 100 mm thick is coated with a 16 mm layer of plaster. Calculate the temperature of the junction of the two materials and the rate of heat transfer per m² of the composite wall when the temperature of the outer (brick) surface is 2°C and that of the inner (plaster) surface 17°C. The thermal conductivities of brick and plaster are, respectively, 0·8 and 0·4 W/m °C.

Let the temperature of the junction be t°C, and consider 1 m² of the composite wall.

From eq. 14.2,

$$\dot{Q} = kA(T_1 - T_2)/x$$

Hence, for the brick,

$$\dot{Q} = 0{\cdot}8(t - 2)/0{\cdot}1$$

and for the plaster,

$$\dot{Q} = 0{\cdot}4(17 - t)/0{\cdot}016$$

The rate of heat transfer, $\dot{Q}$, is the same for both layers.
Hence

$$0{\cdot}8(t - 2)/0{\cdot}1 = 0{\cdot}4(17 - t)/0{\cdot}016$$
$$8(t - 2) = 25(17 - t)$$
$$8t - 16 = 425 - 25t$$
$$33t = 441$$
$$t = 13{\cdot}36°C$$

$\dot{Q}$ may be found by considering either layer of material.

For the brick,

$$\dot{Q} = 0{\cdot}8(\,13.36 - 2)/0{\cdot}1$$
$$= 90{\cdot}9\ W$$

4. At what rate would heat be transferred by radiation from a metal sphere 0·5 m diameter at a temperature of (a) 500°C (b) 1000°C, if the

temperature of its surroundings is 10°C and both sphere and surroundings may be considered 'black'? The Stefan-Boltzmann constant is $5 \cdot 67 \times 10^{-8}$ W/m² K⁴.

From eq. 14.6,

$$\dot{Q} = \sigma A(T_1^4 - T_2^4)$$
$$\text{surface area of sphere } A = 4\pi r^2$$
$$= 4\pi(0 \cdot 25)^2 = 0 \cdot 7854 \text{ m}^2$$

(a) $T_1 = (500 + 273) = 773$ K, $T_2 = (10 + 273) = 283$ K

Therefore,

$$\dot{Q} = 5 \cdot 67 \times 10^{-8} \times 0 \cdot 7854(773^4 - 283^4)$$
$$= 5 \cdot 67 \times 10^{-8} \times 0 \cdot 7854 \ (3570 \times 10^8 - 64 \times 10^8)$$
$$= 5 \cdot 67 \times 0 \cdot 7854 \times 3506$$
$$= 15 \ 600 \text{ W or } 15 \cdot 6 \text{ kW}$$

(b) $T_1 = (1000 + 273) = 1273$ K, $T_2 = (10 + 273) = 283$ K

Therefore,

$$\dot{Q} = 5 \cdot 67 \times 10^{-8} \times 0 \cdot 7854 \ (1273^4 - 283^4)$$
$$= 5 \cdot 67 \times 10^{-8} \times 0 \cdot 7854 \ (26 \ 250 \times 10^8 - 64 \times 10^8)$$
$$= 5 \cdot 67 \times 0 \cdot 7854 \times 26 \ 186$$
$$= 116 \ 300 \text{ W or } 116 \cdot 3 \text{ kW}$$

5. The cylindrical element of an electric radiator is $0 \cdot 3$ m long and 20 mm diameter. Assuming that heat transfer is by radiation only, and treating both the element and its surroundings as black bodies, estimate its surface temperature when its surroundings are at 20°C and it receives a steady electrical input of 1 kW. Take the Stefan-Boltzmann constant as $5 \cdot 67 \times 10^{-8}$ W/m² K⁴.

The surface temperature of the element will rise until energy is being radiated at the same rate as that at which electrical energy is being received. In other words, when operating steadily, $\dot{Q} = 1$ kW.

From eq. 14.6,

$$\dot{Q} = \sigma A(T_1^4 - T_2^4)$$

Here

$$A = 0 \cdot 3 \times 2\pi(0 \cdot 01) = 0 \cdot 01885 \text{ m}^2$$

and

$$T_2 = (20 + 273) = 293 \text{ K}$$

Therefore,

$$1000 = 5\cdot67 \times 10^{-8} \times 0\cdot01885\,(T_1^4 - 293^4)$$

and so

$$T_1^4 - 73\cdot7 \times 10^8 = 1000/(5\cdot67 \times 10^{-8} \times 0\cdot01885)$$
$$= 9355 \times 10^8$$

Hence

$$T_1^4 = 9428\cdot7 \times 10^8$$
$$T_1 = \sqrt[4]{9428\cdot7} \times 10^2$$
$$= 985 \text{ K or } 712°C$$

Problems

1. In a test to determine the thermal conductivity of a material, a slab 200 mm × 200 mm × 30 mm thick was placed between two plates, one being electrically heated and the other water-cooled to maintain a surface temperature of 10°C. The whole assembly was insulated to minimize heat leakage to its surroundings. The power supplied to the heater was 20 W and the surface of the heated plate attained a steady temperature of 64°C. Assuming negligible heat loss from the apparatus, calculate the thermal conductivity of the material.

(*Answer*. 0·278 W/m °C.)

2. One end of a 25 mm diameter copper bar is kept cool by placing it in a water bath, and the other end is heated. If the rate of heat transfer is 200 W, what will be the temperature difference between two points on the bar separated by an axial distance of 50 mm? Neglect heat loss from the surface of the bar, and take the thermal conductivity of copper as 388 W/m °C.

(*Answer*. 52·5 °C.)

3. An electric oven is, approximately, a cube of 0·4 m side. It is insulated by a 20 mm layer of a material having a thermal conductivity of 0·06 W/m °C. What steady electrical power input will maintain an oven temperature of 200°C? The temperature of the outer surface of the lagging may be taken as 50°C and the effect of corners may be neglected.

(*Answer*. 432 W.)

4. One wall of a room is 4 m long and 3 m high and consists of a 120 mm thick layer of concrete to the inner surface of which is attached a 10 mm thick layer of wood. Find (a) the temperature at the junction of the

two materials (b) the rate of heat leakage through the wall when the inner surface of the wood is at 20°C and the outer surface of the concrete is at 3°C. The thermal conductivities of wood and concrete are, respectively, 0·15 and 1·0 W/m °C.

(*Answer.* (a) 13·9°C (b) 1·09 kW.)

5. The wall of a furnace consists of an inner layer of heat-resisting brick 100 mm thick and an outer layer of red brick 200 mm thick. The inner and outer surfaces of the composite wall are at temperatures of 550°C and 50°C respectively, and the thermal conductivities of the heat-resisting brick and the red brick are, respectively, 1·4 and 0·6 W/m °C. Find (a) the temperature at the junction of the two materials (b) the rate of heat transfer per m² of the composite wall.

(*Answer.* (a) 462°C (b) 1·23 kW.)

6. A cylindrical steel forging 300 mm diameter and 2 m long is being allowed to cool by convection and radiation as part of a normalizing process. At what rate is it losing heat by radiation when its surface temperature is (a) 600°C (b) 200°C? The temperature of its surroundings is 20°C and it may be considered a 'black body'. The Stefan-Boltzmann constant is $5·67 \times 10^{-8}$ W/m² K⁴.

(*Answer.* (a) 65·9 kW (b) 4·9 kW.)

7. An unlagged steam pipe 120 mm diameter has a surface temperature of 300°C. Taking the temperature of its surroundings as 25°C, calculate the maximum rate at which heat could be lost by radiation per metre length of pipe. Why is the actual heat loss by radiation likely to be less than this? The Stefan-Boltzmann constant is $5·67 \times 10^{-8}$ W/m² K⁴.

(*Answer.* 2·14 kW.)

8. A solid steel sphere, 200 mm diameter, has its temperature raised to 800°C and is then allowed to cool. Assuming heat to be lost by radiation only, and treating the sphere as a 'black body', calculate the rate at which its temperature will begin to fall if its surroundings are at 20°C. The Stefan–Boltzmann constant is $5·67 \times 10^{-8}$ W/m²K⁴, the density of steel is 7900 kg/m³ and its specific heat is 0·48 kJ/kg K.

(*Answer.* 0·595°C/s.)

15. Gases

15.1 Heat, temperature, and molecular motion

All forms of matter are made up of very small particles called *molecules*. These in turn are combinations of *atoms* (for example, a molecule of water consists of two atoms of hydrogen chemically linked to one atom of oxygen) and the atoms themselves are constructed from even smaller particles—*electrons*, *protons*, and *neutrons*. The molecule, however, is the smallest particle of any substance capable of separate existence. A 'solid object' is in fact an arrangement of a very large number of individual molecules, held in place by inter-molecular forces of attraction and able to resist deformation because of these forces.

In thinking of matter in molecular terms and in drawing diagrams to represent its structure, there is a strong tendency to regard the molecules as stationary: but while this is often convenient it does not represent the true state of affairs. An object may be 'at rest' but its molecules are in continuous motion, and this motion is responsible for the effects which we associate with 'temperature', and for the energy transfer which we call 'heat'. The difference between a hot bar of metal and a cold bar of the same metal is that the molecules of the hot bar are moving faster than those of the cold bar. If the two bars are brought into contact, fast-moving molecules in the hot bar will collide with slower-moving molecules in the cold bar and transfer to them some of their kinetic energy. Thus 'heat' will be transferred until the molecules of both bars are moving at the same speed—that is, until the bars are 'at the same temperature'. This is, of course, a simplified description of heat transfer and it must be pointed out that all the molecules in an object do not move at the same speed. Individual speeds vary considerably so that the temperature of an object is really an *average* value. Furthermore (as will be seen later), temperature is related to the *kinetic energy* of the molecules, and this involves both their speed and their mass.

15.2 Solids, liquids, and gases

In a solid, the molecules are in motion but, owing to the strong forces of attraction, remain in a fixed pattern and merely vibrate about their mean

226

positions. In a liquid, the molecules can move about but the forces of attraction are still fairly strong so that no individual molecule can detach itself from the general mass. The liquid does not retain any particular shape but it still has a definite volume. In a gas, the forces of attraction are very small and the molecules can move freely. Each molecule will, in accordance with Newton's first law of motion, travel in a straight line until it collides either with another molecule or with the wall of its container: in other words, a gas has no particular shape or volume but expands until it fills any vessel into which it is introduced.

15.3 The kinetic theory of gases

It was originally suggested by Daniel Bernoulli that the molecules of a gas could be thought of as small, hard, perfectly elastic spheres moving at high speeds, and that by applying the laws of motion to these particles the behaviour of gases could be explained. This idea was later developed fully by Clerk Maxwell and is known as the *kinetic theory of gases*.

15.4 Pressure of a gas

The collision of a molecule of gas with the wall of its container is, according to the kinetic theory, exactly like the collision of a rubber ball with a solid wall. If the ball is perfectly elastic, it will rebound as in Fig. 15.1. The change in its momentum will be in a direction perpendicular

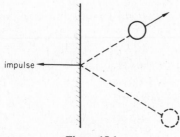

Figure 15.1

to the wall, and, by Newton's second law, the wall will receive an impulse equal to this change in momentum. In the case of, say, a cylinder containing air under normal atmospheric conditions, each square millimetre of its surface will receive millions of such impacts every second so that individual impulses cannot be distinguished and their combined effect is a steady, uniform pressure.

16

15.5   Temperature of a gas

Maxwell showed that the absolute temperature of a gas is proportional not to the average *speed* of its molecules but to their average *kinetic energy*. It will be seen that this statement gives a meaning to the term 'absolute zero temperature': it is the temperature at which the molecules of a gas would have zero kinetic energy—that is, the temperature at which, for a 'perfect gas', molecular motion would cease. Since the kinetic energy of a molecule cannot be *less* than zero, it follows that 0 K is the *lowest possible temperature*.

15.6   Boyle's law

Consider a quantity of gas enclosed in a cylinder (Fig. 15.2a) and compressed until its volume is halved (Fig. 15.2b). If the temperature is kept constant, the speed of the molecules will be unchanged so that the

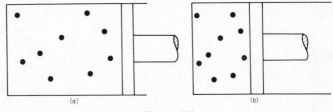

(a)   (b)

Figure 15.2

average molecular impact will produce the same impulse on the piston. Since, however, there are now twice as many molecules per unit volume of the gas there will be twice as many impacts in a given time and the pressure on the piston will be doubled. This is in agreement with the experimental observation (known as Boyle's law) that, for a given mass of gas at constant temperature

$$pV = \text{constant} \tag{15.1}$$

15.7   Charles' law

Consider (Fig. 15.3a and b) that the volume is kept constant but the temperature of the gas is increased until each molecule is moving at twice its former speed. According to Maxwell's theory, the corresponding temperature change will be proportional to the change in molecular kinetic energy—that is, in the average value of $\frac{1}{2}mv^2$. Since m is unchanged

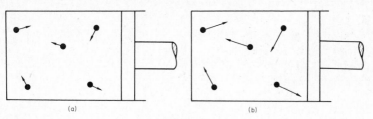

Figure 15.3

but v has been doubled, this means that the absolute temperature of the gas will be four times its original value.

The effect on the gas pressure may now be considered. Since velocities have been doubled, and momentum is the product of mass and velocity, each molecular impact will involve twice the former change in momentum and will produce twice the impulse on the piston. Furthermore, since on the average a molecule will travel from one end of the cylinder to the other in half the previous time, it will rebound from the piston twice as many times in a given period. Thus, in a given period, there are *twice* as many impacts each producing *twice* the original impulse so that the pressure on the piston is increased four times: that is, in the same ratio as the increase in absolute temperature. This may be verified experimentally and is one of the ways in which Charles' law may be stated.

In order to explain the more familiar form of the law, it is necessary to imagine a situation in which the pressure is kept constant. Since each molecular impact produces twice the original impulse, it must be arranged that there are only half as many impacts in a given period. Thus the piston must be moved out until the average molecule takes twice as long to travel from one end to the other and, since it is moving at twice its original speed, this means increasing the length of its journey four times: that is, increasing the volume of the cylinder four times.

Hence, if V is constant,

$$\frac{p}{T} = \text{constant} \qquad (15.2)$$

and, if p is constant,

$$\frac{V}{T} = \text{constant} \qquad (15.3)$$

15.8 Dalton's law of partial pressures

This law states that, when a vessel is occupied by a mixture of gases, the pressure of the mixture is the sum of the pressures which each gas would exert if, at the same temperature, it alone occupied the vessel. (These are known as *partial pressures*.) Figure 15.4a shows a container occupied by a gas A, Fig. 15.4b shows the same container occupied by a gas B, and in Fig. 15.4c both gases occupy the container together. Considering the molecules of gas A, it is seen that, if the temperature is constant;

the speed of the molecules, and hence the impulse due to each collision with the piston, will be the same in Figs. 15.4a and 15.4c;
since there is the same number of molecules of gas A per unit volume in both cases, they will have the same number of collisions with the piston in a given time.

Hence, gas A exerts the same total force on the piston in both cases. The same reasoning applies to gas B, and it follows that

$$p_{(A+B)} = p_A + p_B \qquad (15.4)$$

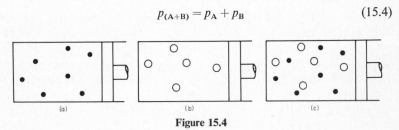

Figure 15.4

15.9 The perfect gas

The kinetic theory of gases is based on the assumptions that

(a) all collisions are perfectly elastic, and take place in negligible time;
(b) the volume occupied by the molecules is negligible compared with the volume of the gas;
(c) forces of attraction between molecules are negligible.

A *perfect gas* is one for which all these assumptions would be justified and which, in consequence, would obey the laws of Boyle and Charles (and all the other laws which may be deduced from the kinetic theory) exactly. In actual gases, such as oxygen and hydrogen, the assumptions are almost, but not quite, true. In particular, assumptions (b) and (c) become completely invalid as a substance approaches the liquid state. Steam, for example, does not obey the gas laws with any degree of accuracy (unless at a very high temperature).

Substances in the gaseous state may thus be divided into two groups: those which may, for practical purposes, be considered perfect gases, and those to which the gas laws do not apply because they are not sufficiently removed from the liquid state and which are generally called 'vapours'. In order to decide whether a particular substance is a 'gas' or a 'vapour', a common practice is to refer to its *critical temperature*—that is, the temperature above which it cannot exist in liquid form. If it is above this temperature, it is considered a gas, and if below it, a vapour.

15.10   The characteristic gas equation

If the state of a given mass of gas is altered so that its pressure, volume, and absolute temperature change from p_1, V_1, and T_1 to p_2, V_2, and T_2, a relationship between the initial and final conditions may be found by considering the change to take place in two stages.

Stage 1. The temperature is kept constant, and the pressure is changed from p_1 to p_2. Boyle' law applies, and

$$p_1 V_1 = p_2 V$$

Hence, at the end of stage 1, $V = p_1 V_1/p_2$.

Stage 2. The pressure is kept constant, and the temperature is changed from T_1 to T_2. Charles' law applies, and

$$V/T_1 = V_2/T_2$$

or, since $V = p_1 V_1/p_2$,

$$p_1 V_1/T_1 p_2 = V_2/T_2$$

Hence

$$\frac{p_1 V_1}{T_1} = \frac{p_2 V_2}{T_2} \tag{15.5}$$

If this relationship is expressed in general terms,

$$pV = kT \tag{15.6}$$

If different masses of the same gas are considered, it is obvious that, for a particular temperature and pressure, volumes will be proportional to masses. Hence, for a particular gas, the constant k is proportional to the mass of gas considered and eq. 15.6 may be re-written,

$$pV = mRT \tag{15.7}$$

This is the *characteristic gas equation* and the constant R (which has different values for different gases) is the *characteristic gas constant* (usually referred to simply as 'the gas constant').

15.11   Units of the characteristic gas equation

pressure p: N/m^2

(It may be noted that this must be the true or absolute pressure—that is, gauge pressure plus atmospheric pressure—and that pressure is often measured in bars. 1 bar $= 10^5$ N/m^2.)

volume V: m^3
mass m: kg
absolute temperature T: K

Transposing the formula,

$$R = \frac{pV}{mT}$$

Hence, the units of R are

$$\frac{\dfrac{N}{m^2} \times m^3}{kg \times K}$$

that is,

$$N\ m/kg\ K$$

or

$$J/kg\ K$$

since 1 newton-metre $=$ 1 joule.

15.12   Avogadro's law

Originally proposed by Amedeo Avogadro on the basis of experimental evidence, and later deduced from the kinetic theory of gases, this law states that *equal volumes of all gases, under the same conditions of temperature and pressure, contain the same number of molecules.*

15.13   The mole

In Fig. 15.5, equal volumes of hydrogen, oxygen, and carbon dioxide are compared. If they are all at the same temperature and pressure, all will contain the same number of molecules and, if this number is n, the mass of gas will in each case be n times the mass of an individual molecule.

Masses of molecules are very small and seldom used in calculations, but the *ratios* of these masses are well known and are referred to as *molecular weights.* The molecular weights of hydrogen, oxygen, and carbon dioxide are, respectively, 2, 32 and 44; and from this it follows that in Fig. 15.5 the masses of the three gases would be in the ratio $2:32:44$. Hence 2 kg hydrogen, 32 kg oxygen, 44 kg carbon dioxide, or in general M kg of a gas whose molecular weight is M will (under the same conditions of temperature and pressure) all occupy the same volume.

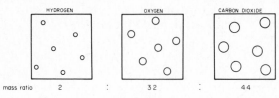

Figure 15.5

A mass of any substance in grammes numerically equal to its molecular weight is called a *mole* or, if the unit of mass is the kilogramme, a kilo-gramme-mole (kmol): thus 1 kmol of hydrogen means a mass of 2 kg, 1 kmol of oxygen a mass of 32 kg, and so on. The statement of the previous paragraph may now be made in the form '1 kmol of any gas will, under the same conditions of temperature and pressure, occupy the same volume'. It is found experimentally that, at standard temperature and pressure (that is, $0°C$ and $101·325 \text{ kN/m}^2$), this volume is $22·41 \text{ m}^3$; and it has been estimated that the number of molecules in 1 kmol is $6·02 \times 10^{26}$.

15.14   The universal gas constant

Transposing the characteristic gas equation,

$$V = mR \times \frac{T}{p}$$

When this is applied to 1 kmol of any gas (that is, to a mass of M kg where M is the molecular weight of the gas)

$$V_M = MR \times \frac{T}{p}$$

From the previous paragraph, if T and p are fixed, the volume of 1 kmol, V_M, is the same for all gases: hence, for all gases, MR has the same value and is known as the *universal gas constant*, symbol R_0. Thus, for 1 kmol of any gas, the characteristic equation becomes

$$pV_M = R_0 T \tag{15.8}$$

The value of R_0 is $8\cdot314\,\text{kJ/kmol K}$ and, since $R_0 = MR$, the gas constant R for any particular gas may readily be calculated. For example, the molecular weight of oxygen is 32; hence, for oxygen, $R = 8\cdot314/32 = 0\cdot260\,\text{kJ/kg K}$.

15.15 Mixtures of gases

The composition of a mixture of gases may be stated in two ways: by mass, and by volume (that is, by the volumes which the individual gases would occupy if, under the same conditions of temperature and pressure, the mixture could be separated into its components). If the proportions of the gases in a mixture by mass are known and the proportions by volume are required (or vice versa), use may be made of the fact that, under the same conditions of temperature and pressure, 1 kmol of any gas occupies the same volume: that is, proportions by volume are the same as proportions by kmol.

If a mixture consists of masses m_A, m_B, and m_C of gases A, B, and C with molecular weights M_A, M_B, and M_C, the proportion of gas A by mass will be $m_A/(m_A + m_B + m_C)$. For a substance with a molecular weight M, a mass of m kg is equivalent to m/M kmol. Hence, by kmol, the proportion of gas A in the mixture is

$$\frac{\dfrac{m_A}{M_A}}{\dfrac{m_A}{M_A} + \dfrac{m_B}{M_B} + \dfrac{m_C}{M_C}}$$

This will also be the proportion of gas A by volume.

15.16 Specific heats of a gas

The *specific heat* of a substance is the quantity of heat which must be transferred to unit mass of the substance in order to raise its temperature by 1 degree. It is found, for example, that to raise the temperature of 1 kg of water by 1 K, a heat transfer of $4\cdot187\,\text{kJ}$ is required. Thus, the specific heat of water, $c = 4\cdot187\,\text{kJ/kg K}$.

For a gas, it is impossible to state a single value of c as in the above example. If the gas is allowed to expand while being heated, it is found that more heat is required to produce the 1 degree temperature rise than if the volume is kept constant. The reason for this is that the expanding gas will do *work* and this output of energy must be balanced by an extra input of energy in the form of heat. (Solids and liquids also expand when heated but by very small amounts so that the work done is negligible.) Thus, the specific heat of a gas depends on whether or not the gas is allowed to expand while being heated: and different amounts of expansion will give different values of specific heat. Normally, however, only two situations are considered.

(a) The gas is not allowed to expand, that is, its volume remains constant.
(b) The gas expands, and its pressure is kept constant.

The corresponding specific heats are (a) the *specific heat at constant colume, c_v,* and (b) *the specific heat at constant pressure, c_p.*

15.17   Relationship between c_p and c_v

If a gas is heated at constant volume, all the heat supplied goes towards increasing the temperature of the gas, that is, increasing the kinetic energy of its molecules. Thus, c_v represents the increase in molecular kinetic energy when the temperature of 1 kg of the gas is raised by 1 K.

If 1 kg of the gas is heated through 1 K at constant pressure, the energy supplied must be sufficient (a) to raise the temperature of the gas and (b) to do work against whatever resists the expansion of the gas (for example, a piston). The energy required for (a) will be, as before, c_v; the increase in volume will have no effect since, according to the kinetic theory, molecular kinetic energy depends only on temperature. Hence, if the work done by the expanding gas is W,

$$c_p = c_v + W \qquad\qquad (15.9)$$

Consider (Fig. 15.6) that 1 kg of a gas, at temperature T K and pressure p N/m² is contained in a cylinder by a freely sliding piston whose area is 1 m². In order to maintain constant gas pressure, a steady force of p newtons acts downwards on the piston. Let the temperature be increased by 1 K so that the volume of the gas increases from V_1 m³ to V_2 m³. It will be seen from Fig. 15.6 that the piston is moved through a distance $(V_2 - V_1)$ metres, hence the work done on the piston by the gas,

$$W = p(V_2 - V_1) \text{ joules}$$

By applying the characteristic gas equation (and noting that in this case $m = 1$)

$$pV_1 = RT \quad \text{and} \quad pV_2 = R(T+1)$$

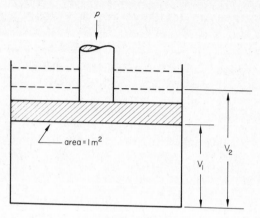

Figure 15.6

Hence

$$W = R(T + 1) - RT$$
$$= R$$

Substituting in eq. 15.9,

$$c_p = c_v + R \tag{15.10}$$

or

$$c_p - c_v = R \tag{15.11}$$

Worked examples

1. A compressed air tank has a volume of 0·5 m³. A pressure gauge fitted to the tank reads 1960 kN/m² (19·6 bar) and the barometric pressure is 1030 millibars. The temperature of the air in the tank is 50°C. Find (a) the absolute pressure of the air in the tank (b) the volume the air would occupy at s.t.p. (c) the mass of air in the tank if the gas constant for air is 0·287 kJ/kg K.

(a) 1 bar = 10⁵ N/m² or 100 kN/m².

Therefore

$$1030 \text{ mbar} = 1 \cdot 03 \text{ bar} = 103 \text{ kN/m}^2$$

Hence,

absolute pressure = 1960 + 103 = 2063 kN/m² or 2·063 MN/m²

(b) Standard temperature and pressure (s.t.p.) are, respectively, 0°C and 101·325 kN/m².

From eq. 15.5,

$$\frac{p_1 V_1}{T_1} = \frac{p_2 V_2}{T_2}$$

Therefore,

$$V_2 = \frac{p_1 V_1 T_2}{p_2 T_1}$$

Here

$p_1 = 2063 \times 10^3 \text{ N/m}^2$, $p_2 = 101 \cdot 325 \times 10^3 \text{ N/m}^2$
$T_1 = (50 + 273) = 323 \text{ K}$, $T_2 = 273 \text{ K}$
$V_1 = 0 \cdot 5 \text{ m}^3$

Hence

$$V_2 = \frac{2063 \times 10^3 \times 0 \cdot 5 \times 273}{101 \cdot 325 \times 10^3 \times 323}$$

$$= 8 \cdot 60 \text{ m}^3$$

(c) From eq. 15.7,

$$p_1 V_1 = mRT_1$$

Hence

$$m = \frac{p_1 V_1}{RT_1}$$

$$= \frac{2063 \times 10^3 \times 0 \cdot 5}{0 \cdot 287 \times 10^3 \times 323} = 11 \cdot 1 \text{ kg}$$

2. The density of helium at a pressure of 100 kN/m² (1 bar) and temperature 25°C is found to be 0·161 kg/m³. What is the value of R for this gas?

From eq. 15.7,

$$pV = mRT$$

Therefore,

$$R = \frac{pV}{mT}$$

or, since density $\rho = m/V$,

$$R = \frac{p}{\rho T}$$

$$= \frac{100 \times 10^3}{0 \cdot 161 \times 298}$$

$$= 2084 \text{ J/kg K or } 2 \cdot 084 \text{ kJ/kg K}$$

3. On a day when the atmospheric pressure was 99 kN/m² (0·99 bar or 990 mbar) and the temperature 29°C, it was found that the atmosphere contained 0·02 kg of water vapour per m³. Calculate the partial pressures of water vapour and of air. It may be assumed that, at low pressures, water vapour behaves as a perfect gas for which $R = 0·462$ kJ/kg K.

Considering 1 m³ of the atmosphere, the partial pressure of the water vapour is that pressure which it would exert if it alone occupied this volume: that is, the pressure of 0·02 kg when at a temperature of 29°C and occupying a volume of 1 m³.

From eq. 15.7,

$$pV = mRT$$

Therefore,

$$p = \frac{mRT}{V}$$

$$= \frac{0·02 \times 0·462 \times 10^3 \times 302}{1}$$

$$= 2790 \text{ N/m}^2 \text{ or } 2·79 \text{ kN/m}^2$$

From Dalton's law, the partial pressure of the air is

$$99 - 2·79 = 96·21 \text{ kN/m}^2$$

(Since 'air' is itself a mixture of gases, it would be more correct to say that 96·21 kN/m² is the sum of the partial pressures of all gases other than water vapour.)

4. A vessel A of volume 0·5 m³ and a vessel B of volume 2 m³ are connected by a valve as shown in Fig. 15.7. Vessel A contains hydrogen at a pressure of 4 MN/m² (40 bar) and vessel B contains nitrogen at a

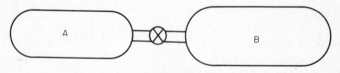

Figure 15.7

pressure of 120 kN/m² (1·2 bar). Both are at a temperature of 20°C. What will be the final pressure if the valve is opened and, after the gases have been allowed to mix, the temperature of both vessels is restored to 20°C?

Assuming that the gases eventually form a uniform mixture, the final pressure will be the sum of the partial pressures of hydrogen and nitrogen.

Partial pressure of hydrogen. This will be the pressure which the hydrogen would exert if no other gas were present—that is, if the vessel B were empty before the valve is opened. Since the initial and final temperatures are the same, Boyle's law may be applied.

$$p_1 V_1 = p_2 V_2$$

Therefore,

$$p_2 = \frac{p_1 V_1}{V_2}$$

$$= \frac{4 \times 10^6 \times 0.5}{2.5} = 8 \times 10^5 \text{ N/m}^2 \text{ or } 800 \text{ kN/m}^2$$

Partial pressure of nitrogen. Again applying Boyle's law, and, in this case, considering vessel A to be empty before opening the valve,

$$p_2 = \frac{p_1 V_1}{V_2}$$

$$= \frac{120 \times 10^3 \times 2}{2.5} = 96 \times 10^3 \text{ N/m}^2 \text{ or } 96 \text{ kN/m}^2$$

Hence, from Dalton's law, the final pressure of the mixture will be

$$800 + 96 = 896 \text{ kN/m}^2$$

5. Taking the universal gas constant as 8·314 kJ/kmol K, find (a) the volume of 1 kmol of any gas at 100 kN/m² (1 bar) and 27°C (b) the value of the gas constant R for carbon dioxide (c) the density of nitrogen at 1 MN/m² (10 bar) and 150°C (d) the specific volume of hydrogen at s.t.p.

(a) From eq. 15.8,

$$p V_M = R_0 T$$

Hence

$$V_M = \frac{R_0 T}{p}$$

$$= \frac{8 \cdot 314 \times 10^3 \times 300}{100 \times 10^3}$$

$$= 24 \cdot 942 \text{ m}^3$$

(b) The molecular weight of carbon dioxide (CO_2) is $12 + (2 \times 16) = 44$.

$$R = \frac{R_0}{M}$$

$$= \frac{8\cdot314 \times 10^3}{44} = 189 \text{ J/kg K or } 0\cdot189 \text{ kJ/kg K}$$

(c) For nitrogen, $M = 28$. Hence,

$$R = \frac{8\cdot314 \times 10^3}{28} = 297 \text{ J/kg K}$$

From eq. 15.7,

$$pV = mRT$$

Therefore,

$$\text{density } \rho = \frac{m}{V} = \frac{p}{RT}$$

$$= \frac{10^6}{297 \times 423}$$

$$= 12\cdot56 \text{ kg/m}^3.$$

(d) For hydrogen, $M = 2$. Hence,

$$R = \frac{8\cdot314 \times 10^3}{2} = 4157 \text{ J/kg K}$$

From eq. 15.7,

$$pV = mRT$$

Therefore,

$$\text{specific volume } v = \frac{V}{m} = \frac{RT}{p}$$

$$= \frac{4157 \times 273}{101325}$$

$$= 11\cdot20 \text{ m}^3/\text{kg}$$

Alternatively, the volume of 1 kmol of any gas at s.t.p. is known to be $22\cdot41$ m^3.

Hence, at s.t.p., 2 kg of hydrogen occupy $22\cdot41$ m^3. Therefore 1 kg would occupy $11\cdot205$ m^3.

6. For a certain gas $c_p = 2 \cdot 19$ kJ/kg K and $c_v = 1 \cdot 67$ kJ/kg K. What would be the specific volume of this gas at 500 kN/m² (5 bar) and 100°C?

From eq. 15.11,

$$c_p - c_v = R$$

Hence, for this gas,

$$R = 2 \cdot 19 - 1 \cdot 67$$
$$= 0 \cdot 52 \text{ kJ/kg K}$$

From eq. 15.7,

$$pV = mRT$$

Therefore,

$$\text{specific volume } v = \frac{V}{m} = \frac{RT}{p}$$

$$= \frac{0 \cdot 52 \times 10^3 \times 373}{500 \times 10^3}$$

$$= 0 \cdot 388 \text{ m}^3/\text{kg}$$

7. If air consists, by volume, of 21 % oxygen and 79 % nitrogen, what is its composition by mass?

Proportions by volume are the same as proportions by kmol. Hence, air contains oxygen and nitrogen in the proportions 21 kmol oxygen to 79 kmol nitrogen. These may be converted to kg by, in each case, multiplying by the molecular weight, and it is usually convenient to show this calculation in the form of a Table.

Component	kmol	Molecular weight	kg	% by mass
Oxygen	21	32	692	23·83
Nitrogen	79	28	2212	76·17
		Total	2904	100·00

8. A sample of flue gases from a furnace was found to consist, by mass, of 80% nitrogen, 5% oxygen, and 15% carbon dioxide. What is its composition by volume?

Proportions by volume are the same as proportions by kmol. If, at the temperature and pressure of the flue gases, 1 kmol of any gas occupies a volume V, the composition of 100 kg of flue gas will be:

Component	kg	Molecular weight	kmol	Volume	% by volume
Nitrogen	80	28	2·857	2·857V	85·18
Oxygen	5	32	0·156	0·156V	4·65
Carbon dioxide	15	44	0·341	0·341V	10·17
			Total	3·354V	100·00

Problems

1. In a diesel engine, at the commencement of the compression stroke, the cylinder contains air at 80 kN/m² (0·8 bar) and 50°C. During the compression stroke the volume is reduced to one-sixteenth of its original value and the pressure rises to 3 MN/m² (30 bar).

What is the temperature of the air after compression?

(*Answer.* 484°C.)

2. If the specific volume of sulphur dioxide is 0·336 m³/kg at s.t.p. (that is, 0°C and 101·325 kN/m²), what will be the specific volume at 200°C and 150 kN/m² (1·5 bar)?

(*Answer.* 0·393 m³/kg.)

3. At a height of 10 km, the atmospheric pressure and temperature are found to be 26·5 kN/m² (0·265 bar) and −50°C. If the gas constant for air is 0·287 kJ/kg K, what is the density of air under these conditions?

(*Answer.* 0·414 kg/m³.)

4. An empty steel cylinder has a volume of 0·04 m³. A certain gas is pumped in until the pressure and temperature in the cylinder are 12 MN/m² (120 bar) and 45°C. The mass of the cylinder is found to have increased by 5 kg. What is the value of R for the gas?

(*Answer.* 0·302 kJ/kg K.)

5. A vessel of volume 0·5 m³ contains oxygen at a pressure of 400 kN/m² (4 bar) and temperature 15°C. 0·6 kg of methane is pumped into the vessel. Taking R for methane as 0·52 kJ/kg K, find the pressure of the mixture when the vessel is at a temperature of 40°C.

(*Answer.* 630 kN/m² (6·3 bar).)

6. A vessel A of volume 1·5 m³ contains a gas at 600 kN/m² (6 bar) and 15°C. It is connected by a valve to a vessel B of volume 2·5 m³ which contains another gas at 2 MN/m² (20 bar) and 15°C. The valve is opened and the gases are allowed to mix. What will be the final pressure if the final temperature is 15°C?

(*Answer.* 1·475 MN/m² (14·75 bar).)

7. The molecular weight of the gas chlorine is 71. What will be the pressure in a vessel of volume 0·2 m³ containing 5 kg of chlorine at 27°C? The universal gas constant is 8·314 kJ/kmol K.

(*Answer.* 878 kN/m² (8·78 bar).)

8. Taking the universal gas constant as 8·314 kJ/kmol K, find (a) the density of oxygen at 15 MN/m² (150 bar) and 20°C (b) the specific volume of nitrogen at 100 kN/m² (1 bar) and 1000°C.

(*Answer.* (a) 197 kg/m³ (b) 3·78 m³/kg.)

9. A cylinder of internal diameter 200 mm is fitted with a freely sliding piston and contains 1 kg of air at 1 MN/m² (10 bar) and 20°C. How much heat must be transferred to the air in order to raise its temperature to 40°C (a) if the piston is fixed so that the process takes place at constant volume (b) if the process takes place at constant pressure? For (b), calculate (c) the force on the piston and (d) the distance through which it moves: show that the work done by the gas is equal to the difference between (a) and (b).

For air, $c_p = 1·005$ kJ/kg K, $c_v = 0·718$ kJ/kg K, and $R = 0·287$ kJ/kg K.

(*Answer.* (a) 14·36 kJ (b) 20·1 kJ (c) 31·42 kN (d) 182·7 mm.)

10. A certain gas is heated by being passed at the rate of 2 kg/min through a duct containing electrical heating elements rated at 3 kW. The gas has a specific heat at constant volume of 1·48 kJ/kg K and its characteristic gas constant is 0·28 kJ/kg K. If the gas enters the duct at 20°C and its pressure remains constant, at what temperature will it leave the duct?

(*Answer.* 71·1°C.)

11. An analysis of the exhaust gas from an engine showed that, after the removal of water vapour, its composition by volume was 84% nitrogen, 3% oxygen, and 13% carbon dioxide. Calculate the percentage composition by mass.

(*Answer.* 77·88% nitrogen, 3·18% oxygen, 18·94% carbon dioxide.)

12. A coal gas has a composition by mass of 8% hydrogen, 44% carbon monoxide (CO), and 48% methane (CH_4). Calculate its percentage composition by volume.

(*Answer.* 46·7% hydrogen, 18·3% carbon monoxide, 35·0% methane.)

13. A compressed air tank has a volume of 1·5 m³ and contains air at 1·2 MN/m² (12 bar) and 25°C. A valve is opened, allowing air to escape until the pressure in the tank falls to 700 kN/m² (7 bar). The valve is then closed, and the temperature of the air in the tank is found to be 15°C. Taking the gas constant for air as 0·287 kJ/kg K, calculate the mass of air allowed to escape.

(*Answer.* 8·34 kg.)

14. A vessel of volume 0·2 m³ contains nitrogen at 200 kN/m² (2 bar) and 20°C. A cylinder of compressed hydrogen is now connected to the vessel and hydrogen is allowed to flow in until the pressure has risen to 1 MN/m² (10 bar) and the temperature of the mixture is 40°C. Calculate the mass of hydrogen admitted. The gas constant for hydrogen is 4·157 kJ/kg K.

(*Answer.* 0·121 kg.)

15. A vessel of volume 0·25 m³ contains 0·3 kg of a gas at 100 kN/m² (1 bar) and 20°C. The gas is heated at constant volume until its pressure rises to 160 kN/m² (1·6 bar). If the amount of heat transferred is 47 kJ, calculate (a) the gas constant, (b) the specific heat at constant volume of the gas, (c) its specific heat at constant pressure.

(*Answer.* (a) 0·824 kJ/kg K (b) 0·891 kJ/kg K (c) 1·175 kJ/kg K.)

16. Combustion of fuels

16.1 The combustion process

The combustion of a fuel is a chemical reaction in which the elements carbon, hydrogen, and, possibly, sulphur (which constitute the bulk of all 'fuels') combine with oxygen (usually provided by the atmosphere) and which is accompanied by a release of energy in the form of heat. The reaction will proceed only if the temperature is high enough; for example, if hydrogen and oxygen are brought into contact, nothing will happen unless their temperature is raised to about 600°C. Once started, however, the reaction will release energy which will maintain a high temperature.

Fuels may be solids, liquids, or gases; and combustion may take place steadily over a long period of time, as in a boiler furnace, or it may be an almost instantaneous process, as in the cylinder of an internal combustion engine. In all cases, however, the three essentials of the combustion process are a supply of fuel, a supply of oxygen or air, and a means of ignition, that is, a way of producing a temperature high enough to start the reaction.

16.2 Calorific values for solid and liquid fuels

The energy released as heat by the complete combustion of unit quantity of a fuel is known as its *calorific value*. It is determined by measuring the amount of heat given out when a known quantity of fuel is burned; for a solid or a liquid fuel, a convenient and accurate way of doing this is to burn the fuel in a *bomb calorimeter*. The 'bomb' is a strong steel vessel in which a small quantity of fuel is ignited in an atmosphere of pure oxygen under high pressure, ensuring perfect combustion. The arrangement is shown diagrammatically in Fig. 16.1. About one gramme of fuel is placed in a small crucible within the bomb and in contact with the 'ignition wire' (usually a piece of fine platinum wire). The two halves of the bomb are screwed together, making a gas-tight joint, an oxygen cylinder is connected to the valve, and oxygen allowed to flow into the bomb until a pressure of about 2·5 MN/m² (25 bar) is reached. The valve is then closed, the oxygen cylinder disconnected, and the bomb immersed in a water bath provided with a sensitive thermometer and a motor-driven stirrer. When enough time has elapsed for the bomb and its contents to reach the same temperature as the water bath, the fuel is ignited by passing an electric current through the ignition wire, and the resulting temperature rise is observed. Assuming no heat losses from the apparatus and neglecting the small amounts of energy supplied by the stirrer and the ignition wire, the heat given out during the combustion of the fuel is equal to the heat taken in by the water bath and the rest of the apparatus (that is, the bomb and its contents, and the water container).

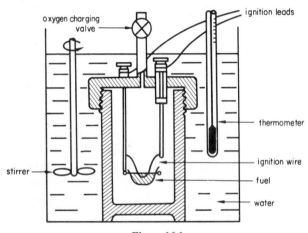

Figure 16.1

This may be calculated, for each part of the apparatus, as the product of mass, specific heat, and temperature rise; but, since many different substances are involved, the usual practice is to find, experimentally, the 'water equivalent' of the apparatus. This is the mass of water which would have the same heat capacity as the apparatus; hence, the heat taken in is given by the product of the temperature rise, the specific heat of water, and (mass of water + water equivalent of apparatus). The calorific value of the fuel will be this quantity of heat divided by the mass of fuel burned.

For greater accuracy, a 'cooling correction' may be added to the observed temperature rise. This compensates for heat losses from the apparatus, and is based on the principle that the rate of heat loss is proportional to the difference in temperature between the apparatus and its surroundings. It is calculated from readings of temperature taken at one-minute intervals from about five minutes before ignition to about ten minutes after maximum temperature has been reached.

16.3 Calorific values for gaseous fuels

The most convenient way of finding the calorific value of a gaseous fuel is to burn it in a *steady-flow calorimeter*, of which the Boys calorimeter and the Junker calorimeter are well known examples. The principle of such a calorimeter is shown in Fig. 16.2. The gas is fed at a steady rate to a burner and the products of combustion pass over tubes through which there is a steady flow of water. When all parts of the apparatus have reached a constant temperature, the heat released by combustion in a given period will be equal to the heat taken in by the water during the same period (assuming no heat losses from the apparatus), and this may

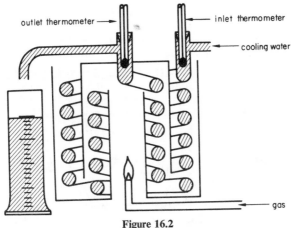

Figure 16.2

be calculated as the product of the mass of water collected during the period, its specific heat, and the difference between inlet and outlet temperatures.

Gases are usually measured by volume rather than by mass. Hence their calorific values are normally stated not per kg but per m³; and this volume must be measured under specified conditions of temperature and pressure. It is therefore necessary to measure the temperature and pressure of the gas fed to the burner as well as the volume used during the test period, and to convert the measured volume to the corresponding volume at the specified conditions; that is, 0°C and 101·325 kN/m² if 's.t.p.' is specified.

Worked examples

1. A bomb calorimeter was used to determine the calorific value of a sample of oil, and the following observations were made: mass of oil in crucible, 1·021 g; mass of water in container, 2·5 kg; temperature before ignition of fuel, 17·520°C; maximum temperature, 20·895°C. The water equivalent of the apparatus was known to be 0·65 kg. Assuming no heat loss from the apparatus and taking the specific heat of water as 4·187 kJ/kg °C, calculate the calorific value of the oil.

heat released by combustion

$$= \text{heat taken in by water and apparatus}$$
$$= (2·5 + 0·65) \times 4·187 \times (20·895 - 17·520)$$
$$= 3·15 \times 4·187 \times 3·375 = 44·50 \text{ kJ}$$

Hence,

$$\text{calorific value of oil} = 44·50/1·021 \times 10^{-3}$$
$$= 43\ 600 \text{ kJ/kg or } 43·6 \text{ MJ/kg}$$

2. In a test on coal gas using a steady flow calorimeter, the following observations were made during a period of four minutes: volume of gas used, 0·01 m³; temperature of gas, 19°C; gauge pressure of gas (measured by a water manometer), 50 mm of water; mass of water collected, 2·03 kg; inlet temperature, 8·16°C; outlet temperature, 28·27°C; barometric pressure 101 kN/m² (1010 mbar). Taking the specific heat of water as 4·187 kJ/kg °C, and its density as 1000 kg/m³, calculate the calorific value of the gas in MJ/m³ at s.t.p.

heat released by combustion

$$= \text{heat taken in by cooling water}$$
$$= 2·03 \times 4·187 \times (28·27 - 8·16)$$
$$= 170·9 \text{ kJ}$$

From eq. 12.2, the absolute pressure of the gas is given by

$$p = \rho g h + p'$$
$$= 1000 \times 9·81 \times 0·05 + 101\ 000$$
$$= 490·5 + 101\ 000 = 101\ 490·5 \text{ N/m}^2$$

From eq. 15.5,

$$p_1 V_1/T_1 = p_2 V_2/T_2$$

Hence volume of gas at s.t.p.,

$$V_2 = p_1 V_1 T_2/p_2 T_1$$
$$= (101\ 490·5 \times 0·01 \times 273)/(101\ 325 \times 292)$$
$$= 0·009367 \text{ m}^3$$

Thus,

> calorific value of gas = 170·9/0·009367
> = 18 250 kJ/m^3 or 18·25 MJ/m^3 at s.t.p.

3. A domestic central heating system uses solid fuel of calorific value 35 MJ/kg. If 75% of the heat released by combustion of the fuel is transferred to the water in the system, what is the hourly fuel consumption when the rate of heat flow from the system is 15 kW?

heat flow from system = 0·75 × heat released by combustion

For a period of 1 hour,

$$15 \times 10^3 \times 3600 = 0.75 \times 35 \times 10^6 \times m$$

where m is the hourly fuel consumption.

Hence,

$$m = 15 \times 10^3 \times 3600/0.75 \times 35 \times 10^6$$
$$= 2.06 \text{ kg}$$

16.4 Chemistry of fuels

As stated in section 15.1, all substances consist of large numbers of *molecules*, and the molecules themselves are combinations of *atoms*. Different arrangements of atoms and molecules give substances with a variety of physical properties, but chemically there are only three basic kinds of substance: elements, compounds, and mixtures.

An *element* is a substance containing only one kind of atom, and may be recognized from the fact that no chemical process can divide it into simpler substances. There are about 100 different kinds of atom, and so there are about one hundred 'elements'; those concerned in combustion processes are given in the Table below, together with their chemical symbols and atomic weights.

Element	Symbol	Atomic weight
Hydrogen	H	1
Carbon	C	12
Sulphur	S	32
Oxygen	O	16
Nitrogen	N	14

The 'atomic weight' of an element means, for practical purposes, the number of times the mass of its atom is greater than that of a hydrogen atom. (Strictly, atomic weights are defined in terms of the mass of the carbon-12 atom, to which is assigned the value 12, and are not exactly whole numbers—for example, the true atomic weight of nitrogen is 14·01—but the values given in the Table are sufficiently accurate for most calculations.) Molecular weights are defined in the same way. For example, one molecule of hydrogen contains two atoms and is represented by the symbol H_2. Its mass is twice that of a hydrogen atom, hence the molecular weight of hydrogen is 2.

A *compound* is formed when two or more elements are combined chemically, and may be distinguished from an element since, by chemical means, it can be divided into simpler substances. Water, for example, is a compound of hydrogen and oxygen and it can be decomposed by means of an electric current into these elements. In any particular compound, all molecules have the same composition; hence, the elements are always present in the same proportions by mass.

A substance in which all the molecules do not have the same composition is called a *mixture*, and it differs from a compound in two ways. Molecules of different kinds may be separated by purely physical means, and the mixture does not have a definite proportional composition. Hydrogen and oxygen, for example, may be mixed together in any proportions; but when combined together as water their proportions by mass are always 1:8.

The chief natural fuels are coal, oil, and natural gas, and all are composed mainly of the elements carbon and hydrogen. Usually these are combined in various ways to form compounds called *hydrocarbons*. Natural gas, for example, consists largely of the hydrocarbon *methane*, in which each atom of carbon is combined with four atoms of hydrogen so that it has the chemical formula CH_4. Crude oil is a mixture of a large number of different hydrocarbons and, since these have different boiling points, can be separated by *fractional distillation* into products ranging from petrol to paraffin wax. Coals consist of a mixture of hydrocarbons and uncombined carbon. In the case of coal and oil, there will probably be present some compounds containing the element sulphur, and there will be various substances which take no part in the combustion process and are left behind as ash.

The combustion of a fuel involves the chemical combination of its constituents with oxygen and is, in fact, a complicated process. If the combustion is complete, however, the final products will be CO_2 (carbon dioxide), H_2O (water), and, if the fuel contains sulphur, SO_2 (sulphur dioxide). In other words, the result of combustion would have been the same had the carbon, hydrogen, and sulphur been burned separately. Hence, for purposes of calculation, there is no need to consider intermediate reactions and each element may be dealt with independently. Furthermore, although the element sulphur is present in many fuels, the amounts involved are small and, in calculations concerned with air requirements and combustion products, are often ignored.

16.5 Combustion of carbon and hydrogen

As with all chemical reactions, the combination of an element with oxygen may be represented by a *chemical equation*. The combustion of carbon is represented by the equation

$$C + O_2 \rightarrow CO_2 \qquad (16.1)$$

The literal meaning of this equation is 'one molecule of carbon (which consists of one atom) and one molecule of oxygen (which consists of two atoms) react to form one molecule of carbon dioxide (which consists of one atom of carbon and two atoms of oxygen)'.

If, instead of considering one molecule of each substance, we consider $6 \cdot 02 \times 10^{26}$ molecules, the amount of each substance becomes 1 kmol (see section 15·13). Thus, an alternative interpretation of the equation is 'one kmol of carbon and one kmol of oxygen react to form one kmol of carbon dioxide'. One kmol of any substance is defined as a mass in kg numerically equal to its molecular weight, hence

$$12 \text{ kg carbon} + 32 \text{ kg oxygen} \rightarrow 44 \text{ kg carbon dioxide}$$

It will be noted that (a) the molecular weight of a substance is the total of the atomic weights of the atoms contained by one molecule, thus the molecular weight of CO_2 is $(12 + 2 \times 16) = 44$; and (b) the total mass after the reaction is equal to the total mass before the reaction. This applies to all chemical reactions and is known as the 'principle of conservation of mass'.

The equation for the combustion of hydrogen is

$$2H_2 + O_2 \rightarrow 2H_2O \qquad (16.2)$$

Hence

$$2 \text{ kmol hydrogen} + 1 \text{ kmol oxygen} \rightarrow 2 \text{ kmol water}$$

or

$$4 \text{ kg hydrogen} + 32 \text{ kg oxygen} \rightarrow 36 \text{ kg water}$$

Since, under the same conditions of temperature and pressure, 1 kmol of any gas occupies the same volume, the volumes in eq. 16.2 will (assuming the H_2O to be a gas, that is, superheated steam) be in the proportions

$$2 \text{ volumes} + 1 \text{ volume} \rightarrow 2 \text{ volumes}$$

It will be noted that (a) the total mass after the reaction is equal to the total mass before the reaction, but this rule does *not* apply to volumes; and (b) eq. 16.2 is *not*

$$H_2 + O \rightarrow H_2O$$

since O represents a single oxygen atom, and the air or oxygen supplied for combustion will contain only oxygen molecules, each consisting of two atoms.

16.6   Air required for combustion

Air is a mixture of gases, and consists, by mass, of $23 \cdot 2\%$ oxygen, $75 \cdot 5\%$ nitrogen, and a further $1 \cdot 3\%$ made up of rare gases such as argon and neon. It also contains a very small amount of carbon dioxide, and varying amounts of water vapour, both of which are ignored in combustion calculations; as are also the rare gases, the whole of the air other than oxygen being considered as 'atmospheric nitrogen'. Usually the percentages are 'rounded off' and, for practical purposes, air is considered to consist, by mass, of 23% oxygen and 77% nitrogen. (By volume, the proportions are, respectively, 21% and 79%.)

The mass of oxygen required for the combustion of the carbon and hydrogen in a fuel may be found by using eq. 16.1 and 16.2. The fuel may contain oxygen, and, if so, the amount of oxygen in the fuel is subtracted from that required for combustion to give the oxygen to be supplied by the air. Since air contains 23% oxygen by mass, this quantity of oxygen must be multiplied by 100/23 to give the mass of air required; this is the minimum amount of air for complete combustion of the fuel, and is known as the 'theoretical air'.

If the amount of air supplied to, say, a boiler furnace is the 'theoretical air', it is unlikely that perfect combustion will result. The fuel and oxygen will both be present in the correct proportions, but it is by no means certain that they will react completely. In practice, some molecules of both fuel and oxygen will pass through the combustion chamber without having come into contact. To avoid the resulting wastage of fuel it is usual to supply more air than the theoretical amount, and the additional amount of air supplied is referred to as the 'excess air'. The percentage of excess air supplied will depend on the design of the combustion chamber; for a furnace burning oil or pulverized fuel it may be as low as 15 per cent of the theoretical air, for a coal-fired boiler furnace 50 per cent, and for a domestic coal fire several hundred per cent.

16.7 Products of combustion

The complete combustion, with excess air, of a fuel consisting of hydrogen, carbon, oxygen, and ash may be represented by a diagram (Fig. 16.3). The gaseous products of combustion are seen to comprise:

(a) carbon dioxide (CO_2) from the combustion of carbon;
(b) water vapour (H_2O) from the combustion of hydrogen;
(c) oxygen (O_2) from the excess air supplied;
(d) nitrogen (N_2) from the total air supplied.

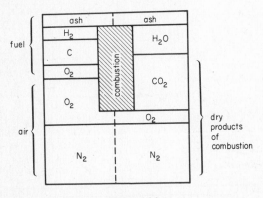

Figure 16.3

If the combustion is incomplete, some of the carbon atoms will combine with only one oxygen atom to form CO (carbon monoxide) instead of CO_2. Hence, in this case, the products of combustion will include carbon monoxide. They may also include unburned hydrocarbons and unburned carbon in the form of 'smoke'.

The composition of the flue gases from a furnace, or the exhaust gases from an internal combustion engine, is thus an indication of whether the combustion is complete, and may also be used to determine whether the correct amount of excess air is being supplied. Products of combustion are usually analysed by chemical means using an 'Orsat apparatus'. This gives an analysis by volume, and, since any water vapour condenses so that its volume becomes negligible, this analysis does not include water vapour. Combustion calculations are therefore often concerned with the estimation of the percentage composition of the dry products of combustion. Percentages may be calculated by mass or by volume, but an estimate of the volumetric composition is usually preferable since this may be compared directly with the results of an analysis using the Orsat apparatus.

Worked examples

4. A coal-fired boiler uses fuel with the following analysis by mass: carbon 81%, hydrogen 5%, oxygen 6%, ash 8%. Find the minimum mass of air necessary for the complete combustion of 1 kg fuel. If 40% excess air is supplied, find the percentage composition of the dry products of combustion (a) by mass (b) by volume. Show that the principle of conservation of mass applies to the combustion process.

From eq. 16.1,

$$C + O_2 \rightarrow CO_2$$

By mass,

$$12 \text{ kg} + 32 \text{ kg} \rightarrow 44 \text{ kg}$$

Hence, 0·81 kg carbon requires

$$0·81 \times 32/12 = 2·16 \text{ kg oxygen}$$

From eq. 16.2,

$$2H_2 + O_2 \rightarrow 2H_2O$$

By mass,

$$4 \text{ kg} + 32 \text{ kg} \rightarrow 36 \text{ kg}$$

Hence, 0·05 kg hydrogen requires

$$0·05 \times 32/4 = 0·4 \text{ kg oxygen}$$

Therefore, total oxygen required is

$$2·16 + 0·4 = 2·56 \text{ kg}$$

The fuel contains 0·06 kg oxygen, and so the oxygen to be supplied is $2·56 - 0·06 = 2·50$ kg.

Air contains 23% oxygen by mass, hence the minimum mass of air required for 1 kg fuel is

$$2·50 \times 100/23 = 10·87 \text{ kg}$$

Products of combustion (by mass)

'40 % excess air' means that the actual air supplied per kg fuel will be $(10.87 \times 140/100) = 15.22$ kg, and this will consist of:

$$\text{oxygen, } 15.22 \times 0.23 = 3.50 \text{ kg}$$
$$\text{and nitrogen, } 15.22 \times 0.77 = 11.72 \text{ kg}$$

The products of the combustion reactions are carbon dioxide and water but, since the composition of the 'dry products of combustion' is required, only the carbon dioxide need be considered.

From the combustion equation for carbon, the CO_2 produced is $0.81 \times 44/12 = 2.97$ kg.

The dry products of combustion will comprise this carbon dioxide, together with the excess oxygen $(3.50 - 2.50 = 1.0$ kg), and the whole of the nitrogen (11.72 kg).

The composition is thus:

carbon dioxide	2.97 kg (18.9 %)
oxygen	1.0 kg (6.4 %)
nitrogen	11.72 kg (74.7 %)
Total	15.69 kg (100 %)

Products of combustion (by volume)

For a mixture of gases, proportions by volume are the same as proportions by kmol (see section 15.15). In the combustion of 1 kg of fuel, the composition by kmol of the dry products of combustion is:

$$CO_2 \ (2.97/44) = 0.0675 \text{ kmol}$$
$$O_2 \ (1.0/32) = 0.0313 \text{ kmol}$$
$$N_2 \ (11.72/28) = 0.4185 \text{ kmol}$$

If, at the temperature and pressure of the combustion products, 1 kmol of any gas occupies a volume V, the composition of the dry products of combustion by volume is therefore:

carbon dioxide	$0.0675V$ (13.1 %)
oxygen	$0.0313V$ (6.0 %)
nitrogen	$0.4185V$ (80.9 %)
Total	$0.5173V$ (100 %)

Conservation of mass

Total mass before combustion must equal total mass after combustion.

$$\text{total mass before combustion} = 1 \text{ kg fuel} + 15.22 \text{ kg air}$$
$$= 16.22 \text{ kg}$$

The mass of the dry gaseous products of combustion is known to be 15·69 kg, and to this must be added the mass of water vapour, which, from the combustion equation for hydrogen, is $(0.05 \times 36/4) = 0.45$ kg, and the mass of ash, 0·08 kg.

Hence,

total mass after combustion $= 15.69 + 0.45 + 0.08 = 16.22$ kg

Thus total masses before and after combustion are seen to be identical. (This is true for any combustion process, and is recommended as a useful check on the accuracy of combustion calculations.)

5. The analysis, by mass, of the petrol used by an engine is 85% carbon, 15% hydrogen. The carburettor gives a mixture with an air/fuel ratio of 16:1 by mass. What percentage of excess air does this represent, and what will be the composition, by mass, of the exhaust gases produced when 1 kg of petrol is burned, assuming complete combustion?

In order to find the percentage of excess air, it is first necessary to find the minimum or theoretical air required for the combustion of 1 kg of fuel.

From eq. 16.1,

$$C + O_2 \rightarrow CO_2$$

By mass,

$$12 \text{ kg} + 32 \text{ kg} \rightarrow 44 \text{ kg}$$

Hence, 0·85 kg carbon requires

$$0.85 \times 32/12 = 2.267 \text{ kg oxygen}$$

From eq. 16.2,

$$2H_2 + O_2 \rightarrow 2H_2O$$

By mass,

$$4 \text{ kg} + 32 \text{ kg} \rightarrow 36 \text{ kg}$$

Hence, 0·15 kg hydrogen requires

$$0.15 \times 32/4 = 1.2 \text{ kg oxygen}$$

Therefore, total oxygen to be supplied is

$$2.267 + 1.2 = 3.467 \text{ kg}$$

and so, minimum air required is

$$3.467 \times 100/23 = 15.08 \text{ kg}$$

The actual mass of air supplied is 16 kg; hence, the mass of excess air per kg of fuel is $16 - 15.08 = 0.92$ kg and the percentage excess air is

$$(0.92/15.08) \times 100\% = 6.1\%$$

Composition of exhaust gases

The 16 kg of air supplied consists of:

oxygen, $16 \times 0.23 = 3.68$ kg
and nitrogen, $16 \times 0.77 = 12.32$ kg

3.467 kg of oxygen are needed for the combustion of the fuel; hence, the remaining 0.213 kg will, together with the 12.32 kg nitrogen, pass through the engine unchanged to become part of the exhaust gases. The other exhaust gases are carbon dioxide and water vapour, and their masses may be found from the combustion equations. Therefore, the exhaust gases produced when 1 kg of petrol is burned consist of:

carbon dioxide $(0.85 \times 44/12) = $ 3.117 kg
water vapour $\quad (0.15 \times 36/4) \quad = $ 1.35 kg
oxygen $\qquad\qquad\qquad\qquad$ 0.213 kg
nitrogen $\qquad\qquad\qquad\qquad$ 12.32 kg

(It may be noted that the total mass of exhaust gas, 17 kg, is equal to the total mass before combustion, namely 16 kg air and 1 kg fuel.)

6. A sample of natural gas is found to consist, by volume, of 87% methane (CH_4), 5% hydrogen and 8% nitrogen. Find (a) the minimum volume of air required for the complete combustion of 1 m³ of natural gas (b) the volumetric analysis of the dry products of combustion if minimum air is supplied and combustion is complete.

The combustion equation for any hydrocarbon may be deduced from three basic facts: (a) the products of combustion are CO_2 and H_2O; (b) the oxygen supplied must comprise a whole number of molecules (each containing two atoms); and (c) the number of atoms of each element does not change during the reaction, only the way in which they are arranged—that is, the equation must 'balance'. Hence, the combustion equation for methane is:

$$CH_4 + 2O_2 \rightarrow CO_2 + 2H_2O$$

Proportions by volume are the same as proportions by kmol, that is,

1 volume + 2 volumes → 1 volume + 2 volumes

Hence, $0\cdot87$ m³ methane require $(2 \times 0\cdot87) = 1\cdot74$ m³ oxygen, and the dry product of its combustion is $0\cdot87$ m³ carbon dioxide.

For hydrogen, from eq. 16.2,

$$2H_2 + O_2 \rightarrow 2H_2O$$

Hence,

$$2 \text{ volumes} + 1 \text{ volume} \rightarrow 2 \text{ volumes}$$

and so $0\cdot05$ m³ hydrogen require $(\frac{1}{2} \times 0\cdot05) = 0\cdot025$ m³ oxygen. There is no 'dry product of combustion'. The total volume of oxygen required is $(1\cdot74 + 0\cdot025) = 1\cdot765$ m³. Air contains 21% oxygen by volume; hence, the minimum air requirement is

$$1\cdot765 \times 100/21 = 8\cdot405 \text{ m}^3$$

Products of combustion

Since minimum air only is supplied, there will be no oxygen in the combustion products; thus the dry products of combustion will comprise nitrogen from the air and from the fuel, and carbon dioxide from the combustion of the methane.

The volume of nitrogen in the air supplied is

$$8\cdot405 \times 0\cdot79 = 6\cdot64 \text{ m}^3$$

The fuel contains $0\cdot08$ m³ nitrogen, and so the total volume of nitrogen is $(6\cdot64 + 0\cdot08) = 6\cdot72$ m³. The composition of the dry combustion products is therefore:

nitrogen	$6\cdot72$ m³	$(88\cdot5\%)$
carbon dioxide	$0\cdot87$ m³	$(11\cdot5\%)$
Total	$7\cdot59$ m³	(100%)

Problems

Air contains 23% oxygen by mass, 21% oxygen by volume. The specific heat of water may be taken as $4\cdot187$ kJ/kg °C.

1. What is meant by the 'calorific value' of a solid fuel? In a test to determine the calorific value of a sample of coal, $1\cdot05$ g of coal was ignited in a bomb calorimeter. The mass of water surrounding the bomb was 2 kg and the observed temperature rise $3\cdot15$°C. Taking the 'water equivalent' of the apparatus as $0\cdot4$ kg and assuming no heat losses, calculate the calorific value of the coal.

(*Answer.* $30\cdot1$ MJ/kg.)

2. A natural gas was tested by means of a steady flow calorimeter and the following results were obtained: volume of gas burned, 0·04 m³; temperature of gas, 15°C; gauge pressure of gas (measured by a water manometer), 60 mm water; mass of water passed through calorimeter, 22·7 kg; inlet water temperature, 9·5°C; outlet water temperature, 23·4°C; barometer reading, 1021 millibars. Taking the density of water as 1000 kg/m³ and the acceleration due to gravity as 9·81 m/s², and assuming no heat losses from the apparatus, calculate the calorific value of the gas per m³ at s.t.p.

(*Answer*. 34·4 MJ/m³.)

3. A domestic heater burns oil of density 790 kg/m³ and calorific value 46·5 MJ/kg. If 1 litre of oil is consumed every 4 hours, what is the rate of heat output?

(*Answer*. 2·55 kW.)

4. A water heater burns gas of calorific value 18 MJ/m³ at s.t.p. Assuming that 80% of the heat produced by combustion is transferred to the water, what volume of gas (measured at a pressure of 103 kN/m² and temperature 17°C) must be burned to produce 5 kg water at 90°C from a water supply at 8°C?

(*Answer*. 0·125 m³.)

5. A sample of dried peat is found to consist, by mass, of 56% carbon, 6% hydrogen, 37% oxygen, and 1% ash. Find the minimum mass of air required for the complete combustion of 1 kg of this fuel.

(*Answer*. 6·97 kg.)

6. Calculate the minimum mass of air required for the complete combustion of 1 kg of an oil with the following analysis by mass: carbon, 86%; hydrogen, 14%. If, in a furnace using this fuel, 20% excess air is supplied, what will be the percentage composition of the dry products of combustion (a) by mass (b) by volume?

(*Answer*. 14·85 kg air (a) 18·0% CO_2, 3·9% O_2, 78·1% N_2 (b) 12·3% CO_2, 3·6% O_2, 84·1% N_2.)

7. A boiler burns 800 kg coal per hour. If the analysis by mass of the coal is 82% carbon, 5% hydrogen, 7% oxygen, and 6% ash, and 50% excess air is supplied, find the mass of air supplied to the furnace per hour.

Find also the total mass of flue gases leaving the furnace per hour, and the mass of each constituent.

(*Answer.* 13 130 kg; 13 880 kg, consisting of 10 110 kg nitrogen, 2400 kg carbon dioxide, 1010 kg oxygen and 360 kg water vapour.)

8. A natural gas consists, by volume, of 84% methane (CH_4), 6% hydrogen, and 10% nitrogen. What will be the volumetric analysis of the dry products of combustion if a mixture of 1 m³ gas and 10 m³ air is burned?

(*Answer.* 9·1% CO_2, 4·2% O_2, 86·7% N_2.)

9. The gas acetylene has the chemical formula C_2H_2. Deduce the chemical equation representing its combustion and hence find (a) the minimum volume of air required for the complete combustion of 1 m³ acetylene (b) the dry products of this combustion by volume.

(*Answer.* (a) 11·9 m³ (b) 2 m³ CO_2, 9·4 m³ N_2.)

10. Deduce the chemical equation for the combustion of octane (C_8H_{18}) and hence find the minimum mass of air required for the complete combustion of 1 kg of octane. If this amount of air is supplied, find the percentage composition of the dry combustion products by mass.

(*Answer.* 15·26 kg: 20·8% CO_2, 79·2% N_2.)

11. Butane (C_4H_{10}) is the main constituent of the various 'bottled gases' used by camping equipment, etc. What is the minimum volume of air required for the complete combustion of 1 m³ of this gas?

(*Answer.* 30·95 m³.)

12. The fuel used by an oil-fired boiler has the following percentage analysis by mass: carbon 86%, hydrogen 12%, oxygen 2%, ash 2%. Find the minimum mass of air required for the complete combustion of 1 kg fuel. If 30% excess air is supplied, find the percentage composition of the dry flue gases by mass.

(*Answer.* 14·05 kg: 17·3% CO_2, 5·3% O_2, 77·4% N_2.)

Index

Printed by William Clowes & Sons Ltd., London, Colchester and Beccles